Introduction to
Linear Algebra

THE UNIVERSITY SERIES IN
UNDERGRADUATE MATHEMATICS

Editors

John L. Kelley, *University of California*
Paul R. Halmos, *University of Michigan*

PATRICK SUPPES—Introduction to Logic
PAUL R. HALMOS—Finite-Dimensional Vector Spaces, 2nd Ed.
EDWARD J. McSHANE AND TRUMAN A. BOTTS—Real Analysis
JOHN G. KEMENY and J. LAURIE SNELL—Finite Markov Chains
PATRICK SUPPES—Axiomatic Set Theory
PAUL R. HALMOS—Naive Set Theory
JOHN L. KELLEY—Introduction to Modern Algebra
R. DUBISCH—Student Manual to Modern Algebra
IVAN NIVEN—Calculus: An Introductory Approach
A. SEIDENBERG—Lectures in Projective Geometry
MAYNARD J. MANSFIELD—Introduction to Topology
FRANK M. STEWART—Introduction to Linear Algebra

A series of distinguished texts for undergraduate mathematics.
Additional titles will be listed and announced as published.

FRANK M. STEWART

Professor of Mathematics
Brown University

Introduction to

Linear Algebra

D. VAN NOSTRAND COMPANY, INC.

Princeton, New Jersey
New York   *Toronto*   *London*

D. VAN NOSTRAND COMPANY, INC.
120 Alexander St., Princeton, New Jersey (*Principal office*)
24 West 40 Street, New York 18, New York

D. VAN NOSTRAND COMPANY, LTD.
358, Kensington High Street, London, W.14, England

D. VAN NOSTRAND COMPANY (Canada), LTD.
25 Hollinger Road, Toronto 16, Canada

To CAROLINE, to BILL, and
to BROWN UNIVERSITY
for its two hundredth birthday

PREFACE

I wrote this book because I believe that linear algebra provides an ideal introduction to the conceptual, axiomatic methods characteristic of mathematics today. The book has a twofold purpose. It is important that the student learn the subject; it is even more important that he learn the language of mathematics.

As to subject matter, there are few novelties here. The two chapters on determinants (Chapters V and VI) are completely independent. Chapter VI presents the subject in the traditional manner. Chapter V emphasizes linear and multilinear forms. Because this is an elementary text, the number of new concepts is kept small. For example, arbitrary fields would present an unnecessary hurdle to the beginner, so they are not mentioned explicitly. Any reader who knows about fields will re-interpret the material accordingly.

The text employs several devices, old and new, intended to help the student to learn how to read and write mathematics.

The Appendices are devoted entirely to questions of language and logic. They are keyed to the text by marginal references whose use is explained in a Note to the Reader. The ablest students—those who use mathematics as their native language—have no call to look at the Appendices. Others should consult them as the need arises.

The definition of a vector space appears in Section 3 along with a few elementary theorems, but the formal development really begins with Chapter III. The delay gives the teacher a chance to drive home the importance of clear and precise writing before the student is plunged into the strange world of mathematical abstraction. Of course, the topics in Chapters I and II are designed to prepare the reader for what is to follow.

Many proofs are given in painful detail. Troublesome questions about their presentation are discussed, sometimes in the text, more often in the Appendices.

Two types of problem help the student to master the language—simple applications of the definitions to concrete cases and very easy proofs.

I have tried to eliminate routine computational exercises except in a few cases where the routines are genuinely important.

Some teachers will want to omit Section 1 and part or all of Chapter II, but ordinarily a minimal course in linear algebra will consist of the introductory chapters, I and II, and of Chapters III (linear independence, bases, etc.), IV (linear equations, transformations, and matrices), and some work with determinants. For physical scientists, inner products (Chapter VII) are fundamental. Only a limited knowledge of determinants is prerequisite for Chapter VII.

All my colleagues at Brown and many of my other friends will find here some of their ideas, borrowed gratefully, but without acknowledgment. I mention no names, not because I am unmindful of my debts, but because the list would be excessively long.

F. M. S.

Providence, Rhode Island
January 1963

NOTE TO THE READER

The prime aim of this book is to teach you about vector spaces, but it is designed to help you also with the grammar and vocabulary of mathematics. When there is some logical difficulty or new trick of notation, you will find, in the margin beside it, a reference to the Appendices. They are there to help you, not to interrupt your train of thought. If you follow an argument without difficulty, do not stop in the middle to look at an Appendix. Only you can decide how often you ought to consult them.

Like any language, mathematics is easier to read than to write. You may understand the proofs in the book, but have difficulty constructing your own. If so, the Appendices were written for you. Read them over once to see what they are about. Later, study them carefully in connection with appropriate parts of the text.

For easy reference, definitions, theorems, corollaries, and lemmas are all numbered consecutively by sections. For example, 11.1 and 11.2 are definitions, 11.3 and 11.4 are theorems, and 11.5 is a corollary. At the very end of the book the definitions, theorems, and corollaries are listed with the numbers of the pages on which they appear. Also, the number of the last theorem (or definition or corollary) on a page is given at the upper inside corner of that page.

Always think before you look up a reference to an earlier result. The context should tell you what sort of theorem is being applied. If you reconstruct it from memory, you will learn it far better than if you simply look it up. If you cannot reconstruct it, be sure to study it carefully when you refer to it.

Beware of memorizing definitions and theorems. It is the ideas and not the words that matter.

Equations are also numbered consecutively by sections. To distinguish equation numbers from theorem numbers the former appear in parentheses while the latter are always identified, e.g., Definition 10.5 or Corollary 17.7. Roman letters are used to denote vectors and Greek letters are used to denote numbers. A Greek alphabet appears at the end of the index of symbols.

Each chapter ends with a summary. You will save yourself much time and effort if you make sure that you are familiar with every result summarized before you go on to the next chapter.

TABLE OF CONTENTS

CHAPTER I   INTRODUCTION

CHAPTER II   THE PLANE

CHAPTER III   LINEAR DEPENDENCE, SPAN, DIMENSION, BASES, SUBSPACES

CHAPTER IV   LINEAR TRANSFORMATIONS

CHAPTER I

INTRODUCTION

As mathematics develops, its concepts become increasingly abstract. Tiny children are already meeting a mathematical abstraction when they learn to count. Two blocks or two pencils are real and concrete, but the idea of two-ness, which they have in common, is a concept created by the mind. Arithmetic is the study of this first-level abstraction, number.

Such abstractions save tremendous amounts of time and effort. Knowing that 3 times 7 is 21, one immediately realizes that if apples cost 7 cents apiece, then 3 of them cost 21 cents, and that 3 rockets costing 7 million dollars apiece together cost 21 million dollars. A single computation solves a myriad different problems.

In elementary algebra we pass to a new level of abstraction, studying the properties of numbers in general rather than such special facts as $3 \times 7 = 21$. This continual increase in generality is characteristic of mathematics. We study a variety of special situations or systems. Next we try to pick out the essential features which they have in common. Finally we explore the consequences of these common properties without reference to the special situation in which they arise.

You will soon have to take a giant step in the direction of generalization, for the special systems which motivate our study are, themselves, abstract. In this chapter and the next we will examine a few examples and write out explicitly the common features which will form the basis of our further study.

Section 1. An Example

The following proposition probably sounds familiar.

> *If the bisectors of two angles of a triangle are equal, then the triangle is isosceles.*

Try to prove it. Whether you use Euclidean methods or analytic

1

ones, you will find it difficult indeed.* We shall prove it analytically, but we use new concepts to abbreviate the dreadful computations a little. Our real interest is in these new concepts and our preliminary calculations will be long and detailed. The reader should study these calculations very carefully, because they are typical of abstract algebra. We introduce new objects and new operations for combining them. Next we list a few of their properties (in this case equations (1.1) to (1.7)). Finally we perform algebraic operations (equations (1.11), (1.12), etc.), using the listed properties and no others.

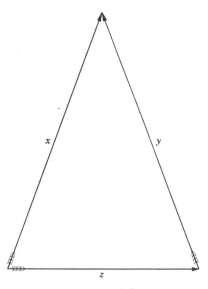

FIGURE 1.1

Think of the sides of the given triangle as if they were arrows laid on the ground and call them x, y, and z (see Fig. 1.1). The letters "x", "y", and "z" stand for the arrows themselves, not for their lengths. To denote their lengths we use "$\|x\|$", "$\|y\|$", and "$\|z\|$".

For a moment we forget about the triangle and talk about "arrows" in general. We think of arrows as unchanged if we move them to positions parallel to their original ones, but we forbid anyone to change the direction in which an arrow points. In other words, two arrows

* A simple proof was discovered in 1960 by L. M. Kelly. It is outlined in the hint to Example 4 on page 16 of H. S. M. Coxeter's fascinating book *Introduction to Geometry* (John Wiley & Sons, New York, 1961). Other proofs, by J. Lipman, G. Gilbert, and D. MacDonnell, are given in the answer booklet and in the German edition of Coxeter's book. The problem has an interesting history, outlined by J. A. McBride in the *Edinburgh Mathematical Notes* no. 33 (1943), pp. 1–13.

are to be regarded as one and the same thing if they have the same length and direction.

If x and y are any two arrows, we may move y to a new position (parallel, of course, to its original position) so that its notch coincides with the head of x (see Fig. 1.2). Now take an arrow whose notch coincides with that of x and whose head coincides with that of y in y's second position. Denote this new arrow by $x \oplus y$.

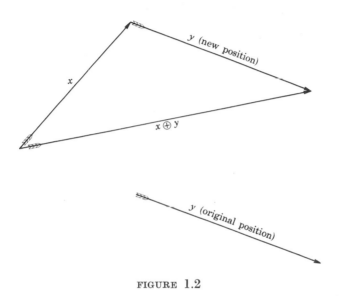

FIGURE 1.2

The operation of putting the arrows x and y together to get a new arrow $x \oplus y$ resembles, in many ways, the operation of adding two numbers. Later, we shall use "$+$" instead of "$\oplus$". Here at first, we use different symbols to emphasize the fact that $\oplus$ and $+$ are different operations used to combine totally different kinds of objects. Were we to use the familiar symbol "$+$" for the new and unfamiliar operation $\oplus$, the inexperienced reader might be tempted to use properties which are valid in the old context but not in the new. With very little practice it becomes easy to see from the context whether one is combining arrows or numbers. As soon as confusion is unlikely, you will find that the analogy between the operations is a tremendous help. Then it will save a good deal of mental effort to use a single symbol, "$+$", to denote both operations.

It is not hard to see (Fig. 1.3) that if we interchange the roles of x and y we get a new arrow, $y \oplus x$, which has the same length and direction as $x \oplus y$.   Since we are considering arrows to be equal if they have the same length and direction,*

APP.
A.2
EQS.

(1.1) $x \oplus y = y \oplus x.$

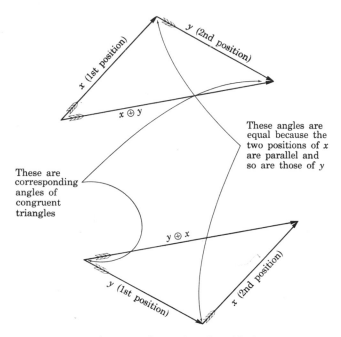

These angles are equal because the two positions of x are parallel and so are those of y

These are corresponding angles of congruent triangles

$x \oplus y$ and $y \oplus x$ make equal angles with the parallel lines y (1st position) and y (2nd position) hence they are parallel

FIGURE 1.3

From Fig. 1.4 you will see that this arrow addition has another familiar property,

(1.2) $x \oplus (y \oplus z) = (x \oplus y) \oplus z.$

If x is any arrow and α is any positive number, $\alpha * x$ will denote the arrow whose direction is the same as that of x, but whose length is α times the length of x.   If α is a negative number, the length of $\alpha * x$ is† $|\alpha| \cdot \|x\|$ and the direction of $\alpha * x$ is opposite to that of x.   If $\alpha = 0$ then $\alpha * x$ is the zero arrow, that is, an arrow whose notch and head coincide.

---

  * As explained in the Note to the Reader, the marginal notations refer to the appendices.   Here "APP. A.2" refers you to Appendix A, Section 2, and "EQS." is intended to remind you of the title of that Appendix, Equations and Identities.

  † Here, as usual, $|\alpha|$ is the absolute value of α, defined to be α if $\alpha \geqslant 0$ and $-\alpha$ if $\alpha \leqslant 0$.

From this definition we infer that

$$(1.3) \qquad \alpha*(\beta*x) = (\alpha\cdot\beta)*x,$$
$$(1.4) \qquad (\alpha+\beta)*x = (\alpha*x) \oplus (\beta*x),$$
$$(1.5) \qquad \alpha*(x \oplus y) = (\alpha*x) \oplus (\alpha*y), \quad \text{and}$$
$$(1.6) \qquad (0*x) \oplus y = y \oplus (0*x) = y = 1*y.$$

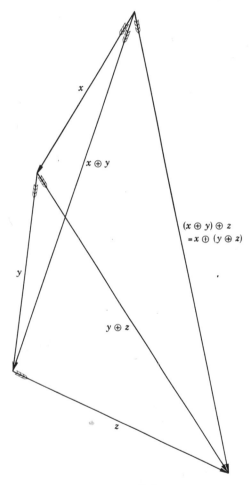

FIGURE 1.4

Moreover, if x and y are non-zero arrows whose directions are neither parallel nor opposite and if $\alpha*x=\beta*y$, then $\alpha=\beta=0$. We shall refer to this property as (1.7).

We now return to the problem of the bisectors. For the remainder of this section A, B, and C will stand for the vertices of a particular triangle and x, y, and z for the arrows from B to C, from A to C, and from B to A.

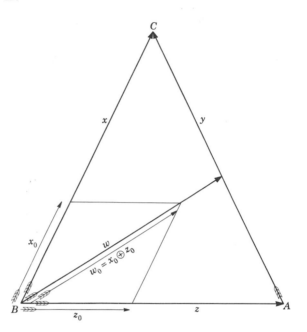

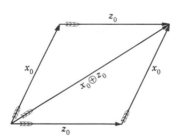

FIGURE 1.5

Note that x is the arrow sum of z and y, i.e.,

APP.
A.3
EQS. (1.8) $x = z \oplus y.$

Let w be the bisector of the angle at B so w is an arrow starting at B, terminating somewhere on the line AC, and making equal angles with x and z. We start by finding an arrow w_0 with the same direction as w. Consider two arrows x_0 and z_0, each one unit long and having the same directions as x and z. In the parallelogram at the bottom of Fig. 1.5 each side is one unit long. A simple appeal to the properties of congruent triangles shows that $x_0 \oplus z_0$ bisects the angle between x_0 and z_0. Let

(1.9)
$$w_0 = x_0 \oplus z_0.$$

Now $(1/\|x\|)*x$ is an arrow with the same direction as x. Its length is $(1/\|x\|)$ times the length of x, i.e., $(1/\|x\|)\cdot\|x\| = 1$. Thus $(1/\|x\|)*x$ is precisely our x_0. Similarly $z_0 = (1/\|z\|)*z$. Substituting in (1.9) we find

(1.10)
$$w_0 = \left[\frac{1}{\|x\|}*x\right] \oplus \left[\frac{1}{\|z\|}*z\right].$$

Since w has the same direction as w_0 there is a number α such that

(1.11)
$$w = \alpha*w_0$$

$$= \alpha*\left\{\left(\frac{1}{\|x\|}*x\right) \oplus \left(\frac{1}{\|z\|}*z\right)\right\} \qquad \text{[by (1.10)]}$$

$$= \left\{\alpha*\left(\frac{1}{\|x\|}*x\right)\right\} \oplus \left\{\alpha*\left(\frac{1}{\|z\|}*z\right)\right\} \qquad \text{[by (1.5)]}$$

$$= \left\{\left(\alpha\cdot\frac{1}{\|x\|}\right)*x\right\} \oplus \left\{\left(\alpha\cdot\frac{1}{\|z\|}\right)*z\right\} \qquad \text{[by (1.3)]}$$

$$= \left\{\frac{\alpha}{\|x\|}*x\right\} \oplus \left\{\frac{\alpha}{\|z\|}*z\right\}.$$

APP.
A.3
EQS.

Hereafter, we will not be so careful about parentheses, since the conventions are analogous to those used in elementary algebra—first perform all multiplications, $\cdot$ and $*$, and then all additions, $\oplus$. (Ordinary addition, $+$, does occur, but is usually accompanied by parentheses, showing that it must be performed before $*$ or $\oplus$.)

Since (1.8) tells us that $x = z \oplus y$, (1.11) yields

(1.12)
$$w = \frac{\alpha}{\|x\|}*(z \oplus y) \oplus \frac{\alpha}{\|z\|}*z$$

$$= \frac{\alpha}{\|z\|}*z \oplus \frac{\alpha}{\|x\|}*(z \oplus y) \qquad \text{[by (1.1)]}$$

$$= \frac{\alpha}{\|z\|}*z \oplus \left[\frac{\alpha}{\|x\|}*z \oplus \frac{\alpha}{\|x\|}*y\right] \qquad \text{[by (1.5)]}$$

$$= \left[\frac{\alpha}{\|z\|}*z \oplus \frac{\alpha}{\|x\|}*z\right] \oplus \frac{\alpha}{\|x\|}*y \qquad \text{[by (1.2)]}$$

$$= \left[\frac{\alpha}{\|z\|} + \frac{\alpha}{\|x\|}\right] *z \oplus \frac{\alpha}{\|x\|}*y \qquad \text{[by (1.4)]}$$

$$= \left[\alpha\,\frac{\|x\| + \|z\|}{\|x\| \cdot \|z\|}\right] *z \oplus \frac{\alpha}{\|x\|}*y$$

To calculate α explicitly we use a standard mathematical trick. We observe that we can get a new formula for something we already know and deduce the consequences.

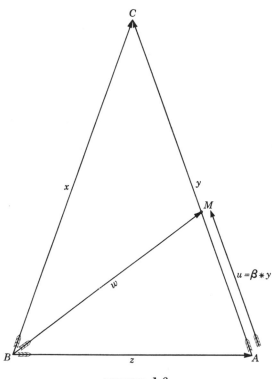

FIGURE 1.6

Let M (Fig. 1.6) be the point where the bisector of the angle B meets the side AC, and let u be the arrow from A to M. Since u has the same direction as y we can choose a number β so $u = \beta *y$. Now

(1.13) $$w = z \oplus u = 1*z \oplus \beta *y$$

so we have two formulas for w. Thus

(1.14) $$1*z \oplus \beta *y = \left[\alpha\,\frac{\|x\| + \|z\|}{\|x\| \cdot \|z\|}\right] *z \oplus \frac{\alpha}{\|x\|}*y.$$

If we could transpose terms and get some multiple of z equal to some multiple of y, we could apply (1.7). Unfortunately, our knowledge of the algebra of $\oplus$ and $*$ is not yet developed to the point where we can justify such transpositions. Nevertheless, the idea of the transposition suggests an alternative argument which is authorized under (1.1)–(1.6). We add $(-1)*z$ and $(-\alpha/\|x\|)*y$ to both sides of (1.14) and obtain

$$(1.15) \quad (-1)*z \oplus \left\{ (1*z \oplus \beta*y) \oplus \frac{-\alpha}{\|x\|}*y \right\}$$

APP.
A.5
EQS.

$$= (-1)*z \oplus \left\{ \left(\left[\alpha \frac{\|x\| + \|z\|}{\|x\| \cdot \|z\|} \right] *z \oplus \frac{\alpha}{\|x\|}*y \right) \oplus \frac{-\alpha}{\|x\|}*y \right\}.$$

(At this stage of our work, all the parentheses really are needed to show which addition is to be made first.) An application of (1.2) to each side yields

$$(1.16) \quad (-1)*z \oplus \left\{ 1*z \oplus \left(\beta*y \oplus \frac{-\alpha}{\|x\|}*y \right) \right\}$$

$$= (-1)*z \oplus \left\{ \left[\alpha \frac{\|x\| + \|z\|}{\|x\| \cdot \|y\|} \right] *z \oplus \left(\frac{\alpha}{\|x\|}*y \oplus \frac{-\alpha}{\|x\|}*y \right) \right\}.$$

To cut a long story short, we combine two applications of (1.2) and four applications of (1.4) into a single step and so obtain

$$(1.17) \qquad 0*z \oplus \left(\beta - \frac{\alpha}{\|x\|} \right) *y = \left(\alpha \frac{\|x\| + \|z\|}{\|x\| \cdot \|z\|} - 1 \right) *z \oplus 0*y.$$

However, according to (1.6), this is the same thing as

$$(1.18) \qquad \left(\beta - \frac{\alpha}{\|x\|} \right) *y = \left(\alpha \frac{\|x\| + \|z\|}{\|x\| \cdot \|z\|} - 1 \right) *z.$$

Since y and z are two sides of a triangle, they cannot have the same direction. Hence, according to (1.7), equation (1.18) implies that

$$\beta - \frac{\alpha}{\|x\|} = 0 \quad \text{and} \quad \alpha \frac{\|x\| + \|z\|}{\|x\| \cdot \|z\|} - 1 = 0.$$

From these we see that

$$\alpha = \frac{\|x\| \cdot \|z\|}{\|x\| + \|z\|} \quad \text{and} \quad \beta = \frac{\alpha}{\|x\|} = \frac{\|z\|}{\|x\| + \|z\|}.$$

Substituting this back in (1.13), we get

$$(1.19) \qquad w = z \oplus \frac{\|z\|}{\|x\| + \|z\|}*y.$$

So far we have been stressing the newness of our algebraic system—that $\oplus$ and $*$ are not ordinary addition and multiplication. We have calculated w in a long and tedious way, taking meticulous care to be sure that we use only algebraic properties explicitly stated in (1.1) to (1.7). The reader should now do it for himself quickly, writing just αx instead of $\alpha * x$, $x + y$ instead of $x \oplus y$, $x - y$ instead of $x \oplus (-1)*y$, and so forth. Do the manipulations as if all the familiar rules of algebra were known to be valid in our new system. For instance, (1.12) would be reduced to

$$w = \frac{\alpha}{\|x\|}\,(z+y) + \frac{\alpha}{\|z\|}\,z$$

$$= \left(\frac{\alpha}{\|x\|} + \frac{\alpha}{\|z\|}\right) z + \frac{\alpha}{\|x\|}\,y$$

$$= \alpha\,\frac{\|z\| + \|x\|}{\|x\|\cdot\|z\|}\,z + \frac{\alpha}{\|x\|}\,y.$$

You should also calculate the other bisector—call it v—although from the symmetry of the situation we can see that it must be

$$v = (-1)*z \oplus \frac{\|z\|}{\|y\| + \|z\|}*x.$$

This concludes the essential part of this section—work in a new algebraic system chosen to illustrate our later abstractions. What remains is simple trigonometry and complicated algebra completing the proof of the theorem.

The fact we borrow from trigonometry is the law of cosines:

> *The square on one side of a triangle is equal to the sum of the squares on the other two sides diminished by twice their product times the cosine of the angle between them.*

Let us apply the law of cosines to the two triangles BAC and BAM and, to abbreviate a little, let $a = \|x\|$, $b = \|y\|$, $c = \|z\|$, $p = a + c$, and $q = b + c$.

In the triangle BAC the angle at A is between sides of length c and b, while the third side has length a. Thus the law of cosines says

(1.20) $a^2 = c^2 + b^2 - 2cb \cos A.$

In the triangle BAM the angle A is between the side BA, of length c, and the side AM, of length $\|\beta * y\| = \{\|z\|/(\|x\| + \|z\|)\}\|y\| = cb/(a + c).$

The third side, BM, is the bisector of the angle CBA and its length is $\|w\|$. Hence

(1.21) $$\|w\|^2 = c^2 + \left(\frac{cb}{a+c}\right)^2 - 2c\,\frac{cb}{a+c}\cos A.$$

From (1.20) we see that

$$2cb\,\cos A = b^2 + c^2 - a^2 = b^2 + (c-a)(c+a).$$

Substituting this in (1.21), we obtain

(1.22) $$\|w\|^2 = c^2 + \left(\frac{cb}{a+c}\right)^2 - \frac{c}{a+c}[b^2 + (c-a)(c+a)]$$

$$= c^2 + \left(\frac{cb}{a+c}\right)^2 - \frac{cb^2}{a+c} - c(c-a)$$

$$= c^2 + \frac{c^2b^2}{(a+c)^2} - \frac{cb^2(a+c)}{(a+c)^2} - c^2 + ac$$

$$= ac - \frac{acb^2}{(a+c)^2} = ac - \frac{acb^2}{p^2}.$$

Similarly

(1.23) $$\|v\|^2 = bc - \frac{bca^2}{(b+c)^2} = bc - \frac{bca^2}{q^2}.$$

The hypothesis of the theorem is that $\|w\| = \|v\|$, whence $\|w\|^2 = \|v\|^2$ and, using (1.22) and (1.23),

$$\frac{ca}{p^2}(p^2 - b^2) = \frac{cb}{q^2}(q^2 - a^2).$$

Multiplying both sides by p^2q^2 and dividing by c, yields

$$q^2a(p^2 - b^2) = p^2b(q^2 - a^2),$$

or $$q^2a(p+b)(p-b) = p^2b(q+a)(q-a).$$

However, $p+b$ and $q+a$ are both equal to $a+b+c$, so we may divide both sides by this non-zero factor and infer

$$q^2a(p-b) = p^2b(q-a)$$

or $$q^2ap - q^2ab = p^2bq - p^2ba.$$

Transposing, we get

$$q^2ap - p^2bq + p^2ba - q^2ab = 0,$$

$$qp[qa - pb] + ab(p^2 - q^2) = 0,$$

$$qp[(c+b)a - (c+a)b] + ab(p+q)(p-q) = 0,$$

$$qp[ca - cb] + ab(p+q)(a-b) = 0,$$

and finally $\qquad\qquad \{q\,pc + ab(p+q)\}(a-b) = 0.$

Since the factor $\{q\,pc + ab(p+q)\}$ is positive, the factor $a-b$ must be zero and we infer, at long last,

$$a = b \quad \text{or} \quad \|x\| = \|y\|.$$

Q.E.D.

Section 2.   Further Examples

In Section 1 we introduced an algebraic system, our arrows with the operations $\oplus$ and $*$, to solve a particular problem; but the real power of modern algebra comes from the fact that it solves problems wholesale rather than individually.

Look at another example of an algebraic system with two operations $\oplus$ and $*$.   (Of course, $\oplus$ and $*$ now stand for operations in this new system, not for operations on the arrows of Section 1.)   Let $\mathscr{R}^4$ be the set of all ordered quadruples of real numbers.   Thus the members of $\mathscr{R}^4$ are objects of the form $(\xi_1, \xi_2, \xi_3, \xi_4)$ where ξ_1, ξ_2, ξ_3, and ξ_4 are real numbers.   If x and y are two such objects—say $x = (\xi_1, \xi_2, \xi_3, \xi_4)$ and $y = (\eta_1, \eta_2, \eta_3, \eta_4)$, and α is any real number—let us define $x \oplus y$ and $a * x$ by the formulas

$$x \oplus y = (\xi_1 + \eta_1, \xi_2 + \eta_2, \xi_3 + \eta_3, \xi_4 + \eta_4)$$

and $\qquad\qquad \alpha * x = (\alpha\xi_1, \alpha\xi_2, \alpha\xi_3, \alpha\xi_4).$

Clearly $x \oplus y$ and $\alpha * x$ are quadruples of numbers, that is, members of $\mathscr{R}^4$.   You will have no difficulty in proving that (1.1) to (1.6) hold in $\mathscr{R}^4$.   Thus any proposition which is derived from (1.1) to (1.6) alone is just as valid in $\mathscr{R}^4$ as in our "arrow" system.

A system which has these basic properties is called a vector space, and the study of vector spaces is important because there is an inexhaustible supply of such systems.   If we prove a theorem using (1.1) to (1.6) (or, as is customary, an equivalent set of basic assumptions), then we know that the result is valid in each and every one of this tremendous host of systems.   By studying vector spaces in this abstract fashion we get our theorems at wholesale rates.   The theorems we prove will be applicable whenever we meet a collection of objects satisfying (1.1) to (1.6), whether it be in quantum theory or in economics, in rocket engineering or in the geometry of surfaces.   A list of topics where vector spaces play a dominant role would include most of mathematics, physics, and engineering, as well as large and rapidly developing portions of economics and chemistry.

Before looking at further examples let us rewrite (1.1) to (1.6) in a more conventional way.

APP.
C.2
SETS

DEFINITION 2.1. We consider a set $\mathscr{V}$ of objects $x, y, \ldots$, and two operations $\oplus$ and $*$. We shall say that $\mathscr{V}$ is a *real vector space with respect to $\oplus$ and $*$* if and only if the following propositions hold.

For all x, y, and z in $\mathscr{V}$:

(2.1) $$x \oplus y \text{ is in } \mathscr{V},$$

APP.
B.2
VAR.

(2.2) $$x \oplus y = y \oplus x, \quad \text{and}$$

(2.3) $$(x \oplus y) \oplus z = x \oplus (y \oplus z).$$

APP.
B.4
VAR.

(2.4) For each x and y in $\mathscr{V}$ there is a z in $\mathscr{V}$ such that $x \oplus z = y$.

For all real numbers α and β and all x and y in $\mathscr{V}$

(2.5) $$\alpha * x \text{ is in } \mathscr{V},$$

(2.6) $$\alpha * (\beta * x) = (\alpha\beta) * x,$$

(2.7) $$1 * x = x,$$

(2.8) $$\alpha * (x \oplus y) = (\alpha * x) \oplus (\alpha * y), \quad \text{and}$$

(2.9) $$(\alpha + \beta) * x = (\alpha * x) \oplus (\beta * x).$$

Naturally the objects in a vector space will be called vectors.

Different authors refer to (2.4) and to (2.7) in different ways, but the other conditions have standard names. Equations (2.1) and (2.5) are called *closure axioms*. Roughly speaking, they say that the operations $\oplus$ and $*$ cannot lead one out of $\mathscr{V}$. Equation (2.2) is a *commutative law*. Equations (2.3) and (2.6) are called *associative laws*, while (2.8) and (2.9) are *distributive laws*.

In Definition 2.1 the word "real" appears twice. If we replace "real" by "complex," we get the definition of a complex vector space.* Real and complex vector spaces are equally important and it is pointless to go through all our arguments twice, once for the real case and

---

* Readers who know little or nothing of complex numbers need not be alarmed. A few of the problems demand a slight acquaintance with the algebra of complex numbers, but most of the text does not. In Chapter VII, where the complex numbers do play a significant role, we explain those of their properties which are needed.

once for the complex. At a later stage we will prove results which are valid only for complex vector spaces, but until then it is easier to treat both together. Instead of writing "real number" or "complex number" we will write "scalar." If, throughout, we think of scalars as real numbers, we have all the propositions about real vector spaces and similarly we obtain the theory of complex vector spaces by interpreting scalars as complex numbers.

To describe a particular vector space you first specify a set $\mathscr{V}$ and then define two operations. To define $\oplus$ you give a rule which enables your reader to calculate $\cdots \oplus$ --- whenever the blanks, $\cdots$ and ---, are filled with the names of elements of $\mathscr{V}$. To define $*$ you give a rule for calculating $\cdots * $ --- when the first blank is occupied by the name of a scalar and the second by the name of a vector.

Let us look at some examples. These will reappear often in the problems, so we give each a distinctive symbol. In this text the symbols $\mathscr{R}^n$, $\mathscr{C}^n$, $C(-\infty, +\infty)$, $C[\alpha, \beta]$, $\mathscr{S}$, $\mathscr{P}$, and $\mathscr{P}_n$, will stand for the vector spaces described below.

EXAMPLE $\mathscr{R}^n$. The set $\mathscr{R}^n$ consists of all ordered n-tuples of real numbers; i.e., a typical element of $\mathscr{R}^n$ is $(\xi_1, \xi_2, \ldots, \xi_n)$ where $\xi_1, \xi_2, \ldots, \xi_n$ are real numbers. If x and y are elements of $\mathscr{R}^n$, then each of them is an n-tuple. Say

$$x = (\xi_1, \xi_2, \ldots, \xi_n) \quad \text{and} \quad y = (\eta_1, \eta_2, \ldots, \eta_n).$$

We need a rule saying what the n-tuple $x \oplus y$ is to be. The simplest and most useful rule says that $x \oplus y$ is the n-tuple with $\xi_i + \eta_i$ in the i-th place. In a formula

$$(2.10) \quad (\xi_1, \xi_2, \ldots, \xi_n) \oplus (\eta_1, \eta_2, \ldots, \eta_n) = (\xi_1 + \eta_1, \xi_2 + \eta_2, \ldots, \xi_n + \eta_n).$$

Similarly, we define $*$ by the formula

$$(2.11) \qquad \alpha*(\xi_1, \xi_2, \ldots, \xi_n) = (\alpha\xi_1, \alpha\xi_2, \ldots, \alpha\xi_n).$$

To anyone used to looking at such formulae, it is immediately obvious that the operations $\oplus$ and $*$ as defined by (2.10) and (2.11) have the required properties (2.1) to (2.9). The novice should verify a few of them in detail and try to check the rest mentally. To see how the verification goes, let us look at (2.3). We want to prove that if x, y, and z are in $\mathscr{R}^n$ then

$$(x \oplus y) \oplus z = x \oplus (y \oplus z).$$

Consider three arbitrary elements of $\mathscr{R}^n$ and call them $(\xi_1, \xi_2, \ldots, \xi_n)$, $(\eta_1, \eta_2, \ldots, \eta_n)$, and $(\zeta_1, \zeta_2, \ldots, \zeta_n)$. We have

$$[(\xi_1, \xi_2, \ldots, \xi_n) \oplus (\eta_1, \eta_2, \ldots, \eta_n)] \oplus (\zeta_1, \zeta_2, \ldots, \zeta_n)$$
$$= [(\xi_1 + \eta_1, \xi_2 + \eta_2, \ldots, \xi_n + \eta_n)] \oplus (\zeta_1, \zeta_2, \ldots, \zeta_n)$$
$$= (\xi_1 + \eta_1 + \zeta_1, \xi_2 + \eta_2 + \zeta_2, \ldots, \xi_n + \eta_n + \zeta_n)$$
$$= (\xi_1, \xi_2, \ldots, \xi_n) \oplus (\eta_1 + \zeta_1, \eta_2 + \zeta_2, \ldots, \eta_n + \zeta_n)$$
$$= (\xi_1, \xi_2, \ldots, \xi_n) \oplus [(\eta_1, \eta_2, \ldots, \eta_n) \oplus (\zeta_1, \zeta_2, \ldots, \zeta_n)],$$

which is exactly the formula we wanted to establish.

EXAMPLE $\mathscr{C}^n$. The set $\mathscr{C}^n$ consists of all ordered n-tuples of complex numbers with $\oplus$ and $*$ defined by the equations (2.10) and (2.11).

*EXAMPLE $C(-\infty, +\infty)$. The set $C(-\infty, +\infty)$ consists of all real valued functions which are defined and continuous for all real values of the independent variable. If x and y belong to $C(-\infty, +\infty)$ then $x \oplus y$ should also be a function in $C(-\infty, +\infty)$. We must tell what function $x \oplus y$ is. We do so by giving a formula for the value of this function at τ: _{APP. F.10 FNS.}

(2.12) $(x \oplus y)(\tau) = x(\tau) + y(\tau).$

Similarly we define $*$ by the formula

(2.13) $(\alpha * x)(\tau) = \alpha \cdot x(\tau),$

for all real numbers τ.

To prove that $C(-\infty, +\infty)$ is a vector space one must show that the conditions (2.1) to (2.9) are satisfied. In the case of $\mathscr{R}^n$ the very definition of $\oplus$ made it plain that $x \oplus y$ belongs to $\mathscr{R}^n$ if x and y belong to it, i.e., $\mathscr{R}^n$ satisfies condition (2.1). It should be equally clear that if x and y belong to $C(-\infty, +\infty)$ then $x \oplus y$ is some sort of function, but it is not obvious that $x \oplus y$ belongs to $C(-\infty, +\infty)$. In fact, the proof that $C(-\infty, +\infty)$ satisfies (2.1) is one of the basic theorems of the calculus: the sum of two continuous functions is continuous. The verification of (2.5) also comes from the calculus. The remaining conditions provide relatively straightforward exercises.

EXAMPLE $C[\alpha, \beta]$. The set $C[\alpha, \beta]$ consists of all those continuous real valued functions which have for their domain the set of all real

---

* Any reader who has not studied the calculus should omit this example and the next two.

numbers τ such that $\alpha \leqslant \tau \leqslant \beta$. The operations $\oplus$ and $*$ are defined by equations (2.12) and (2.13). Here, of course, we require that these

equations be satisfied only for $\alpha \leqslant \tau \leqslant \beta$, not for all real τ.

If $\mathscr{V}$ is a vector space with respect to $\oplus$ and $*$, then any subset of $\mathscr{V}$ necessarily has the properties (2.2), (2.3), (2.6), (2.7), (2.8), and (2.9). Thus to verify that a subset of $\mathscr{V}$ is a vector space, one needs to check only (2.1), (2.4), and (2.5). A subset of $\mathscr{V}$ which is itself a vector space is called a subspace of $\mathscr{V}$.

EXAMPLE $\mathscr{S}$. In the study of differential equations one considers the set $\mathscr{S}$ consisting of all twice differentiable functions, x, with the property that

$$(2.14) \qquad x''(\tau) + a(\tau)x'(\tau) + b(\tau)x(\tau) = 0,$$

where a and b are given continuous functions of the real variable τ. Use (2.12) and (2.13) to define the operations $\oplus$ and $*$ for $\mathscr{S}$.

If x and y are in $\mathscr{S}$, then, by the familiar differentiation formulas,

$$(x \oplus y)'(\tau) = x'(\tau) + y'(\tau)$$

and
$$(x \oplus y)''(\tau) = x''(\tau) + y''(\tau).$$

Hence

$$(x \oplus y)''(\tau) + a(\tau)(x \oplus y)'(\tau) + b(\tau)(x \oplus y)(\tau)$$
$$= x''(\tau) + y''(\tau) + a(\tau)[x'(\tau) + y'(\tau)]$$
$$+ b(\tau)[x(\tau) + y(\tau)]$$
$$= [x''(\tau) + a(\tau)x'(\tau) + b(\tau)x(\tau)]$$
$$+ [y''(\tau) + a(\tau)y'(\tau) + b(\tau)y(\tau)]$$
$$= 0 + 0 = 0.$$

Thus $\mathscr{S}$ has property (2.1). Similarly the rule for differentiating a constant times a function enables us to see that (2.5) is satisfied in $\mathscr{S}$. Finally if x and y are given members of $\mathscr{S}$ and we let $z(\tau) = y(\tau) - x(\tau)$, then z is in $\mathscr{S}$ and $x \oplus z = y$, so (2.4) also holds. Thus $\mathscr{S}$ is a vector space. The fact that the set of all solutions of a linear homogeneous differential equation such as (2.14) form a vector space is the basis for much of the theory of differential equations.

EXAMPLE $\mathscr{P}$. The set $\mathscr{P}$ is the set of all polynomials with real coefficients. Thus x belongs to $\mathscr{P}$ if and only if x is a function defined by an equation of the form

$$x(\tau) = \alpha_0 + \alpha_1 \tau + \cdots + \alpha_{n-1} \tau^{n-1} + \alpha_n \tau^n,$$

where $\alpha_0, \alpha_1, \ldots, \alpha_n$, are real numbers. If

$$y(\tau) = \beta_0 + \beta_1 \tau + \cdots + \beta_{m-1} \tau^{m-1} + \beta_m \tau^m$$

and $m > n$, then

$$(2.15) \quad (x \oplus y)(\tau) = (\alpha_0 + \beta_0) + (\alpha_1 + \beta_1)\tau + \cdots + (\alpha_n + \beta_n)\tau^n$$
$$+ \beta_{n+1}\tau^{n+1} + \cdots + \beta_m \tau^m.$$

If $m \leqslant n$, (2.15) must be modified accordingly. We define $\gamma * x$ by the formula

$$(\gamma * x)(\tau) = \gamma \alpha_0 + \gamma \alpha_1 \tau + \cdots + \gamma \alpha_{n-1} \tau^{n-1} + \gamma \alpha_n \tau^n.$$

EXAMPLE $\mathscr{P}_n$. The set $\mathscr{P}_n$ consists of those polynomials in $\mathscr{P}$ whose degree is not greater than n. The operations in $\mathscr{P}_n$ are precisely the same as those in $\mathscr{P}$.

Section 3. Elementary Properties

Although the use of unfamiliar symbols such as $\oplus$ and $*$ is a help in stressing the fact that we are dealing with new operations, it is, in the long run, both clumsy and unnecessary. From now on we will write just $x + y$ instead of $x \oplus y$ and αx or $\alpha \cdot x$ instead of $\alpha * x$. With very little practice you will come to recognize instinctively whether "$+$" stands for the ordinary addition of scalars or for the addition symbol in the vector space. If it appears between names of scalars, it must stand for the former; if between names of vectors, for the latter. If α is a scalar and x is a vector, $\alpha + x$ is meaningless. Similarly, if α and β are scalars and x a vector, then the first, second, and fourth dots in $\alpha \cdot (\beta \cdot x) = (\alpha \cdot \beta) \cdot x$ must signal the multiplication of a vector by a scalar, while the third dot can only stand for the ordinary multiplication of scalars.

This double meaning of our symbols is not dangerous. If a formula would look correct in the context of elementary algebra and if it is meaningful in the context of vector algebra, it is virtually certain that it is a valid vector formula. Thus from a practical point of view, the ambiguous notation is immensely helpful.

From a more severe logical point of view, it is not so satisfactory. The novice is tempted to use formulas which are at best unverified and may even be nonsense. For example, at this stage of our study $0 \cdot x = 0$ is nonsense. The left-hand side is clear enough. The "x" must denote a vector and "0" is the name of a certain number. Hence "$0 \cdot x$" will be the name of a vector. If "$0 \cdot x = 0$" is a valid formula, the "0" on the right-hand side must also denote some vector, but in our abstract system we have, as yet, no vector named "0". Our first chore must be to prove several trivial identities so that we can manipulate vectors as easily and confidently as we manipulate numbers.

APP.
c.2
SETS
We begin by restating the fundamental definition in terms of our changed notation. The symbol "$\in$" is an abbreviation for such phrases as "is an element of", "is a member of", or sometimes just "in". The symbol "$\notin$" stands for "is not an element of", etc. Here and later we will use lower case roman letters for vectors and Greek for scalars.

DEFINITION 3.1. A set $\mathscr{V}$ with two operations $+$ and $\cdot$ is called a *vector space over the scalar field* $\mathscr{F}$* if and only if it satisfies the following axioms:

APP.
B.3
VAR.
(3.1)   if $x, y \in \mathscr{V}$ then $x + y \in \mathscr{V}$,

(3.2)   if $x, y \in \mathscr{V}$ then $x + y = y + x$,

(3.3)   if $x, y, z \in \mathscr{V}$ then $(x + y) + z = x + (y + z)$,

APP.
B.4
VAR.
(3.4)   if $x, y \in \mathscr{V}$ then for some $z \in \mathscr{V}$, $x + z = y$,

(3.5)   if $\alpha \in \mathscr{F}$ and $x \in \mathscr{V}$ then $\alpha \cdot x \in \mathscr{V}$,

(3.6)   if $\alpha, \beta \in \mathscr{F}$ and $x \in \mathscr{V}$ then $\alpha \cdot (\beta \cdot x) = (\alpha \cdot \beta) \cdot x$,

(3.7)   if $x \in \mathscr{V}$ then $1 \cdot x = x$,

(3.8)   if $\alpha \in \mathscr{F}$ and $x, y \in \mathscr{V}$ then $\alpha \cdot (x + y) = (\alpha \cdot x) + (\alpha \cdot y)$,   and

(3.9)   if $\alpha, \beta \in \mathscr{F}$ and $x \in \mathscr{V}$ then $(\alpha + \beta) \cdot x = (\alpha \cdot x) + (\beta \cdot x)$.

THEOREM 3.2. *If $\mathscr{V}$ is a vector space, then there is an $o \in \mathscr{V}$ such that for all $x \in \mathscr{V}$, $x + o = x$. Moreover, for all $y, z \in \mathscr{V}$, if $y + z = y$, then*
APP.
B.5
VAR.
$z = o$.

APP.
D.3
PRF.
PROOF.   Note carefully what must be proved.   Axiom (3.4) guarantees that if we are given one *particular* x we can find an o (which might change when x is changed) such that $x + o = x$. The first half of the theorem goes much further. It says we can choose o once and for all and that with this particular o the equation $x + o = x$ is valid for all x. The second half says more than that there is only one vector o with this property. It says that if a vector z satisfies one equation of the

---

* You may think of $\mathscr{F}$ either as the set of all real numbers or as the set of all complex numbers, but our work is valid in a far more general setting. In Chapters I–VI we will use only the most elementary properties of the number system. There are many other mathematical systems which share these properties. Any such system is called a *field*. With one small exception in Chapter V all the proofs remain valid when $\mathscr{F}$ is an arbitrary field.

form $y+z=y$, then z must be o and hence it will satisfy every equation of this form.

Choose any particular vector, v. By (3.4) there is a vector, o, such that

$$(3.10) \qquad\qquad v+o = v.$$

If x is any vector then, using (3.4) again, there is a $w \in \mathscr{V}$ so

$$(3.11) \qquad\qquad v+w = x.$$

Hence

$$(3.12)$$
$$
\begin{aligned}
x+o &= (v+w)+o && \text{[by (3.11)]}\\
&= v+(w+o) && \text{[by (3.3)]}\\
&= v+(o+w) && \text{[by (3.2)]}\\
&= (v+o)+w && \text{[by (3.3)]}\\
&= v+w && \text{[by (3.10)]}\\
&= x. && \text{[by (3.11)]}
\end{aligned}
$$

Now assume that $y+z=y$. Choose y' so $y+y'=o$. By the first part of the proof, $z+o=z$, so

$$
\begin{aligned}
z = z+o &= z+(y+y') = (z+y)+y'\\
&= (y+z)+y' = y+y' = o.
\end{aligned}
$$

$$\text{Q.E.D.}$$

We have just shown that there is one and only one element of $\mathscr{V}$ with the property that if you add it to any element of $\mathscr{V}$, the sum is that same element; i.e., this element behaves in vector addition exactly as zero behaves in scalar addition. Just as it is convenient to use a single symbol, "$+$", for both scalar and vector addition, so it is convenient to use the same symbol, "0", both for the scalar zero and this new vector zero. Whenever it occurs, it will be clear from the context what meaning is to be assigned to this theoretically ambiguous symbol, "0".

DEFINITION 3.3.   If $\mathscr{V}$ is a vector space, 0 is the (unique) element of $\mathscr{V}$ such that for all $x \in \mathscr{V}$, $x+0=x$.

In the proof of Theorem 3.2 we have carefully used parentheses to show which addition is to be performed first. Strictly speaking, an expression such as "$x+y+z$" is undefined. Axiom (3.1) says that the sum of two vectors is a vector, but says nothing about the sum of three vectors. However, (3.3) tells us that if we add the three vectors in either of the ways that do make sense—y to x and then z to their sum, or z to y and then this sum to x—we get the same result. It is natural to let $x+y+z$ stand for the vector which can be obtained in either of these two ways. By repeated application of the same principle it can be shown that no matter how one inserts parentheses to make a sum, $x_1+x_2+\cdots+x_n$, meaningful, one always obtains the same vector. Naturally, we shall usually omit these unessential parentheses, as also for such products as $\alpha_1\cdot\alpha_2\cdot\ldots\cdot\alpha_n\cdot x$.

On the other hand, one can insert parentheses in $\alpha\cdot x+y$ in two ways to get vectors $(\alpha\cdot x)+y$ and $\alpha\cdot(x+y)$, which are entirely different as a rule. To save writing these really essential parentheses we adopt the usual convention: except where parentheses explicitly indicate the contrary, perform all multiplications before adding the results.

The skill you developed in elementary algebra should make it possible for you to combine several applications of (3.2), (3.3), (3.6), (3.8), and (3.9) into a single step. For instance, you should have no difficulty with the following abbreviated version of (3.12):

$$x+o = (v+w)+o = (v+o)+w = v+w = x.$$

THEOREM 3.4. *If $\mathscr{V}$ is a vector space and $x, y \in \mathscr{V}$, then there is exactly one $z \in \mathscr{V}$ such that $x+z=y$.*

APP.
D.4
PRF.
PROOF. Our axiom (3.4) tells us that there is at least one such z. If z' also has the property that $x+z'=y$, then, choosing x' so $x+x'=0$, we have

$$z = z+0 = z+x+x' = y+x' = x+z'+x'$$
$$= z'+x+x' = z'+0 = z',$$

and z' is really the same element as z.

Q.E.D.

DEFINITION 3.5. If $\mathscr{V}$ is a vector space and x, y, then $y-x$ is the element of $\mathscr{V}$ such that $x+(y-x)=y$, and $-x$ is $0-x$.

We conclude this chapter with some examples of very minor theorems. Several similar theorems are included in the problems at the end of the chapter. Such phrases as "if $\mathscr{V}$ is a vector space" and "if $\ldots \in \mathscr{V}$" are to be understood whenever appropriate.

THEOREM 3.6. $0\cdot x=0$.

APP.
D.5
PRF.
PROOF. From Theorem 3.2 we know that if $x+z=x$, then $z=0$. But

(3.13)
$$x+0\cdot x = 1\cdot x+0\cdot x \qquad \text{[by (3.7)]}$$
$$= (1+0)\cdot x \qquad \text{[by (3.9)]}$$
$$= 1\cdot x$$
$$= x. \qquad \text{[by (3.7)]}$$

Q.E.D.

THEOREM 3.7. $(-1)x = -x$.

PROOF. By Definition 3.5, $-x$ is the only element which satisfies the equation $x + (-x) = 0$. However,

$$x + (-1)x = 1x + (-1)x = (1 + (-1))x = 0 \cdot x = 0.$$

Q.E.D.

THEOREM 3.8. $\alpha \cdot 0 = 0$.

PROOF. Since $\alpha \cdot 0 + \alpha \cdot 0 = \alpha(0 + 0) = \alpha \cdot 0$, it follows from the second part of Theorem 3.2 that

$$\alpha \cdot 0 = 0.$$

Q.E.D.

THEOREM 3.9. $x + (-y) = x - y$.

PROOF. By definition $x - y$ is the unique vector z such that $y + z = x$. But

$$y + [x + (-y)] = y + [x + (0 - y)]$$
$$= [y + (0 - y)] + x = 0 + x = x.$$

Q.E.D.

Hereafter we may adopt the usual conventions about omitting parentheses in expressions containing "$-$". For example, $x - y - z$ means $x + (-y) + (-z)$, not $x - (y - z)$.

Section 4. Problems

1. Starting from equations (1.8) and (1.19), prove that

$$w = x \oplus \frac{-\|x\|}{\|x\| + \|z\|} * y.$$

2. Let $x, y, z, w, v, \oplus$, and $*$ be defined as in Section 1. Prove that

$$v = (-1) * z \oplus \frac{\|z\|}{\|y\| + \|z\|} * x.$$

3. Let x and y be "arrows" whose notches lie at a point O and whose heads lie at A and B respectively. Show that the altitude arrow of the triangle OAB, dropped from the vertex A to the base OB is

$$\frac{\|x\|^2 + \|y\|^2 - \|y \oplus (-1) * x\|^2}{2\|y\|^2} * y \oplus (-1) * x$$

4. If x and y are "arrows" show that

$$\|x \oplus y\|^2 + \|x \oplus (-1) * y\|^2 = 2[\|x\|^2 + \|y\|^2].$$

5. Let x, y, z, w, and v be defined as in Section 1, but denote the addition of arrows by "$+$" and the multiplication of an arrow by a number by "$\cdot$" Without stopping to justify your steps by (1.1)–(1.7), calculate v.

6. If $\oplus$ and $*$ stand for ordinary addition and multiplication, show that the complex numbers form a real vector space, and that the real numbers do not form a complex vector space.

7. (a) Prove that the set $\mathscr{V}$ of all those ordered triples (ξ_1, ξ_2, ξ_3) of real numbers such that $\xi_3 = \xi_1 + \xi_2$ forms a real vector space. (It is taken for granted that $\oplus$ and $*$ are defined by (2.10) and (2.11).)

APP.
C.2
SETS
(b) Consider the set $\mathscr{T}$ of all those ordered triples of real numbers (ξ_1, ξ_2, ξ_3) such that $\xi_3 = \xi_1 + \xi_2^2$. Let $x = (1, 1, 2)$ and $y = (1, 2, 5)$. Show that x and y are both in $\mathscr{T}$. Show that $x \oplus y$ is not in $\mathscr{T}$.

8. Consider the following seven sets, $\mathscr{A}$, $\mathscr{B}$, $\mathscr{C}$, $\mathscr{D}$, $\mathscr{E}$, $\mathscr{G}$, $\mathscr{H}$. (We do not introduce a set $\mathscr{F}$ because we want the letter $\mathscr{F}$ to stand always for the scalar field.) Each of them is a subset of $C[0, 1]$ and we may use (2.12) and (2.13) to define operations $\oplus$ and $*$ for these subsets. For each subset (i) decide whether the subset is a vector space; (ii) if it is a vector space, show that (2.1), (2.4), and (2.5) are satisfied; (iii) if it is not a vector space, give an explicit example (like that in Problem 7b) showing that one of the axioms (2.1), (2.4), or (2.5) does not hold.

$\mathscr{A}$ = the set of those functions $x \in C[0, 1]$ such that $x(0) = x(1)$.

$\mathscr{B}$ = the set of those $x \in C[0, 1]$ such that $\int_0^1 x(\tau)\, d\tau = 1$.

$\mathscr{C}$ = the set of those $x \in C[0, 1]$ such that $x(0) = 2x'(1/2)$.

$\mathscr{D}$ = the set of those $x \in C[0, 1]$ such that $x''(\tau) = 0$ for all, $0 < \tau < 1$.

$\mathscr{E}$ = the set of those $x \in C[0, 1]$ such that $x(\tau) \geqslant 0$ for all τ, $0 \leqslant \tau \leqslant 1$.

$\mathscr{G}$ = the set of those $x \in C[0, 1]$ such that $x(\tau) = \mu\tau + \nu$ where μ and ν are integers.

$\mathscr{H}$ = the set of those $x \in C[0, 1]$ such that $x(0) = [x(1)]^2$.

9. Show that the set of all polynomials in one variable with complex coefficients (with the usual operations) forms a complex vector space. Does it form a real vector space?

10. Let $\mathscr{V}$ be a vector space over the scalar field $\mathscr{F}$. Prove the following assertions, making your arguments as complete and detailed as those of Theorems 3.2 and 3.6.

(a) For all x, y, $z \in \mathscr{V}$, $x - (y - z) = x - y + z$.

APP.
D.10
PRF.
(b) If $\alpha \in \mathscr{F}$, $x \in \mathscr{V}$, and $\alpha x = 0$ then either $\alpha = 0$ or $x = 0$ (or both).

(c) For all $\alpha \in \mathscr{F}$ and all x, y, $\in \mathscr{V}$, $\alpha(x - y) = \alpha x - \alpha y$.

11. Let $\mathscr{V}$ be a vector space over the scalar field $\mathscr{F}$. Prove the following assertions, giving an amount of detail comparable to that in the proofs of Theorems 3.4, 3.8, and 3.9.

(a) If 0 is the zero element of $\mathscr{V}$, then $-0 = 0$. (We need the introductory phrase here because the equation itself does not tell us whether 0 is the scalar zero or the vector zero.)

(b) $(-\alpha)x = -(\alpha x)$.

(c) $-(-x) = x$.

12. Let $\mathscr{V}$ be a real vector space and let $\mathscr{W}$ consist of all ordered pairs of elements of $\mathscr{V}$. For all $x = (x_1, x_2)$ and $y = (y_1, y_2)$ in $\mathscr{W}$ and all complex numbers $\alpha = \alpha_1 + i\alpha_2$ let

$$x + y = (x_1 + y_1, x_2 + y_2) \quad \text{and}$$
$$\alpha x = (\alpha_1 x_1 - \alpha_2 x_2, \alpha_2 x_1 + \alpha_1 x_2).$$

Prove that $\mathscr{W}$ is a complex vector space.

13. Let $\mathscr{A}$ be the set of all positive real numbers, and let $\mathscr{F}$ be the set of all real numbers. Define two operations $\oplus$ and $*$ by the formulas

$$x \oplus y = xy \quad \text{for} \quad x, y \in \mathscr{A}$$
$$\alpha * x = x^\alpha \quad \text{for} \quad x \in \mathscr{A}, \alpha \in \mathscr{F}.$$

Either prove that $\mathscr{A}$ is a vector space with respect to $\oplus$ and $*$ or prove that one of the axioms (2.1)–(2.9) does not hold for $\mathscr{A}$.

14. Let $\mathscr{V}$ be a vector space over $\mathscr{F}$, with operations $|$ and $\cdot$. Let $\mathscr{A}$ consist of all elements of $\mathscr{V}$ and one additional element which we will denote by e. Let the operations $\oplus$ and $*$ be defined by:

$$x \oplus y = x + y \quad \text{if} \quad x, y \in \mathscr{V},$$
$$x \oplus e = e \oplus x = x \quad \text{if} \quad x \in \mathscr{A},$$
$$\alpha * x = \alpha \cdot x \quad \text{if} \quad x \in \mathscr{V}, \alpha \in \mathscr{F}, \quad \text{and}$$
$$\alpha * e = e \quad \text{if} \quad \alpha \in \mathscr{F}.$$

Which of the axioms (2.1)–(2.9) does $\mathscr{A}$ satisfy?

Summary

The essential point of this chapter is the definition of a *vector space*. You must be prepared to recognize vector spaces whenever you meet them.

Hereafter, the elementary algebra of vectors as contained in Theorems 3.2, 3.4, 3.6–3.9 and Problems 4.10 and 4.11 will be taken for granted. These results are essential, but there is no need to memorize them. Your familiarity with elementary algebra will enable you to use them naturally and easily.

The sort of reasoning used in the proofs in Section 3 is important. You will meet it again and again both in this book and elsewhere, and you must be prepared to discover and write out the proofs of similar theorems.

CHAPTER II

THE PLANE

In this chapter we shall continue the study of the plane begun in Section 1. Our purpose is the same—to introduce important concepts in terms of familiar examples. When we study arbitrary vector spaces the intuition gained by working with the simplest of vector spaces proves to be enormously helpful.

Analytic geometry begins by assigning to each point in the plane an ordered pair of real numbers, that is, an element of $\mathscr{R}^2$. The most helpful picture of the relationship between the plane and $\mathscr{R}^2$ is the one used in Section 1. We visualize our vectors as arrows starting at the origin and terminating at a point (ξ_1, ξ_2) or, when convenient, as any arrow with the same length and direction. It is easy to see that the addition described pictorially in Section 1 is precisely the addition operation in $\mathscr{R}^2$.

There are two vital features of the Euclidian (or Cartesian) plane which are nowhere mentioned in our axioms (3.1)–(3.9): (i) the plane is two-dimensional, and (ii) the concept of distance plays a central role. Dimensionality is important in all vector spaces, and we shall study it in the next chapter. Much of the theory of finite-dimensional vector spaces is independent of any notion of distance, but those spaces in which distance is defined have particularly important applications. Such spaces will be the subject of Chapter VII.

Section 5. Dimension, Bases

The most obvious way to describe the fact that the plane is two-dimensional is simply to point to $\mathscr{R}^2$ and observe that its elements are pairs of scalars. Unfortunately, this scheme does not lead to the most fruitful view of dimensionality, so we examine two other ways of looking at $\mathscr{R}^2$.

Besides the origin there are two members of $\mathscr{R}^2$ which have a particularly simple form, $(1, 0)$ and $(0, 1)$. Let us call them x_1 and x_2 respectively. If $x = (\xi_1, \xi_2)$ is an element of $\mathscr{R}^2$ then there are scalars

α_1 and α_2 such that $x = \alpha_1 x_1 + \alpha_2 x_2$. In fact, there is exactly one such pair of scalars; we must have $\alpha_1 = \xi_1$ and $\alpha_2 = \xi_2$. Although x_1 and x_2 make the calculation particularly simple, *almost* any other pair of vectors would do as well. For instance, if $y_1 = (1, 3)$ and $y_2 = (-1, 2)$ and if $x = (\xi_1, \xi_2)$ is an element of $\mathscr{R}^2$ then

$$x = \alpha_1 y_1 + \alpha_2 y_2$$

where $\alpha_1 = (2\xi_1 + \xi_2)/5$ and $\alpha_2 = (-3\xi_1 + \xi_2)/5$.

Such pairs of vectors as x_1, x_2 or y_1, y_2 are called *bases*. Specifically, z_1 and z_2 form a basis for a vector space $\mathscr{V}$ if and only if for each x in $\mathscr{V}$ there is a uniquely determined pair of scalars α_1 and α_2 such that $x = \alpha_1 z_1 + \alpha_2 z_2$. More generally a set of vectors, $z_1, z_2, \ldots, z_n$, is a basis for $\mathscr{V}$ if and only if each x in $\mathscr{V}$ determines one and only one set of scalars, $\alpha_1, \alpha_2, \ldots, \alpha_n$, such that $x = \alpha_1 z_1 + \alpha_2 z_2 + \cdots + \alpha_n z_n$.

If one basis for a given vector space consists of n vectors then, as we shall prove in the next chapter, every basis consists of exactly n vectors. A vector space is said to be n-dimensional if each of its bases is made up of n vectors. According to this definition, $\mathscr{R}^2$ is two-dimensional because $(1, 0)$ and $(0, 1)$ are a basis for $\mathscr{R}^2$. Similarly, $(1, 0, 0)$, $(0, 1, 0)$, and $(0, 0, 1)$ form a basis for $\mathscr{R}^3$, so $\mathscr{R}^3$ is, as one would expect, three-dimensional.

How can we recognize those pairs of vectors which form bases for $\mathscr{R}^2$? Say $y = (\eta_1, \eta_2)$ and $z = (\zeta_1, \zeta_2)$ are two given vectors. The pair y, z form a basis for $\mathscr{R}^2$ if and only if, for each $x \in \mathscr{R}^2$, the equation

(5.1) $$x = \alpha y + \beta z$$

has a unique solution for the unknowns α and β. If $x = (\xi_1, \xi_2)$, this equation is just

$$
\begin{aligned}
(\xi_1, \xi_2) &= \alpha(\eta_1, \eta_2) + \beta(\zeta_1, \zeta_2) \\
&= (\alpha\eta_1, \alpha\eta_2) + (\beta\zeta_1, \beta\zeta_2) \\
&= (\alpha\eta_1 + \beta\zeta_1, \alpha\eta_2 + \beta\zeta_2)
\end{aligned}
$$

or, equivalently,

(5.2) $$\begin{cases} \eta_1\alpha + \zeta_1\beta = \xi_1 \\ \eta_2\alpha + \zeta_2\beta = \xi_2. \end{cases}$$

Multiplying the first equation by ζ_2 and the second by ζ_1 and subtracting, we see that if (5.2) is satisfied then

$$(\eta_1\zeta_2 - \eta_2\zeta_1)\alpha = \xi_1\zeta_2 - \xi_2\zeta_1.$$

A similar calculation yields

$$(\eta_1\zeta_2 - \eta_2\zeta_1)\beta = \eta_1\xi_2 - \eta_2\xi_1.$$

If $\eta_1\zeta_2 - \eta_2\zeta_1 \neq 0$, we see that the only pair of numbers which could possibly satisfy (5.1), or equivalently (5.2), is

$$\alpha = \frac{\xi_1\zeta_2 - \xi_2\zeta_1}{\eta_1\zeta_2 - \eta_2\zeta_1}, \qquad \beta = \frac{\eta_1\xi_2 - \eta_2\xi_1}{\eta_1\zeta_2 - \eta_2\zeta_1}.$$

By substituting these values in (5.1) we can show that they do, in fact, satisfy the equation. Thus if $\eta_1\zeta_2 - \eta_2\zeta_1 \neq 0$ then y and z constitute a basis for $\mathscr{R}^2$.

When $\eta_1\zeta_2 - \eta_2\zeta_1 = 0$ two things happen. On the one hand, there are always certain x's for which (5.1) has no solution and, on the other hand, if x is a vector such that (5.1) does have a solution, this solution is never unique. To show this we must consider two cases. One possibility is that $\eta_1 = \eta_2 = \zeta_1 = \zeta_2 = 0$ so $y = z = 0$. In this case $\alpha y + \beta z = 0$ for every α and β so (5.1) has a solution only if $x = 0$ and if $x = 0$ then every pair α, β is a solution. The other possibility is that at least one of η_1, η_2, ζ_1, and ζ_2 is not zero. To be specific let us assume that $\eta_2 \neq 0$. Then $\zeta_1 = \eta_1\zeta_2/\eta_2$ and (5.2) becomes

$$\left\{ \begin{array}{l} \eta_1\alpha + \dfrac{\eta_1\zeta_2}{\eta_2}\beta = \xi_1 \\[2mm] \eta_2\alpha + \zeta_2\beta = \xi_2 \end{array} \right.$$

or

$$\left\{ \begin{array}{l} \dfrac{\eta_1}{\eta_2}(\eta_2\alpha + \zeta_2\beta) = \xi_1 \\[2mm] \eta_2\alpha + \zeta_2\beta = \xi_2 \end{array} \right.$$

These have a solution only if $\xi_1 = (\eta_1/\eta_2)\xi_2$; and if this is the case, then, for every number γ, a solution is

$$\alpha = (\xi_2 - \zeta_2\gamma)/\eta_2, \qquad \beta = \gamma.$$

We will meet the quantity $\eta_1\zeta_2 - \eta_2\zeta_1$ again in Section 8, and Chapters V and VI will be devoted largely to it and its generalizations.

For the present we concentrate on an even more important aspect of the situation. The equation $\alpha y + \beta z = 0$ always has a solution. If y and z form a basis, its only solution is $\alpha = \beta = 0$. If the pair y, z is not a basis, then $\alpha y + \beta z = 0$ has a solution with at least one of α and β different from zero.

A set of vectors $y_1, y_2, \ldots, y_n$ is said to be *linearly independent* if the only solution of

$$(5.3) \qquad\qquad \alpha_1 y_1 + \alpha_2 y_2 + \cdots + \alpha_n y_n = 0$$

is $\alpha_1 = \alpha_2 = \cdots = \alpha_n = 0$. If (5.3) has a solution in which at least one of the α's is different from zero, then $y_1, y_2, \ldots, y_n$ are said to be *linearly dependent*.

We have shown that a pair of vectors form a basis for $\mathscr{R}^2$ if and only if they are linearly independent. What happens if we have three linearly independent vectors in $\mathscr{R}^2$? In fact, this cannot occur. (See Problem 9.1.)

It follows immediately from the definition of a basis that every basis is a linearly independent set of vectors. In the next chapter we shall prove a sort of converse: in an n-dimensional vector space any set of n linearly independent vectors form a basis. Thus the dimension of a space is the number of elements in those linearly independent sets which are as large as possible. The plane is two dimensional. The set consisting of $(1, 0)$ and $(0, 1)$ is linearly independent. Any set of three vectors in the plane is linearly dependent.

To see one application of linear independence look at the use we made of (1.7). That axiom asserts that two "arrows" which do not have the same direction are linearly independent.

Section 6.   Distance and Inner Products

This chapter illustrates the relationship between geometry and vector algebra. It does not attempt to give a logically adequate discussion of either. However, the main difficulty is psychological not logical. Traditionally, analytic geometry pictures the elements of $\mathscr{R}^2$ only as points. Sometimes we want to picture them as arrows starting at the origin and terminating at the point. Usually the context suggests the proper picture. If confusion seems likely, we may speak of "the vector x" when we want to visualize the arrow and of "the point x" when we want to think only of the tip of the arrow.

If x and y are points of $\mathscr{R}^2$ then the distance between them is the length of the vector $x-y$. As in Section 1 we shall denote this length by $\|x-y\|$. The most characteristic feature of distance in the Euclidean plane is given by the Pythagorean theorem: if x and y are perpendicular, then $\|x\|^2 + \|y\|^2 = \|x-y\|^2$. For vectors which are not perpendicular we have a more general formula, the law of cosines. One form of this reads: if θ is the angle between x and y, then

$$\|x\|^2 + \|y\|^2 - \|x-y\|^2 = 2 \cdot \|x\| \cdot \|y\| \cdot \cos \theta.$$

The quantity $\|x\| \cdot \|y\| \cdot \cos \theta$, which appears in this equation, has algebraic properties which make it far more convenient to use than distance. Because of its importance it is given a special name and notation. It is called the *scalar product* or *inner product* of x and y and is denoted by $\langle x, y \rangle$. (In physical applications it is often called the dot product and denoted by $x \cdot y$.   Mathematicians commonly use $(\ ,\ )$ instead of $\langle\ ,\ \rangle$.)   Thus

$$\langle x, y \rangle = (\|x\|^2 + \|y\|^2 - \|x-y\|^2)/2.$$

Let us now compute a formula for $\langle x, y \rangle$.   If $x = (\xi_1, \xi_2) \in \mathscr{R}^2$, then $\|x\|$ is given by the ordinary distance formula

$$\|x\| = \sqrt{\xi_1^2 + \xi_2^2}.$$

Thus if $x = (\xi_1, \xi_2)$ and $y = (\eta_1, \eta_2)$, we have $x - y = (\xi_1 - \eta_1, \xi_2 - \eta_2)$ and

$$
\begin{aligned}
(6.1) \quad \langle x, y \rangle &= (\|x\|^2 + \|y\|^2 - \|x-y\|^2)/2 \\
&= \{[\xi_1^2 + \xi_2^2] + [\eta_1^2 + \eta_2^2] - [(\xi_1 - \eta_1)^2 + (\xi_2 - \eta_2)^2]\}/2 \\
&= \{\xi_1^2 + \xi_2^2 + \eta_1^2 + \eta_2^2 - [\xi_1^2 - 2\xi_1\eta_1 + \eta_1^2 + \xi_2^2 - 2\xi_2\eta_2 + \eta_2^2]\}/2 \\
&= \xi_1\eta_1 + \xi_2\eta_2.
\end{aligned}
$$

It is now easy to derive the algebraic properties of $\langle x, y \rangle$ which make it so useful.   Let $x = (\xi_1, \xi_2)$, $y = (\eta_1, \eta_2)$ and $z = (\zeta_1, \zeta_2)$ be elements of $\mathscr{R}^2$ and let α be any real number.   Then

$$(6.2) \qquad \langle y, x \rangle = \xi_1\eta_1 + \xi_2\eta_2 = \langle x, y \rangle,$$

$$
\begin{aligned}
(6.3) \qquad \langle x + y, z \rangle &= \langle (\xi_1 + \eta_1, \xi_2 + \eta_2), (\zeta_1, \zeta_2) \rangle \\
&= (\xi_1 + \eta_1)\zeta_1 + (\xi_2 + \eta_2)\zeta_2 \\
&= \xi_1\zeta_1 + \xi_2\zeta_2 + \eta_1\zeta_1 + \eta_2\zeta_2 \\
&= \langle x, z \rangle + \langle y, z \rangle,
\end{aligned}
$$

$$
\begin{aligned}
(6.4) \qquad \langle \alpha x, y \rangle &= \langle (\alpha\xi_1, \alpha\xi_2), (\eta_1, \eta_2) \rangle \\
&= \alpha\xi_1 \cdot \eta_1 + \alpha\xi_2 \cdot \eta_2 \\
&= \alpha(\xi_1\eta_1 + \xi_2\eta_2) \\
&= \alpha\langle x, y \rangle,
\end{aligned}
$$

$$(6.5) \qquad \langle x, x \rangle = \xi_1^2 + \xi_2^2 \geqslant 0,$$

$$(6.6) \qquad \langle x, x \rangle = 0 \quad \text{if and only if} \quad x = 0, \quad \text{and}$$

$$(6.7) \qquad \|x\| = \sqrt{\xi_1^2 + \xi_2^2} = \sqrt{\langle x, x \rangle}.$$

We also note that the vectors x and y are perpendicular if and only if $\langle x, y \rangle = 0$.

As an example of how the study of inner products can be based on (6.2)–(6.6) we shall derive an important inequality.   If $x \neq 0$ and

$y \neq 0$, then, letting $\alpha = [(y, y)/(x, x)]^{1/4}$, $\beta = \alpha^{-1} = [(x, x)/(y, y)]^{1/4}$ we have

$$
\begin{aligned}
0 \leqslant & \langle \alpha x - \beta y, \alpha x - \beta y \rangle && \text{[by (6.5)]}\\
= & \langle \alpha x, \alpha x - \beta y \rangle + \langle -\beta y, \alpha x - \beta y \rangle && \text{[by (6.3)]}\\
= & \alpha \langle x, \alpha x - \beta y \rangle + (-\beta) \langle y, \alpha x - \beta y \rangle && \text{[by (6.4)]}\\
= & \alpha \langle \alpha x - \beta y, x \rangle - \beta \langle \alpha x - \beta y, y \rangle && \text{[by (6.2)]}\\
= & \alpha [\langle \alpha x, x \rangle + \langle -\beta y, x \rangle] - \beta [\langle \alpha x, y \rangle + \langle -\beta y, y \rangle] && \text{[by (6.3)]}\\
= & \alpha [\alpha \langle x, x \rangle - \beta \langle y, x \rangle] - \beta [\alpha \langle x, y \rangle - \beta \langle y, y \rangle] && \text{[by (6.4)]}\\
= & \alpha^2 \langle x, x \rangle - 2\alpha\beta \langle x, y \rangle - \beta^2 \langle y, y \rangle && \text{[by (6.2)]}\\
= & \sqrt{\langle y, y \rangle / \langle x, x \rangle} \langle x, x \rangle - 2 \langle x, y \rangle + \sqrt{\langle x, x \rangle / \langle y, y \rangle} \langle y, y \rangle\\
= & 2[\sqrt{\langle x, x \rangle \langle y, y \rangle} - \langle x, y \rangle].
\end{aligned}
$$

Thus $\langle x, y \rangle \leqslant \sqrt{\langle x, x \rangle} \sqrt{\langle y, y \rangle}$. Similarly, by computing $\langle \alpha x + \beta y, \alpha x + \beta y \rangle$ we get $-\langle x, y \rangle \leqslant \sqrt{\langle x, x \rangle} \sqrt{\langle y, y \rangle}$. Hence

(6.8) $$ |\langle x, y \rangle| \leqslant \sqrt{\langle x, x \rangle} \sqrt{\langle y, y \rangle}. $$

Although our derivation of (6.8) was based on the assumption $x \neq 0$, $y \neq 0$, the formula itself is obviously valid when one or both of them is zero. Moreover, if x and y are linearly independent, then $\alpha x - \beta y \neq 0$ and $\langle \alpha x - \beta y, \alpha x - \beta y \rangle > 0$ by (6.6). The same reasoning we used in deriving (6.8) serves to demonstrate:

(6.9)   If x and y are linearly independent, then

$$ |\langle x, y \rangle| < \sqrt{\langle x, x \rangle} \sqrt{\langle y, y \rangle}. $$

Furthermore, the reader should be able to demonstrate the converse of (6.9).

Section 7. Some Geometry

In order to become more familiar with the concepts introduced in Sections 5 and 6 we now rephrase some elementary geometry in these new terms.

Straight lines, circles, and the other loci studied in geometry are sets of points, and it is helpful to have a notation for the set of all points which fulfill a given condition. One standard notation is to write $\{x \mid \cdots\}$ for the set of all points x such that $\cdots$. Thus $\{x \mid \|x - a\| = \rho\}$ is the set of all vectors x such that the distance from x to a is ρ, i.e., the circle with center at a and radius ρ. Finite sets may be described by this device, but it is usually more convenient to

APP. C.3 SETS

denote a finite set simply by listing its members in braces. Thus $\{x, y, a, b\}$ is the set consisting of the elements x, y, a, and b.

THEOREM 7.1. *The straight line through the distinct points a and b is*

$$\{x \mid x-a \text{ and } b-a \text{ are linearly dependent}\}.$$

PROOF. Let $a = (\alpha_1, \alpha_2)$, $b = (\beta_1, \beta_2)$ and let $x = (\xi_1, \xi_2)$ be any point of $\mathscr{R}^2$. Because we are reserving roman letters for vectors we may not use the customary letters in the equation of the line. Remembering that with the traditional letters the equation of the line through the points (x_1, y_1) and (x_2, y_2) is $(y_2 - y_1)(x - x_1) = (x_2 - x_1)(y - y_1)$, we see (replacing x_1 by α_1, y_1 by α_2, x_2 by β_1, y_2 by β_2, x by ξ_1, and y by ξ_2) that x lies on the line if and only if

(7.1) $$(\beta_2 - \alpha_2)(\xi_1 - \alpha_1) = (\beta_1 - \alpha_1)(\xi_2 - \alpha_2).$$

If we set $b - a = c = (\gamma_1, \gamma_2)$ and $x - a = z = (\zeta_1, \zeta_2)$, we see that (7.1) is just $\gamma_2\zeta_1 = \gamma_1\zeta_2$ or $\zeta_1\gamma_2 - \zeta_2\gamma_1 = 0$. But, as we showed in Section 5, this is precisely the condition that z and c do not form a basis or, equivalently, that they are linearly dependent. We have proved that x lies on the line if and only if it satisfies the condition: $x - a$ and $b - a$ are linearly dependent. That is to say, the line is $\{x \mid x - a \text{ and } b - a$ are linearly dependent}.

APP.
c.3
SETS

Q.E.D.

THEOREM 7.2. *The straight line through the points a and b is*

$$\{x \mid x-a \text{ and } x-b \text{ are linearly dependent}\}.$$

NOTE. When we speak of the line through a and b, it is to be understood that a and b are distinct.

PROOF. In view of Theorem 7.1, what we want to show is that the condition

$$x - a \text{ and } x - b \text{ are linearly dependent,}$$

is equivalent to:

$$x - a \text{ and } b - a \text{ are linearly dependent.}$$

Assume $x - a$ and $x - b$ are linearly dependent. Thus there are scalars α and β not both zero such that

$$0 = \alpha(x-a) + \beta(x-b),$$

or, equivalently,

(7.2) $$0 = (\alpha+\beta)(x-a) + (-\beta)(b-a).$$

Since α and β are not both zero, $(\alpha+\beta)$ and $-\beta$ are not both zero.

Thus (7.2) tells us that there are two scalars, $\alpha+\beta$ and $-\beta$, not both zero, such that the first times $x-a$ plus the second times $b-a$ is zero. But to say that $x-a$ and $b-a$ are linearly dependent is just to say that there are two scalars with these properties. Thus we have shown that the first of our two conditions implies the second.

We give the converse more briefly. Assume that $x-a$ and $b-a$ are linearly dependent. Then there are scalars α and β, not both zero such that

$$0 = \alpha(x-a)+\beta(b-a)$$
$$= (\alpha+\beta)(x-a)+(-\beta)(x-b).$$

Since α and β are not both zero, $\alpha+\beta$ and $-\beta$ are not both zero and hence $x-a$ and $x-b$ are linearly dependent.

Q.E.D.

THEOREM 7.3.   *The straight line through the points a and b is $\{x \mid \text{for some } \tau,\ x=\tau b+(1-\tau)a\}=\{x \mid \text{for some } \tau,\ x=a+\tau(b-a)\}$.*

PROOF.   Assume that $x \in \{x \mid \text{for some } \tau,\ x=\tau b+(1-\tau)a\}$, which is just a fancy way of saying: for some τ, $x = \tau b+(1-\tau)a$. Then $\tau(x-b)+(1-\tau)(x-a)=0$. Since τ and $1-\tau$ cannot vanish simultaneously, $x-b$ and $x-a$ are linearly dependent and the point x lies on the given line.

APP. c.3 & c.7 SETS

Conversely, assume that x lies on the line so that, by Theorem 7.1, we have α and β, not both zero, and

(7.3) $\alpha(x-a)+\beta(b-a) = 0.$

Now $b \neq a$ so $b-a \neq 0$. Were $\alpha=0$ we should have $\beta(b-a)=0$ and, by Problem 4.10b, $\beta=0$. Thus $\alpha \neq 0$, so β/α is meaningful. Solving (7.3), we have $x=a+(\beta/\alpha)(b-a)=a+\tau(b-a)$ where $\tau=\beta/\alpha$.

Q.E.D.

Both Theorems 7.2 and 7.3 have analogs in spaces of higher dimensions. A point x lies in the same plane as a, b, and c if and only if $x-a$, $x-b$, and $x-c$ are linearly dependent. A point x lies on the line through a and b if and only if, for some τ, $x=a+\tau(b-a)$.

THEOREM 7.4.   *The shortest distance from the point c to the line through a and $a+b$ is*

$$\sqrt{\|c-a\|^2-\langle c-a,\ b\rangle^2/\|b\|^2}.$$

PROOF.   By Theorem 7.3 the points on the line are precisely the vectors of the form $a+\tau b$, for some number τ, so we wish to find the minimum value of $\|c-(a+\tau b)\|$ as τ varies. Let $d=c-a$ and let $\rho=\langle d,\ b\rangle/\langle b,\ b\rangle$. We want to show that the minimum of $\|d-\tau b\|$ is

$\sqrt{\|d\|^2 - \langle d, b \rangle^2 / \|b\|^2}$. Now the value of τ which makes $\|d - \tau b\|$ a minimum also minimizes

$$
\begin{aligned}
\|d - \tau b\|^2 &= \langle d - \tau b, d - \tau b \rangle \\
&= \langle d, d \rangle - 2\tau \langle d, b \rangle + \tau^2 \langle b, b \rangle \\
&= \langle d, d \rangle + \langle b, b \rangle [-2\tau \rho + \tau^2] \\
&= \langle d, d \rangle + \langle b, b \rangle [\rho^2 - 2\rho \tau + \tau^2] - \langle b, b \rangle \rho^2 \\
&= \langle d, d \rangle - \langle b, b \rangle \rho^2 + \langle b, b \rangle [\rho - \tau]^2.
\end{aligned}
$$

Clearly this minimum occurs when $\tau = \rho$ and is

$$
\begin{aligned}
\langle d, d \rangle - \langle b, b \rangle \rho^2 &= \langle d, d \rangle - \langle b, b \rangle [\langle d, b \rangle / \langle b, b \rangle]^2 \\
&= \|d\|^2 - \langle d, b \rangle^2 / \|b\|^2.
\end{aligned}
$$

Q.E.D.

Section 8.   Area

Consider a triangle whose vertices lie at the origin, $0 = (0, 0)$, and at the points $x = (\xi_1, \xi_2)$ and $y = (\eta_1, \eta_2)$. Its area is one-half the product of the length of the side from 0 to x times the length of the altitude from y to the side $0x$. The length of the side $0x$ is the length, $\|x\|$, of the vector x and the altitude is just the perpendicular distance from y to the line through 0 and x. Applying Theorem 7.4 we find that this altitude is

$$
\sqrt{\|y\|^2 - \langle y, x \rangle^2 / \|x\|^2} = \sqrt{\langle y, y \rangle - \frac{\langle y, x \rangle^2}{\langle x, x \rangle}}.
$$

Multiplying this by one-half the length, $\|x\| = \sqrt{\langle x, x \rangle}$, we find the area to be $\frac{1}{2} \sqrt{\langle x, x \rangle \langle y, y \rangle - \langle y, x \rangle^2}$.

Using the formula (6.1) for the inner products of two vectors in terms of their coordinates, we get

$$
\begin{aligned}
\langle x, x \rangle \langle y, y \rangle - \langle y, x \rangle^2 &= (\xi_1^2 + \xi_2^2)(\eta_1^2 + \eta_2^2) - (\xi_1 \eta_1 + \xi_2 \eta_2)^2 \\
&= \xi_1^2 \eta_1^2 + \xi_1^2 \eta_2^2 + \xi_2^2 \eta_1^2 + \xi_2^2 \eta_2^2 - \xi_1^2 \eta_1^2 - 2\xi_1 \eta_1 \xi_2 \eta_2 - \xi_2^2 \eta_2^2 \\
&= \xi_1^2 \eta_2^2 - 2\xi_1 \eta_2 \xi_2 \eta_1 + \xi_2^2 \eta_1^2 \\
&= (\xi_1 \eta_2 - \xi_2 \eta_1)^2.
\end{aligned}
$$

Thus the area of the triangle is $\frac{1}{2} \sqrt{(\xi_1 \eta_2 - \xi_2 \eta_1)^2}$.

THEOREM 8.1. *The area of the triangle with vertices at* $0 = (0, 0)$, $x = (\xi_1, \xi_2)$, *and* $y = (\eta_1, \eta_2)$ *is**

$$
|\xi_1 \eta_2 - \xi_2 \eta_1| / 2.
$$

---

* To avoid ambiguity, the square root of a positive number always means the positive square root. Thus $\sqrt{a^2} = a$ if $a > 0$, but $\sqrt{a^2} = -a$ if $a < 0$, and, of course, $\sqrt{0} = 0$. In other words, the naïve formula $\sqrt{a^2} = a$ is false and the correct formula is $\sqrt{a^2} = |a|$.

For algebraic purposes the absolute value is extremely inconvenient and one wants to deal not with the area but with the simpler quantity $(\xi_1\eta_2 - \xi_2\eta_1)/2$. This new quantity must not be confused with the area; so to talk about it we need a new name—preferably one both suggesting its relation to and stressing its difference from the ordinary area.

DEFINITION 8.2. The *oriented area* of the triangle with vertices at $0 = (0, 0)$, $x = (\xi_1, \xi_2)$, and $y = (\eta_1, \eta_2)$ is

$$(\xi_1\eta_2 - \xi_2\eta_1)/2.$$

The oriented area has a number of simple algebraic properties.

THEOREM 8.3. *If $\varphi(x, y)$ denotes the oriented area of the triangle with vertices at 0, x, and y, then for all vectors x, y, and z and all real numbers α,*

(8.1) $$\varphi(x, y) = -\varphi(y, x),$$

(8.2) $$\varphi(x+y, z) = \varphi(x, z) + \varphi(y, z),$$

(8.3) $$\varphi(\alpha x, y) = \alpha\varphi(x, y), \quad \text{and}$$

(8.4) $$\varphi(x + \alpha y, y) = \varphi(x, y).$$

The proof of this easy theorem and some further results about oriented area are left as problems.

The theory of area properly belongs to geometry and analysis, not to algebra. We will not develop it further in this book, but a generalization of the concept of oriented area will be the prime goal of Chapter V.

The algebraic simplicity achieved by introducing oriented areas carries with it no penalty in the form of lost geometric information. As soon as you know the oriented area of a triangle, you can calculate its ordinary area by taking the absolute value. This means that all the powerful algebraic tools to be developed in Chapter V will be immediately applicable to geometric problems. In fact, the central subject of that chapter, the theory of alternating forms, is the basis of much modern work in differential geometry.

Section 9.   Problems

1. Let x, y, and z be elements of $\mathscr{R}^2$. By considering the two cases (i) x and y are linearly dependent, and (ii) x and y are linearly independent (and hence form a basis) show that x, y, and z are linearly dependent.

2. For each of the following pairs of vectors x and y: (i) decide whether x and y are linearly independent or linearly dependent; (ii) if they are linearly independent, find scalars α and β so that $(3, -2) = \alpha x + \beta y$; and (iii) if they are linearly dependent, find scalars α and β, not both zero such that $\alpha x + \beta y = 0$ and either find two solutions of $(3, -2) = \alpha x + \beta y$, or show that this equation has no solutions.

(a) $x = (1, 2)$, $y = (2, 1)$,

(b) $x = (1, 2)$, $y = (2, 4)$,

(c) $x = (2, -3)$, $y = (-2, 3)$,

(d) $x = (-6, 4)$, $y = (2, -1)$,

(e) $x = (-6, 4)$, $y = (3, -2)$,

(f) $x = (-3, 2)$, $y = (6, -4)$,

(g) $x = (3, 0)$, $y = (0, 2)$.

3. State and prove the converse of (6.9). NOTE: This result, (6.8), and (6.9) are sometimes combined and restated as: for all vectors x and y

$$\langle x, x \rangle \langle y, y \rangle \geqslant \langle x, y \rangle^2$$

where equality holds if and only if x and y are linearly dependent.

4. Basing your work on (6.2), (6.3), and (6.4), show that

$$\langle \alpha x + \beta y, \gamma x + \delta y \rangle = \alpha \gamma \langle x, x \rangle + (\alpha \delta + \beta \gamma) \langle x, y \rangle + \beta \delta \langle y, y \rangle.$$

5. Show that x and y are linearly independent if and only if $x + y$ and $x - y$ are linearly independent.

6. Use the calculations of Theorem 7.4 and the fact that the perpendicular is the shortest distance from a point to a line to prove: the perpendicular from c to $\{x \mid$ for some $\tau, x = a + \tau b\}$ is $\{x \mid$ for some $\tau, x = c + \tau[d - \rho b]\}$ where $d = c - a$ and $\rho = \langle d, b \rangle / \langle b, b \rangle$.

7. Let a and b be any vectors and let $c = a - [\langle a, b \rangle / \langle b, b \rangle] \cdot b$. Show that $\langle c, b \rangle = 0$.

8. Show that if $\langle a, b \rangle = 0$, $a \neq 0$, and $b \neq 0$, then a and b are linearly independent.

9. Assume that $a, b \in \mathscr{R}^2$, $a \neq 0$, $b \neq 0$, and $\langle a, b \rangle = 0$. Show that $\langle x, b \rangle = 0$ if and only if for some α, $x = \alpha a$.
HINT: Use the fact that a and b form a basis.

10. Using the results of Problems 6, 7, 8, and 9, prove: The straight line through c and perpendicular to $\{x \mid$ for some $\tau, x = a + \tau b\}$ is $\{x \mid \langle x - c, b \rangle = 0\}$.

11. Prove Theorem 8.3.

12. Let $\psi(x, y)$ be the area of the triangle with vertices at 0, x, and y. Show that

$$\psi(x, y) = \psi(y, x),$$
$$\psi(\alpha x, y) = |\alpha| \psi(x, y), \quad \text{and}$$
$$\psi(x + \alpha y, y) = \psi(x, y).$$

HINT: This is very easy using Theorem 8.3. It is only a little harder if you start from Theorem 8.1.

13. Let $\psi(x, y)$ denote the area of the triangle with vertices at 0, x, and y. For each of the following triples of vectors, x, y, z, calculate $\psi(x, z)$, $\psi(y, z)$, and $\psi(x+y, z)$:

(a) $x = (1, 2)$, $\quad y = (-1, 4)$, $\quad z = (1, -3)$;

(b) $x = (2, 4)$, $\quad y = (2, 1)$, $\qquad z = (3, 5)$;

(c) $x = (2, 5)$, $\quad y = (-1, 2)$, $\quad z = (-1, 3)$.

Show that

for case (a), $\qquad\qquad \psi(x+y, z) = \psi(x, z) + \psi(y, z)$;

for case (b), $\qquad\qquad \psi(x+y, z) = -\psi(x, z) + \psi(y, z)$;

and for case (c), $\qquad \psi(x+y, z) = \psi(x, z) - \psi(y, z)$.

NOTE: It is this inconstancy in the formula for $\psi(x+y, z)$ which makes the area less convenient than the oriented area.

14. Let θ be a function of two vectors which satisfies the following identities

(9.1) $$\theta(x, y) = -\theta(y, x),$$

(9.2) $$\theta(\alpha x, y) = \alpha\theta(x, y), \quad \text{and}$$

(9.3) $$\theta(x+y, z) = \theta(x, z) + \theta(y, z).$$

(a) Use (9.1) to show that $\theta(x, x) = 0$.

(b) Use part (a) together with (9.2) and (9.3) to show that

$$\theta(x+\alpha y, y) = \theta(x, y).$$

(c) Use (9.1) and (9.3) to show that

$$\theta(x_1+x_2, y_1+y_2) = \theta(x_1, y_1) + \theta(x_1, y_2) + \theta(x_2, y_1) + \theta(x_2, y_2).$$

(d) Let $z_1 = (1, 0)$, $z_2 = (0, 1)$, $x = (\xi_1, \xi_2)$ and $y = (\eta_1, \eta_2)$. Use parts (c) and (a), (9.2), and the fact that $x = \xi_1 z_1 + \xi_2 z_2$, $y = \eta_1 z_1 + \eta_2 z_2$ to show that

$$\theta(x, y) = (\xi_1\eta_2 - \xi_2\eta_1) \cdot \theta(z_1, z_2).$$

(e) Use part (d) to show that there is a scalar ρ, independent of x and y, such that

$$\theta(x, y) = \rho \cdot \varphi(x, y),$$

where $\varphi(x, y)$ is the oriented area of the triangle with vertices at 0, x, y.

(f) Finally prove:

THEOREM 9.1. *If θ is a function which satisfies the identities* (9.1), (9.2), *and* (9.3) *and if* $\theta((1, 0), (0, 1)) = 1/2$, *then* $\theta(x, y)$ *is the oriented area of the triangle with vertices at* 0, x, *and* y.

15. Show that the area of the triangle with vertices at $x = (\xi_1, \xi_2)$, $y = (\eta_1, \eta_2)$, and $z = (\zeta_1, \zeta_2)$ is

$$|\xi_1\eta_2 - \xi_2\eta_1 + \eta_1\zeta_2 - \eta_2\zeta_1 + \zeta_1\xi_2 - \zeta_2\xi_1|/2.$$

Summary

The important concepts introduced in this chapter will be reintroduced later.   In preparation for the more formal treatment to follow you should be familiar with the following facts in $\mathscr{R}^2$:

1. By definition, two vectors x and y form a basis for $\mathscr{R}^2$ if and only if for each $z \in \mathscr{R}^2$ there are uniquely determined scalars α and β such that $z = \alpha x + \beta y$.

2. By definition, the vectors x and y are linearly independent if and only if the unique solution of $\alpha x + \beta y = 0$ is $\alpha = \beta = 0$.

3. In $\mathscr{R}^2$, x and y form a basis if and only if they are linearly independent.

4. The vectors $x = (\xi_1, \xi_2)$ and $y = (\eta_1, \eta_2)$ are linearly independent if and only if $\xi_1 \eta_2 - \xi_2 \eta_1 \neq 0$.

5. The inner product has the properties (6.2)–(6.8).

6. By attaching a suitable sign to the area of a triangle we obtain a quantity with the simple algebraic properties (8.1) to (8.4).

CHAPTER III

LINEAR DEPENDENCE, SPAN, DIMENSION, BASES, SUBSPACES

Up to this point our work has been anticipatory, merely a suggestion of what is to follow. Now we plunge into the main stream of mathematics. The new material is abstract—formal definitions, theorems, and proofs—but always it is suggested by the specific examples and directed towards its eventual application.

The formal material demands of the reader both sophistication and patience. You must be sophisticated enough to accept the abstractions as such and to use no properties except those explicitly set forth. Yet all the while, you should keep in the back of your mind the examples which suggested the abstractions. Patience is needed because mastery of the subject is essential. A half-understood definition or theorem is worse than useless. You must know exactly what each one says.

Of course, it is the ideas which are important, not the words. Do not try to memorize the definitions verbatim. Instead, check your memory, every so often, by making a list of all the concepts defined in a particular section. Then, in your own words, give a definition for each of them. Finally, compare your definitions with those in the text to see that you have said precisely what you mean.

You will probably not be able to remember all the theorems individually. If you are sure you know what each one says, when you read it, and understand each application that appears in a later proof, you may hope to remember enough to use the theorem when the need arises.

It is important to understand each detail in the proofs. Only by doing so can you learn how proofs are constructed. Do not, however, try to memorize proofs. The important thing is to be able to give your own proofs, both of known theorems and of new results. If a theorem is so important that you must know how to prove it, first see if your mathematical education has progressed to the point where you can prove it without outside help. If not, read the proof and try to pick out the key ideas. Get the skeleton of the proof clearly in mind and you will be able to fill in the details.

Section 12 is the heart of the present chapter. In it we develop the fundamental facts about bases, and bases are the essential tool for all our later work.

The material in Sections 10 and 11 is important in its own right, but the primary aim of those sections is to prepare the ground for Section 12.

The purpose of Section 13 is less obvious. If you find the theorems interesting and the proofs ingenious, well and good. Otherwise, you will have to possess your soul in patience, confident that the material will find important applications eventually.

Most of the time we will speak as if we were confining our attention to a single vector space, $\mathscr{V}$. When we speak of a vector we always mean a vector in the space $\mathscr{V}$. Obviously, everything we say applies to any vector space. Throughout, $\mathscr{F}$ is the scalar field of $\mathscr{V}$.

Section 10.   Linear Dependence and Independence

For the sake of honesty, we begin by pointing out a terminological difficulty even though its practical importance is negligible. In our very first definition we will use the phrase "$x_1, x_2, \ldots, x_n$, are linearly dependent." Soon we will need to look at some, but not all, of the x's and the notion of a subset appears to be made to order for this purpose. Unfortunately, in studying linear dependence and independence, possible repetitions of elements are important whereas in listing the elements of a set, repetitions are to be neglected. For example the sets $\{(1, 0), (0, 1), (1, 0)\}$ and $\{(1, 0), (0, 1)\}$ are identical, but it will turn out that the vectors $(1, 0)$, $(0, 1)$, and $(1, 0)$ are linearly dependent while the vectors $(1, 0)$ and $(0, 1)$ are linearly independent.

APP.
C.7
SETS

For convenience, we will continue to use the traditional, but inexact, phrase "the set of vectors $x_1, x_2, \ldots, x_n$ is linearly dependent" and will talk of subsets of $x_1, x_2, \ldots, x_n$ even when we wish to take account of possible repetitions in the list. Our one concession to purists will be the omission of the braces, { }, when we use the word "set" in this imprecise way. After this long word of warning, you may safely dismiss from your mind the whole troublesome question.

DEFINITION 10.1.   The vectors $x_1, x_2, \ldots, x_n$ are *linearly independent* if* the condition:

APP.
E.2
IND.

$$\sum_{i=1}^{n} \alpha_i x_i = 0,$$

* In definitions the single word "if" is often used instead of the more accurate phrase "if and only if."

implies that $\alpha_i = 0$, for $i = 1, 2, \ldots, n$. They are said to be *linearly dependent* if they are not linearly independent, i.e., if there are scalars $\alpha_1, \alpha_2, \ldots, \alpha_n$, not all zero, such that

APP.
B.7
VAR.

$$\sum_{i=1}^{n} \alpha_i x_i = 0.$$

THEOREM 10.2.   *Each subset* of a linearly independent set of vectors is linearly independent.*

PROOF.   The order of the elements is immaterial, so it will be sufficient to prove that if $x_1, x_2, \ldots, x_n$ are linearly independent and $m \leqslant n$ then $x_1, x_2, \ldots, x_m$ are linearly independent.

Assume that $x_1, x_2, \ldots, x_n$ are linearly independent and that $m \leqslant n$. Referring to the definition we see that what we must prove is:

$$\text{if } \sum_{i=1}^{m} \alpha_i x_i = 0 \quad \text{then} \quad \alpha_1 = \alpha_2 = \cdots = \alpha_m = 0.$$

APP.
D.8
PRF.

Assume $\sum_{i=1}^{m} \alpha_i x_i = 0$ and introduce new scalars $\alpha_{m+1}, \alpha_{m+2}, \ldots, \alpha_n$ each equal to zero.   Using our assumption, we have

$$\sum_{i=1}^{n} \alpha_i x_i = \sum_{i=1}^{m} \alpha_i x_i + \sum_{i=m+1}^{n} \alpha_i x_i$$

APP.
E.3
IND.

$$= 0 + \sum_{i=m+1}^{n} 0 \cdot x_i = 0 + 0 = 0.$$

Since $x_1, x_2, \ldots, x_n$, are linearly independent, Definition 10.1 tells us that this equation implies that all the α's are zero.   In particular, $\alpha_1 = \alpha_2 = \cdots = \alpha_m = 0$.

$$\text{Q.E.D.}$$

COROLLARY 10.3.   *If a subset of a set of vectors is linearly dependent then the original set is linearly dependent.*

THEOREM 10.4.   *If $x_1, x_2, \ldots, x_n$ are linearly independent elements of $\mathscr{V}$, then for each $y \in \mathscr{V}$, the equation*†

$$\sum_i \alpha_i x_i = y$$

has at most one solution.

---

* For completeness, one should consider the empty set (see Appendix C.8) which is a subset of every set.   Like most arguments involving the empty set, the proof that it is linearly independent has the appearance of a logical quibble.   For the amusement of readers who enjoy such quibbles, the proof is given in Appendix C.10.   Usually, we will ignore the existence of the empty set.

†When the limits of summation are quite clear from the context, we often omit them.

PROOF. If the equation has no solution there is nothing to prove, so let us assume that $\alpha_1, \alpha_2, \ldots, \alpha_n$ is a solution. We want to prove that if $\alpha_1', \alpha_2', \ldots, \alpha_n'$ is a solution then it is the one we already know, i.e., that $\alpha_i' = \alpha_i$ for $i = 1, 2, \ldots, n$.

If both the α''s and the α's are solutions, we have

APP.
E.4
IND.
$$(10.1) \qquad 0 = y - y = \sum_i \alpha_i' x_i - \sum_i \alpha_i x_i = \sum_i (\alpha_i' - \alpha_i) x_i.$$

APP.
D.1
PRF.
Since the x's are linearly independent, Definition 10.1 tells us that $\alpha_i' - \alpha_i = 0$ for $i = 1, 2, \ldots, n$.

Such that $\alpha_i' = \alpha_i$ ——————————————— Q.E.D.

DEFINITION 10.5. A vector y is said to be a *linear combination* of $x_1, x_2, \ldots, x_n$ if there are scalars $\alpha_1, \alpha_2, \ldots, \alpha_n$ such that $x = \sum_i \alpha_i x_i$.

Note that we do not require any of the α's to be different from zero. In fact, zero is a linear combination of every set of vectors. The linear combination $\sum_i 0 \cdot x_i$ is called the trivial linear combination of the x's. Thus Definition 10.1 can be rephrased: $x_1, x_2, \ldots, x_n$ are linearly dependent if some non-trivial linear combination of them is zero; they are linearly independent if no non-trivial linear combination of them is zero.

DEFINITION 10.6. If $\mathscr{A}$ is a subset of the vector space $\mathscr{V}$, the *span* of $\mathscr{A}$ is the set $\mathrm{Sp}\mathscr{A}$ consisting of all linear combinations of finite subsets of $\mathscr{A}$.

This definition calls for several comments. It differs from those that precede it in that here we think about infinite sets of vectors. As we shall prove later, in a finite-dimensional vector space it is always possible to choose, from any set $\mathscr{A}$, a finite subset whose span is the same as that of $\mathscr{A}$, but we do not always want to take the trouble to make such a selection. Combining Definitions 10.5 and 10.6, we see that $\mathrm{Sp}\mathscr{A}$ consists of all vectors of the form $\sum_{i=1}^{n} \alpha_i x_i$ where the α's are scalars and the x's are elements of $\mathscr{A}$. The word "span" is also used as a verb. We will say that $\mathscr{A}$ spans $\mathrm{Sp}\mathscr{A}$. Elsewhere you may meet the verb "generate": $\mathscr{A}$ generates $\mathrm{Sp}\mathscr{A}$. Finally, the notation "$\mathrm{Sp}\mathscr{A}$" is far from universal.

It is a great help to visualize the situation in $\mathscr{R}^3$. First consider the case where $\mathscr{A}$ consists of a single vector x. The linear combinations of x alone are simply multiples of x, and the span of x consists of all the vectors with the same direction as x. If $\mathscr{A}$ consists of two linearly independent vectors x and y then the multiples of x lie on one line through the origin and the multiples of y lie on another. The span of

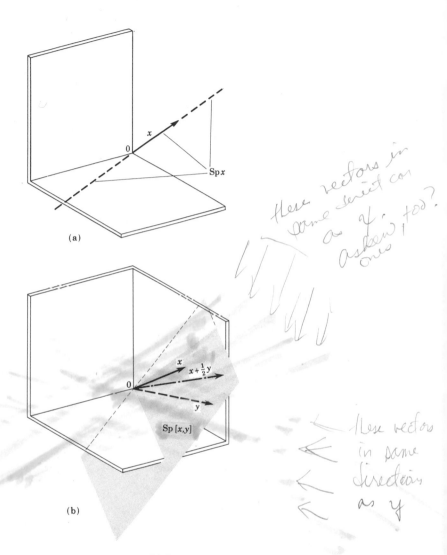

FIGURE 10.1

x and y consists of the plane which contains these two lines (see Fig. 10.1). As we will prove later, any three linearly independent vectors in $\mathscr{R}^3$ span the whole of $\mathscr{R}^3$. On the other hand if x, y, z are linearly dependent but do not all lie on a single line, their span is the plane containing them (Fig. 10.2). Let us call the whole of $\mathscr{R}^3$, planes through the origin, lines through the origin, and the set consisting of

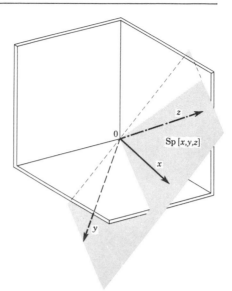

FIGURE 10.2

the zero vector alone, subspaces. In general Sp$\mathscr{A}$ is the smallest
subspace containing $\mathscr{A}$. For instance in Fig. 10.3 $\mathscr{A}$ is an infinite
set lying wholly in a plane containing the origin; Sp$\mathscr{A}$ is that plane.

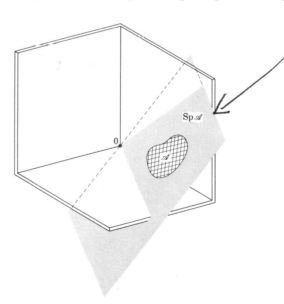

FIGURE 10.3

since Sp𝒜 *contains* 𝒜

THEOREM 10.7. *If* $\mathscr{A} \subseteq \mathrm{Sp}\mathscr{B}$, *then* $\mathrm{Sp}\mathscr{A} \subseteq \mathrm{Sp}\mathscr{B}$.

APP.
C.7
SETS

PROOF. Assume that $x \in \mathrm{Sp}\mathscr{A}$ so there are scalars $\alpha_1, \alpha_2, \ldots, \alpha_m$ and vectors $x_1, x_2, \ldots, x_m \in \mathscr{A}$ such that

$$x = \sum_{i=1}^{m} \alpha_i x_i.$$

Our assumption is that $\mathscr{A} \subseteq \mathrm{Sp}\mathscr{B}$ so each x_i, because it lies in $\mathscr{A}$, must also belong to $\mathrm{Sp}\mathscr{B}$. To say that $x_i \in \mathrm{Sp}\mathscr{B}$ is to say that there are scalars $\beta_1^i, \beta_2^i, \ldots, \beta_{n_i}^i$ and vectors $y_1^i, y_2^i, \ldots, y_{n_i}^i \in \mathscr{B}$ so

APP.
E.7
IND.

$$x_i = \sum_{j=1}^{n_i} \beta_j^i y_j^i.$$

Thus

(10.2)
$$\begin{aligned}
x &= \sum_{i=1}^{m} \alpha_i \left(\sum_{j=1}^{n_i} \beta_j^i y_j^i \right) \\
&= (\alpha_1 \beta_1^1 y_1^1 + \alpha_1 \beta_2^1 y_2^1 + \cdots + \alpha_1 \beta_{n_1}^1 y_{n_1}^1) \\
&\quad + (\alpha_2 \beta_1^2 y_1^2 + \alpha_2 \beta_2^2 y_2^2 + \cdots + \alpha_2 \beta_{n_2}^2 y_{n_2}^2) \\
&\quad + \cdots \\
&\quad + (\alpha_m \beta_1^m y_1^m + \alpha_m \beta_2^m y_2^m + \cdots + \alpha_m \beta_{n_m}^m y_{n_m}^m).
\end{aligned}$$

That is to say, x is a linear combination of elements, $y_1^1, \ldots, y_{n_1}^1, y_1^2, \ldots, y_{n_2}^2, \ldots, y_1^m, \ldots, y_{n_m}^m$, in $\mathscr{B}$. By Definition 10.6, $x \in \mathrm{Sp}\mathscr{B}$.

$$\text{Q.E.D.}$$

It is often necessary to find linearly independent sets of vectors. The next theorem is particularly useful because it tells us that, out of any finite set of vectors, it is always possible to choose a linearly independent set with the same span as the original set. Moreover, if we happen to know that certain vectors in the original set are linearly independent, the choice can be made in such a way as to include these vectors in the final set.

The theorem is very formal and it may help to have a picture of what is going on. We will be given a finite collection of vectors, $x_1, x_2, \ldots, x_n$, and the first m of them will be linearly independent. Figure 10.4 illustrates a case where $n = 5$ and $m = 2$. We want to choose a subset $\mathscr{A}$ from among x_1, x_2, x_3, x_4, and x_5 in such a way that the subset is linearly independent and has the same span as the original set. We start by putting x_1 in $\mathscr{A}$. Next we look at x_2. Examining Fig. 10.4, we see that $x_2 \notin \mathrm{Sp}x_1$. Such a vector is put in $\mathscr{A}$. In Fig. 10.4 the span of x_1 and x_2 is the shaded plane; x_3 lies in this plane. The set $\mathscr{A}$ will consist precisely of those x's which do not lie in the span of their predecessors. Thus, since $x_3 \in \text{Sp}[x_1, x_2]$, we will not include it in $\mathscr{A}$. In the illustration x_4 does not lie in $\text{Sp}[x_1, x_2, x_3]$ so we put x_4 in $\mathscr{A}$. In this case x_1, x_2, x_3, and x_4, span the whole of $\mathscr{R}^3$, so certainly $x_5 \in \text{Sp}[x_1, x_2, x_3, x_4]$. Accordingly we

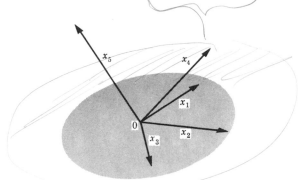

FIGURE 10.4

do not put it in $\mathscr{A}$. This exhausts our original set. We have put x_1, x_2, and x_4 in $\mathscr{A}$ and omitted x_3 and x_5. In this example then, $\mathscr{A} = \{x_1, x_2, x_4\}$.

THEOREM 10.8.   *If x_1, x_2, ..., x_n are vectors and if the first m of them, x_1, x_2, ..., x_m, are linearly independent, then there is a subset $\mathscr{A}$ of x_1, ..., x_m, x_{m+1}, ..., x_n with the following properties:*

   (i) *$\mathscr{A}$ is linearly independent,*

   (ii) *x_1, x_2, ..., $x_m \in \mathscr{A}$, and*

   (iii) *$\text{Sp}\mathscr{A} = \text{Sp}[x_1, x_2, ..., x_n]$.*

APP.
E.9
IND.

PROOF.   Let $\mathscr{A}$ consist of x_1 and of those x_j such that $x_j \notin \text{Sp}[x_1, x_2, ..., x_{j-1}]$. Let j_1 be the least index such that $x_{j_1} \in \mathscr{A}$ (in fact $j_1 = 1$), let j_2 be the next index such that $x_{j_2} \in \mathscr{A}$, and so on until we come to the largest index, call it j_l, such that $x_{j_l} \in \mathscr{A}$. Thus $\mathscr{A}$ consists of x_{j_1}, x_{j_2}, ..., x_{j_l}.

We must show that $\mathscr{A}$ has each of the required properties.

PROOF OF (i).   Assume, to the contrary, that there are scalars α_{j_1}, α_{j_2}, ..., α_{j_l}, not all zero, such that

$$\sum_{i=1}^{l} \alpha_{j_i} x_{j_i} = 0.$$

Let k be the largest integer such that $\alpha_{j_k} \neq 0$. We would have

$$\alpha_{j_1} x_{j_1} + \cdots + \alpha_{j_{k-1}} x_{j_{k-1}} + \alpha_{j_k} x_{j_k} + 0x_{j_{k+1}} + \cdots + 0x_{j_l} = 0.$$

Since $\alpha_{j_k} \neq 0$, we could solve for x_{j_k}, getting

$$x_{j_k} = \sum_{i=1}^{k-1} \left(\frac{-\alpha_{j_i}}{\alpha_{j_k}} \right) x_{j_i},$$

APP.
E.2
IND.

which says that x_{j_k} is a linear combination of some of the x's which precede it: i.e.,

(10.3) $x_{j_k} \in \mathrm{Sp}[x_1, x_2, \ldots, x_{j_{k-1}}].$

Since $x_{j_k} \in \mathscr{A}$ and $\mathscr{A}$ is made up of precisely those x's which do not satisfy (10.3), this is impossible. Thus the assumption that $\mathscr{A}$ is linearly dependent leads to a contradiction and we may conclude that $\mathscr{A}$ is linearly independent.

PROOF OF (ii).   Were any one of the first m of the x's not in $\mathscr{A}$, say $x_i \notin \mathscr{A}$, we would have, by the definition of $\mathscr{A}$: $x_i \in \mathrm{Sp}[x_1, x_2, \ldots, x_{i-1}]$ where $1 \leqslant i \leqslant m$. According to the definition of span, this means that there are scalars $\alpha_1, \alpha_2, \ldots, \alpha_{i-1}$ such that

$$x_i = \alpha_1 x_1 + \alpha_2 x_2 + \cdots + \alpha_{i-1} x_{i-1}$$

and hence

$$\alpha_1 x_1 + \alpha_2 x_2 + \cdots + \alpha_{i-1} x_{i-1} + (-1) x_i = 0.$$

In this linear relation among $x_1, x_2, \ldots, x_i$ at least one coefficient, namely the final -1, is different from zero. If there were such a relation, it would mean that $x_1, x_2, \ldots, x_i$ would be linearly dependent. Since $x_1, x_2, \ldots, x_i$ is a subset of the linearly independent set $x_1, x_2, \ldots, x_m$, Theorem 10.2 says that this is impossible.

PROOF OF (iii).   If we can show that every one of the x's lies in $\mathrm{Sp}\mathscr{A}$, we may apply Theorem 10.7 with the $\mathscr{A}$ of the theorem replaced by the set $x_1, x_2, \ldots, x_n$ and the $\mathscr{B}$ replaced by $\mathscr{A}$. The conclusion will be $\mathrm{Sp}[x_1, x_2, \ldots, x_n] \subseteq \mathrm{Sp}\mathscr{A}$. The reverse inclusion, $\mathrm{Sp}\mathscr{A} \subseteq \mathrm{Sp}[x_1, x_2, \ldots, x_n]$ should be completely obvious so the proof will be complete.

APP.
C.7
SETS

Once more we work by contradiction. Were one of the x's not in $\mathrm{Sp}\mathscr{A}$ there would be a least index i such that $x_i \notin \mathrm{Sp}\mathscr{A}$. Of course, each x_{j_k} is a linear combination of elements of $\mathscr{A}$, explicitly $x_{j_k} = 1 \cdot x_{j_k}$, so i could not be one of $j_1, j_2, \ldots, j_l$. Thus our definition of $\mathscr{A}$ would tell us that $x_i \in \mathrm{Sp}[x_1, x_2, \ldots, x_{i-1}]$. On the other hand, i was chosen so that $x_1, x_2, \ldots, x_{i-1} \in \mathrm{Sp}\mathscr{A}$. Thus Theorem 10.7 with $\mathscr{A}$ replaced by $[x_1, x_2, \ldots, x_{i-1}]$ and $\mathscr{B}$ replaced by $\mathscr{A}$ would yield the contradiction $x_i \in \mathrm{Sp}[x_1, x_2, \ldots, x_{i-1}] \subseteq \mathrm{Sp}\mathscr{A}$.

Q.E.D.

COROLLARY 10.9. *Every finite set of vectors contains a linearly independent subset whose span is the same as that of the original set.*

COROLLARY 10.10. *Every linearly dependent set of vectors contains a proper subset whose span is the same as that of the original set.*

COROLLARY 10.11. *Every linearly dependent set of vectors includes one which is a linear combination of the others.*

All the results we will get about dimension and bases rest ultimately upon the knowledge that certain sets of vectors are linearly dependent and others linearly independent. The next theorem, the most important in this section, provides the basic criterion for deciding that certain sets are linearly dependent.

The theorem itself is essentially theoretical, but its proof describes an effective method for computing non-trivial linear relations. A numerical example will clarify the ideas.

Assume that three vectors, x_1, x_2, and x_3, are given and that four others are determined from them by the equations:

$$y_0 = 2x_1 - 2x_2 + x_3,$$

$$y_1 = 3x_1 + 2x_2 - x_3,$$

$$y_2 = -x_1 + x_2 + 3x_3, \quad \text{and}$$

$$y_3 = x_1 + 3x_2 - 4x_3.$$

By adding suitable multiples of the first equation to the others we can infer new relations involving only x_1 and x_2. Specifically, we add 1 times the first to the second, -3 times the first to the third, and 4 times the first to the fourth. We thus infer that

$$y_1 + y_0 = 5x_1,$$

$$y_2 - 3y_0 = -7x_1 + 7x_2, \quad \text{and}$$

$$y_3 + 4y_0 = 9x_1 - 5x_2.$$

Now it is not terribly hard to see the relationship

$$35(y_3 + 4y_0) + 25(y_2 - 3y_0) = 28(y_1 + y_0),$$

but it is important to have some systematic procedure.

Introduce the abbreviations

$$z_0 = y_1 + y_0, \quad z_1 = y_2 - 3y_0, \quad \text{and} \quad z_2 = y_3 + 4y_0.$$

Then

$$z_0 = 5x_1$$

$$z_1 = -7x_1 + 7x_2, \quad \text{and}$$

$$z_2 = 9x_1 - 5x_2.$$

To eliminate x_2 we cannot use the first of these equations because, in it, the coefficient of x_2 is zero. However, the second equation will do just as well. We want to leave the first equation unchanged; but, to be systematic, we may say that we add 0 times the second to it and 5/7 times the second to the third. This yields

$$z_0 = 5x_1, \quad \text{and}$$

$$z_2 + (5/7)z_1 = 9x_1 - 5x_2 + (5/7)(-7x_1 + 7x_2)$$

$$= (28/7)x_1.$$

Clearing fractions, we get

$$7z_2 + 5z_1 = 28x_1.$$

Now the linear relationship

$$28z_0 - 5(7z_2 + 5z_1) = 0$$

should be completely obvious. Returning to the y's we have

$$0 = 28z_0 - 25z_1 - 35z_2$$

$$= 28(y_1 + y_0) - 25(y_2 - 3y_0) - 35(y_3 + 4y_0)$$

$$= -37y_0 + 28y_1 - 25y_2 - 35y_3.$$

In the inductive proof to follow, the general step consists of two parts. The first part corresponds to the elimination of one of the x's with the introduction of the z's; the second corresponds to the return to the original y's. The starting point for the induction corresponds to the noting of the obvious linear relation when everything is expressed in terms of the single vector x_1.

Theorem 10.12. *If $x_1, x_2, \ldots, x_n$ are n vectors and $y_0, y_1, \ldots, y_n$ are $n+1$ vectors lying in $\mathrm{Sp}[x_1, x_2, \ldots, x_n]$, then $y_0, y_1, \ldots, y_n$ are linearly dependent.*

PROOF. Since this is our first example of a standard inductive proof, we give it in great detail. The theorem asserts that every positive integer has a certain property, which we will call property P. A positive integer n has property P if and only if every set of $n+1$ vectors, which lie in the span of a set of n vectors, is linearly dependent. Like every inductive proof, this one has two parts. To start with, we show that 1 has property P; then we give the general inductive step showing that if $n-1$ has property P then so does n. From these two facts it is clear intuitively that every positive integer has property P. The proof of this intuitively obvious inference takes one deep into the foundations of mathematics. We will accept the inference without any further justification.

PART 1. We must show that if two vectors lie in the span of a single vector then they are linearly dependent.

Assume then, that y_0, $y_1 \in \mathrm{Sp}[x]$. This means that there are scalars α_0 and α_1 such that $y_0 = \alpha_0 x$ and $y_1 = \alpha_1 x$. Hence

$$-\alpha_1 y_0 + \alpha_0 y_1 = -\alpha_1 \alpha_0 x + \alpha_0 \alpha_1 x = 0,$$

so if either $\alpha_0 \neq 0$ or $\alpha_1 \neq 0$, the y's satisfy a non-trivial relation and are linearly dependent. On the other hand if $\alpha_0 = \alpha_1 = 0$, then $y_0 = y_1 = 0$ and y_0 and y_1 are, again, linearly dependent (see Problem 14.4).

PART 2. Let us assume that every set of n vectors lying in the span of a set of $n-1$ vectors is linearly dependent. (This assumption will be referred to as "the inductive hypothesis.") We must consider an arbitrary set of $n+1$ vectors, say y_0, y_1, ..., y_n, lying in the span of a set of n vectors, say x_1, x_2, ..., x_n, and show that the y's are linearly dependent.

By Definitions 10.5 and 10.6 there are scalars α_j^i, $i = 1, 2, \ldots, n$; $j = 0, 1, \ldots, n$; such that

APP.
E.7
IND.

$$y_j = \sum_i \alpha_j^i x_i.$$

There are two alternatives to consider: either, for some value of the index j, $\alpha_j^n \neq 0$, or, for all $j = 0, 1, \ldots, n$, $\alpha_j^n = 0$.

In the latter case the y's lie in the span of the $n-1$ vectors x_1, x_2, ..., x_{n-1}; and hence, by the inductive hypothesis, any set consisting of n of the y's is linearly dependent. Since a subset of the y's is linearly dependent, Corollary 10.3 assures us that the whole set of y's is linearly dependent.

It only remains to show that the y's are linearly dependent under the alternative assumption that there is a j such that $\alpha_j^n \neq 0$.

Consider the set of n vectors, z_0, ..., z_{j-1}, z_{j+1}, ..., z_n, defined by $z_k = y_k - (\alpha_k^n / \alpha_j^n) y_j$. Upon substituting, in this equation, the formula for the y's in terms of the x's, we get:

(10.4)
$$z_k = \sum_i \alpha_k^i x_i - (\alpha_k^n / \alpha_j^n) \sum_i \alpha_j^i x_i$$

$$= \sum_i (\alpha_k^i - \alpha_k^n \alpha_j^i / \alpha_j^n) x_i$$

APP.
E.5 &
E.6
IND.

$$= \sum_{i \neq n} (\alpha_k^i - \alpha_k^n \alpha_j^i / \alpha_j^n) x_i + (\alpha_k^n - \alpha_k^n \alpha_j^n / \alpha_j^n) x_n$$

$$= \sum_{i \neq n} (\alpha_k^i - \alpha_k^n \alpha_j^i / \alpha_j^n) x_i.$$

Thus the z's lie in the span of the $n-1$ vectors $x_1, x_2, \ldots, x_{n-1}$ and, by the inductive hypothesis, there are scalars $\beta_0, \ldots, \beta_{j-1}, \beta_{j+1}, \ldots, \beta_n$, not all zero, such that

(10.5)
$$\sum_{k \neq j} \beta_k z_k = 0.$$

From the definition of the z's, this yields

(10.6)
$$0 = \sum_{k \neq j} \beta_k [y_k - (\alpha_k^n / \alpha_j^n) y_j]$$

$$= \sum_{k \neq j} \beta_k y_k + [\sum_{k \neq j} (-\beta_k \alpha_k^n / \alpha_j^n)] y_j$$

$$= \sum_{k=0}^{n} \gamma_k y_k,$$

where $\gamma_k = \beta_k$ for $k \neq j$ and $\gamma_j = \sum_{k \neq j} (-\beta_k \alpha_k^n / \alpha_j^n)$. Since each of the β's is one of the γ's and at least one of the β's is different from zero, one of the γ's is different from zero. Thus equation (10.6) says that the y's are linearly dependent.

Q.E.D.

COROLLARY 10.13. *If $y_1, y_2, \ldots, y_m$ are linearly independent vectors and $y_1, y_2, \ldots, y_m \in \mathrm{Sp}[x_1, x_2, \ldots, x_n]$, then $m \leqslant n$.*

In the numerical example which preceded the theorem we saw a linear relation among the z's, but such a relation may not be obvious. If it is not, one passes from the z's to a new set of variables by repeating the process which led from the y's to the z's. Eventually this method leads to a set of vectors which satisfy some obvious linear relation. In the next chapter we use a very similar procedure to solve complicated systems of simultaneous linear equations.

Section 11. Dimension

It is quite possible to have linearly independent sets of vectors with arbitrarily large numbers of members. For instance, if $\mathscr{V}$ is the space consisting of all polynomials in τ then the set $\{1, \tau, \tau^2, \ldots, \tau^n\}$ consists of $n+1$ distinct elements of $\mathscr{V}$. It is not hard to prove that these elements are linearly independent.

In this text we are primarily concerned with spaces where this cannot happen—with spaces where there is an upper bound to the number of elements in a linearly independent set. Such spaces are called finite-dimensional.

There are various possible definitions of the dimension of a finite-dimensional vector space. In Section 5 we suggested two of these: (i) the number of elements in a basis, and (ii) the number of elements in a "maximal" linearly independent set. These definitions are perfectly acceptable, but they suffer from a common disadvantage. At this stage of our work definition (i) is meaningless. It is quite conceivable that a given vector space might have bases, $x_1, x_2, \ldots, x_m$ and $y_1, y_2, \ldots, y_n$, with $m \neq n$. If this could occur, we would be at a loss to decide whether m or n was the dimension of the space. Before we could use this definition we would have to prove that all bases for a particular space have exactly the same number of elements. Similar remarks apply to definition (ii).

Of course, we could prove the theorem referred to in the preceding paragraph and then give our definition, but instead we give a definition which, by its very nature, precludes ambiguity. Later, we will see that the other approaches to dimension yield precisely the same results. Thus, in the long run, it is immaterial which definition we adopt.

We take for granted the principle that every non-empty set of natural numbers has a least member. This implies that the phrase "the least natural number such that..." has a precise meaning as soon as it is established that there is at least one natural number such that ....

DEFINITION 11.1. A vector space $\mathscr{V}$ is said to be *finite-dimensional* if there is some natural number N such that each set of $N + 1$ vectors in $\mathscr{V}$ is linearly dependent. If $\mathscr{V}$ is finite dimensional, its *dimension*, dim $\mathscr{V}$, is the least natural number N such that every set of $N + 1$ vectors in $\mathscr{V}$ is linearly dependent.

One peculiar special case is important. The set $\{0\}$ consisting of the zero vector alone is a perfectly good vector space. The only set of $0 + 1$ vectors in this space is the set with the single member 0, and this set is linearly dependent (see Problem 14.4). Thus, according to Definition 11.1, a vector space whose only member is zero has dimension 0, just as one might expect. The dimension of a vector space with more than one element is positive.

Before proving any results about dimension, we make precise the notion of a maximal linearly independent set. The concept of a set which is "maximal" with respect to some property plays an important role in mathematics. The arguments in this section provide an introduction to the way "maximality" can be used in proofs.

APP. c.7 SETS DEFINITION 11.2. A set $\mathscr{A}$ of linearly independent vectors is a *maximal linearly independent* set if every set of vectors which contains $\mathscr{A}$ as a proper subset is linearly dependent.

Since we have defined linear dependence and independence only for finite sets, this definition is useful for us only if $\mathscr{A}$ is a finite set.

Of course, the word "maximal" varies its meaning with the context. A set of vectors may be maximal with respect to linear independence, but not with respect to some other property. If two or more sorts of maximality are being studied simultaneously, it is essential to write very carefully, but such complicated situations are rare.

THEOREM 11.3. *If $x_1, x_2, \ldots, x_n$ is a maximal linearly independent set of vectors in a finite dimensional space $\mathscr{V}$ then*

$$\mathscr{V} = \mathrm{Sp}[x_1, x_2, \ldots, x_n].$$

APP. D.1 PRF.

PROOF. The span of the x's consists of all linear combinations of them and these, of course, lie in $\mathscr{V}$ so $\mathrm{Sp}[x_1, x_2, \ldots, x_n] \subseteq \mathscr{V}$. What we must show is that $\mathscr{V} \subseteq \mathrm{Sp}[x_1, x_2, \ldots, x_n]$, i.e., if $y \in \mathscr{V}$ then there are scalars $\alpha_1, \alpha_2, \ldots, \alpha_n$ such that $y = \sum_i \alpha_i x_i$.

APP. C.7 SETS

Since the set $x_1, x_2, \ldots, x_n$ is maximal with respect to linear independence, the larger set $y, x_1, x_2, \ldots, x_n$ must be linearly dependent. Hence we can find scalars $\beta, \beta_1, \ldots, \beta_n$, not all zero, so

(11.1) $$\beta y + \sum_i \beta_i x_i = 0.$$

Were $\beta = 0$, we would have a vanishing linear combination of the x's alone, with at least one coefficient different from zero. Since the x's are linearly independent, this is impossible and we conclude that $\beta \neq 0$.

Since $\beta \neq 0$, we can solve (11.1) for y and, letting $\alpha_i = -\beta_i/\beta$, we have

$$y = (-1/\beta) \sum_i \beta_i x_i = \sum_i \alpha_i x_i.$$

Q.E.D.

THEOREM 11.4. *A set of n linearly independent vectors in a finite-dimensional vector space $\mathscr{V}$ is maximal if and only if $n = \dim \mathscr{V}$.*

PROOF. Let $x_1, x_2, \ldots, x_n$ be a set of linearly independent vectors in $\mathscr{V}$. By Definition 11.1, we know that $n \leqslant \dim \mathscr{V}$.

APP. D.9 PRF.

Furthermore, if $n = \dim \mathscr{V}$ then, still by Definition 11.1, any larger set is linearly dependent. Thus $x_1, x_2, \ldots, x_n$ is maximal.

The only thing which really needs proof is that if the set is maximal then $n \geqslant N$ where $N = \dim \mathscr{V}$.

Assume then, that $x_1, x_2, \ldots, x_n$ is a maximal linearly independent set. By Definition 11.1, there is some set of N vectors, say $y_1, y_2, \ldots, y_N$, which is linearly independent. According to Theorem 11.3, $\mathscr{V} = \mathrm{Sp}[x_1, x_2, \ldots, x_n]$ so the y's all lie in the span of the x's. Corollary 10.13 says that in this case $N \leqslant n$.

Q.E.D.

COROLLARY 11.5.   *If N linearly independent vectors, $x_1, x_2, \ldots, x_N$, lie in a vector space, $\mathscr{V}$, of dimension N then $\mathscr{V} = \mathrm{Sp}[x_1, x_2, \ldots, x_N]$.*

Section 12.   Bases

DEFINITION 12.1.   A *basis* for a vector space $\mathscr{V}$ is a set of vectors, $x_1, x_2, \ldots, x_n$, with the property that, for each $y \in \mathscr{V}$, there is one and only one set of scalars $\alpha_1, \alpha_2, \ldots, \alpha_n$, such that

$$(12.1) \qquad\qquad y = \sum_i \alpha_i x_i.$$

Definition 12.1 gives the most useful property of a basis, but there are several other ways of characterizing bases. Since it is important to be able to decide whether or not a given set of vectors is a basis, we need theorems which provide such characterizations.

THEOREM 12.2.   *If $x_1, x_2, \ldots, x_n$ is a basis for $\mathscr{V}$, then $x_1, x_2, \ldots, x_n$ is a maximal linearly independent set.*

PROOF.   If $x_1, x_2, \ldots, x_n$ is a basis then the equation

$$(12.2) \qquad\qquad \sum_i \alpha_i x_i = 0$$

has exactly one solution. Obviously this solution is $\alpha_1 = \alpha_2 = \cdots = \alpha_n = 0$; i.e., (12.2) implies that all the α's are zero. According to Definition 10.1, this is precisely what it means to say that the x's are linearly independent.

If the x's did not form a maximal linearly independent set, we could find a larger independent set. However, Definition 12.1 tells us that all the vectors in $\mathscr{V}$ lie in the span of $x_1, x_2, \ldots, x_n$ and Corollary 10.13 tells us that there cannot be a set of more than n linearly independent vectors lying in the span of $x_1, x_2, \ldots, x_n$.

Q.E.D.

THEOREM 12.3.   *If $x_1, x_2, \ldots, x_n$, are linearly independent vectors in $\mathscr{V}$ and $\mathscr{V} = \mathrm{Sp}[x_1, x_2, \ldots, x_n]$ then $x_1, x_2, \ldots, x_n$, is a basis for $\mathscr{V}$.*

PROOF.   By the definition of span, the hypotheses of the theorem imply that equation (12.1) always has a solution and, using Theorem 10.4, they also imply that this solution is unique.

Q.E.D.

COROLLARY 12.4.   *If $x_1, x_2, \ldots, x_n$ is a maximal linearly independent set of vectors in $\mathscr{V}$ then it is a basis for $\mathscr{V}$.*

PROOF.   See Theorem 11.3.

THEOREM 12.5.   *If $\mathscr{V}$ is an N-dimensional vector space then each set of N vectors which span $\mathscr{V}$ is a basis for $\mathscr{V}$.*

PROOF.   Let $x_1, x_2, \ldots, x_N$ be a set of N vectors which span $\mathscr{V}$. By Theorem 12.3, all we need to show is that the x's are linearly independent.   According to Corollary 10.10, every linearly dependent set of vectors contains a smaller set with the same span.   Thus, were the x's linearly dependent there would be a set of m vectors, $m < N$, which span $\mathscr{V}$.   By Theorem 10.12, every set of $m + 1$ vectors in $\mathscr{V}$ would be linearly dependent.   This is impossible.   (Why?)

Q.E.D.

These various characterizations of bases are so important that the reader must have them at his finger tips.   Accordingly, we now summarize them.   Assume that $\mathscr{V}$ is an N-dimensional vector space and consider a set, $x_1, x_2, \ldots, x_m$, of vectors lying in $\mathscr{V}$.   If such a set has any one of the following properties A–E then it has all the others.

A. The x's form a basis for $\mathscr{V}$.

B. The x's constitute a maximal linearly independent set of vectors in $\mathscr{V}$.

C. The x's are linearly independent and $m = N$.

D. The x's span $\mathscr{V}$ and $m = N$.

E. The x's are linearly independent and span $\mathscr{V}$.

To see that these conditions are equivalent we first observe that: A implies B by Theorem 12.2; B implies C by Theorem 11.4; C implies E by Corollary 11.5; and E implies A by Theorem 12.3.   Only D is left out of this circuit.   However, D implies A by Theorem 12.5 while C and E together obviously imply D.

We now turn to the question of finding bases.

THEOREM 12.6.   *If $\mathscr{V}$ is a finite-dimensional vector space then it has a basis.*

PROOF.   Let the dimension of $\mathscr{V}$ be N.   By the very definition of dimension there must be a set of N linearly independent vectors in $\mathscr{V}$. This set fulfills our condition C.

Q.E.D.

At first glance the next proof appears overelaborate.   The theorem says that out of a set $\mathscr{A}$ which spans $\mathscr{V}$ we can choose a basis for $\mathscr{V}$. The bright but unwary reader may think that Theorem 10.8 says that out of any set we can choose a linearly independent subset with the same span as the original set.   Such a set would have property E. Unfortunately, Theorem 10.8 applies only to *finite* sets.   In the following proof the z's are introduced to prepare the ground for an application of Theorem 10.8.

THEOREM 12.7.   *If $\mathscr{V}$ is a vector space of dimension N and $\mathrm{Sp}\mathscr{A} = \mathscr{V}$ then $\mathscr{V}$ has a basis $x_1, x_2, \ldots, x_N$ such that $x_i \in \mathscr{A}$, for $i = 1, 2, \ldots, N$.*

APP.
E.7
IND.   PROOF.   Let $y_1, y_2, \ldots, y_N$ be some basis for $\mathscr{V}$. Since $\mathrm{Sp}\mathscr{A} = \mathscr{V}$, each y_i is a linear combination of certain vectors $z_1^i, z_2^i, \ldots, z_{m_i}^i \in \mathscr{A}$. Let $\mathscr{Z}$ be the set of all the z_j^i, $i = 1, 2, \ldots, N$, $j = 1, 2, \ldots, m_i$. The y's all lie in the span of the z's and, according to Theorem 10.7, this implies that the span of the y's, namely $\mathscr{V}$ itself, lies in the span of the z's. Corollary 10.9 informs us that every finite set has a linearly independent subset with the same span as the original set. Choose such a subset of $\mathscr{Z}$. Each of the elements of this subset is one of the z's and so lies in $\mathscr{A}$. On the other hand the subset was chosen in a way which guarantees that it has property E and hence is a basis.

Q.E.D.

COROLLARY 12.8.   *If*

    (i) *$\mathscr{V}$ is an N-dimensional vector space,*

    (ii) *$x_1, x_2, \ldots, x_m$ are linearly independent, and*

    (iii) *$\mathrm{Sp}\mathscr{A} = \mathscr{V}$,*

then there are vectors $y_1, y_2, \ldots, y_{N-m} \in \mathscr{A}$ such that $x_1, \ldots, x_m, y_1, \ldots, y_{N-m}$ is a basis for $\mathscr{V}$.

PROOF.   By the theorem there is a basis $z_1, z_2, \ldots, z_N$ whose members all belong to $\mathscr{A}$. Obviously, the larger set $x_1, \ldots, x_m, z_1, \ldots, z_N$ spans the whole of $\mathscr{V}$. By Theorem 10.8, we can find a set $\mathscr{B}$ with the properties $x_1, x_2, \ldots, x_m \in \mathscr{B}$, $\mathscr{B}$ is linearly independent, and $\mathrm{Sp}\mathscr{B} = \mathrm{Sp}[x_1, \ldots, x_m, z_1, \ldots, z_N] = \mathscr{V}$. The set $\mathscr{B}$ is the desired basis.

Q.E.D.

One very special case is so useful that we state it separately.

COROLLARY 12.9.   *If $\mathscr{V}$ is a finite-dimensional vector space and $x_1, x_2, \ldots, x_m$ are linearly independent vectors in $\mathscr{V}$, then there are vectors $y_1, y_2, \ldots, y_n$ such that $x_1, \ldots, x_m, y_1, \ldots, y_n$ is a basis for $\mathscr{V}$.*

Section 13.   Subspaces

In Chapter I we mentioned the concept of a subspace. In particular we showed that the set of all solutions of a second-order linear homogeneous differential equation is a subspace of the space of continuous functions. For the study of linear equations of any sort—simultaneous linear equations, linear differential equations, linear integral equations, etc.—subspaces are important. In this text, attention is focused on finite-dimensional spaces, but many of the ideas are usable in the infinite-dimensional spaces introduced in studying, for example, differential equations.

DEFINITION 13.1. A *subspace* of a vector space $\mathscr{V}$ is any subset of $\mathscr{V}$ which is itself a vector space.

It is to be understood that the scalar field and the operations in the subspace are the same as those of the original space. It is obvious that every subset $\mathscr{A}$ of $\mathscr{V}$ satisfies axioms (3.2), (3.3), (3.6), (3.7), (3.8), and (3.9), and it is easy to show that if it satisfies (3.1) and (3.5) then it satisfies (3.4). Thus $\mathscr{A}$ is a subspace of $\mathscr{V}$ if and only if, for all $x, y \in \mathscr{A}$ and all $\alpha \in \mathscr{F}$, the scalar field of $\mathscr{V}$, $x + y \in \mathscr{A}$ and $\alpha x \in \mathscr{A}$. Often it is convenient to replace the two conditions (3.1) and (3.5) by the single condition

$$\text{if} \quad x, y \in \mathscr{V} \quad \text{and} \quad \alpha, \beta \in \mathscr{F} \quad \text{then} \quad \alpha x + \beta y \in \mathscr{V},$$

which is equivalent to them.

The set $\{0\}$ consisting of the zero vector alone and $\mathscr{V}$ itself are both subspaces of $\mathscr{V}$. These rather special subspaces may be called improper subspaces; all others are called proper subspaces.

THEOREM 13.2. *If $\mathscr{A}$ is a subset of $\mathscr{V}$ then $\mathrm{Sp}\mathscr{A}$ is a subspace of $\mathscr{V}$.*

PROOF. See Problem 14.18.

We next introduce three operations. These operations serve to combine arbitrary subsets of a vector space to yield new subsets. All three have important uses, but only the two which we will denote by "$\bigcap$" and "$\sum$" are needed in the study of subspaces.

DEFINITION 13.3. If $\mathscr{A}_1, \mathscr{A}_2, \ldots, \mathscr{A}_n$ are subsets of a vector space $\mathscr{V}$, then

$$\bigcap_{i=1}^{n} \mathscr{A}_i = \{x \mid \text{for all } i = 1, 2, \ldots, n, \, x \in \mathscr{A}_i\},$$

$$\bigcup_{i=1}^{n} \mathscr{A}_i = \{x \mid \text{for some } i = 1, 2, \ldots, n, \, x \in \mathscr{A}_i\},$$

$$\sum_{i=1}^{n} \mathscr{A}_i = \{x \mid \text{for some } x_1, x_2, \ldots, x_n, \, x_i \in \mathscr{A}_i \text{ and } x = \sum_{i=1}^{n} x_i\}.$$

APP.
C.5
SETS

The sets $\bigcap_i \mathscr{A}_i$, $\bigcup_i \mathscr{A}_i$, and $\sum_i \mathscr{A}_i$ are called, respectively, the *intersection*, the *union*, and the *sum* of the $\mathscr{A}$'s and are often denoted by

$$\mathscr{A}_1 \cap \mathscr{A}_2 \cap \cdots \cap \mathscr{A}_n, \qquad \mathscr{A}_1 \cup \mathscr{A}_2 \cup \cdots \cup \mathscr{A}_n, \quad \text{and}$$
$$\mathscr{A}_1 + \mathscr{A}_2 + \cdots + \mathscr{A}_n.$$

It is quite easy to introduce the union and intersection of infinitely many sets, but we have no need for such infinite unions and intersections.

THEOREM 13.4. *If* $\mathscr{X}_1, \mathscr{X}_2, \ldots, \mathscr{X}_n$ *are subspaces of* $\mathscr{V}$, *then* $\bigcap_i \mathscr{X}_i$ *and* $\sum_i \mathscr{X}_i$ *are subspaces of* $\mathscr{V}$.

APP.
D.11
PRF.

PROOF. Assume that $x, y \in \bigcap_i \mathscr{X}_i$ and $\alpha \in \mathscr{F}$. Then, for each i, $x, y \in \mathscr{X}_i$ and, since $\mathscr{X}_i$ is a subspace $x + y$ and αx belong to $\mathscr{X}_i$. Since $x + y$ and αx belong to each $\mathscr{X}_i$, they belong to $\bigcap_i \mathscr{X}_i$.

Now assume $x, y \in \sum_i \mathscr{X}_i$, $\alpha \in \mathscr{F}$. By definition, there are vectors $x_1, x_2, \ldots, x_n$; $y_1, y_2, \ldots, y_n$ such that $x_i, y_i \in \mathscr{X}_i$ and $x = \sum_i x_i$, $y = \sum_i y_i$. Since $\mathscr{X}_i$ is a subspace the vectors z_i and w_i defined by $z_i = x_i + y_i$ and $w_i = \alpha x_i$, for $i = 1, 2, \ldots, n$, lie each in the corresponding $\mathscr{X}_i$. Since

$$x + y = \sum_i x_i + \sum_i y_i = \sum_i (x_i + y_i) = \sum_i z_i$$

and $z_i \in \mathscr{X}_i$, it follows from Definition 13.3 that $x + y \in \sum_i \mathscr{X}_i$. Similarly, $\alpha x = \sum_i w_i \in \sum_i \mathscr{X}_i$.

Q.E.D.

It is quite easy to see that the operations $\cap$, $\cup$, and $+$ are commutative. That is to say

$$\mathscr{A} \cap \mathscr{B} = \mathscr{B} \cap \mathscr{A},$$

$$\mathscr{A} \cup \mathscr{B} = \mathscr{B} \cup \mathscr{A}, \quad \text{and}$$

$$\mathscr{A} + \mathscr{B} = \mathscr{B} + \mathscr{A}.$$

They are also associative:

$$(\mathscr{A} \cap \mathscr{B}) \cap \mathscr{C} = \mathscr{A} \cap (\mathscr{B} \cap \mathscr{C}),$$

$$(\mathscr{A} \cup \mathscr{B}) \cup \mathscr{C} = \mathscr{A} \cup (\mathscr{B} \cup \mathscr{C}), \quad \text{and}$$

$$(\mathscr{A} + \mathscr{B}) + \mathscr{C} = \mathscr{A} + (\mathscr{B} + \mathscr{C}).$$

Other algebraic identities which one might expect are less obvious and some which look very plausible are false.

Because the union of subspaces is not, as a rule, a subspace, unions are not very useful in the study of vector spaces. We will say no more about them.

Once again pictures in $\mathscr{R}^3$ are helpful, even though some interesting phenomena appear only in higher dimensions. The one-dimensional subspaces of $\mathscr{R}^3$ are the straight lines through the origin and the two-dimensional subspaces are the planes through the origin. The only three-dimensional subspace of $\mathscr{R}^3$ is $\mathscr{R}^3$ itself and $\{0\}$ is, as always, the only zero dimensional subspace.

The sum of two subspaces is the smallest subspace containing them.

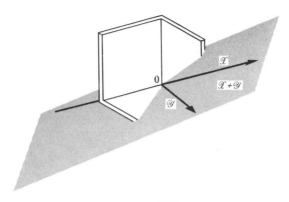

FIGURE 13.1

Thus if $\mathscr{X}$ and $\mathscr{Y}$ are two distinct lines through the origin $\mathscr{X} + \mathscr{Y}$ is the plane containing them (see Fig. 13.1). If $\mathscr{X}$ and $\mathscr{Y}$ are distinct planes through the origin then $\mathscr{X} \cap \mathscr{Y}$ is the line in which $\mathscr{X}$ and $\mathscr{Y}$ intersect (Fig. 13.2). If $\mathscr{X}$ is a line and $\mathscr{Y}$ is a plane which does not

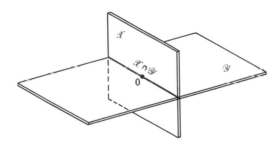

FIGURE 13.2

contain $\mathscr{X}$, then $\mathscr{X} \cap \mathscr{Y} = \{0\}$ and $\mathscr{X} + \mathscr{Y} = \mathscr{R}^3$. On the other hand if $\mathscr{Y}$ is a plane containing the line $\mathscr{X}$, then $\mathscr{X} + \mathscr{Y}$ is just the plane $\mathscr{Y}$ and $\mathscr{X} \cap \mathscr{Y}$ is the line $\mathscr{X}$. Compare Fig. 13.3a with Fig. 13.3b.

THEOREM 13.5. *If $\mathscr{V}$ is finite-dimensional and $\mathscr{X}$ is a subspace of $\mathscr{V}$, then* $\dim \mathscr{X} \leqslant \dim \mathscr{V}$. *Moreover, if* $\dim \mathscr{X} = \dim \mathscr{V}$, *then* $\mathscr{X} = \mathscr{V}$.

PROOF. Any set of linearly independent vectors in $\mathscr{X}$ is a set of linearly independent vectors in $\mathscr{V}$; so the first assertion is an immediate consequence of the definition of dimension.

Assume now that $\dim \mathscr{X} = \dim \mathscr{V} = N$. Then $\mathscr{X}$ has a basis

$x_1, x_2, \ldots, x_N$ with N elements. These form a set of N linearly independent elements of $\mathscr{V}$ so they are a basis for $\mathscr{V}$ also. Thus $\mathscr{X} = \mathrm{Sp}[x_1, x_2, \ldots, x_N] = \mathscr{V}$.

Q.E.D.

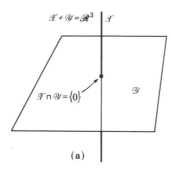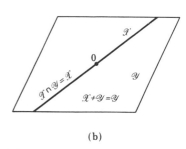

(a)   (b)

FIGURE 13.3

THEOREM 13.6. *If $\mathscr{V}$ is finite-dimensional and $\mathscr{X}$ and $\mathscr{Y}$ are subspaces of $\mathscr{V}$, then*

$$\dim \mathscr{X} + \dim \mathscr{Y} = \dim (\mathscr{X} \cap \mathscr{Y}) + \dim (\mathscr{X} + \mathscr{Y}).$$

PROOF. The proof depends on choosing suitable bases for the four subspaces, $\mathscr{X}, \mathscr{Y}, \mathscr{X} \cap \mathscr{Y}$, and $\mathscr{X} + \mathscr{Y}$. We shall choose z_i, $i = 1, 2, \ldots, l$; x_j, $j = 1, 2, \ldots, m$; and y_k, $k = 1, 2, \ldots, n$; so that the z's are as basis for $\mathscr{X} \cap \mathscr{Y}$, the z's and x's together form a basis for $\mathscr{X}$, the z's and y's together form a basis for $\mathscr{Y}$, and all three together form a basis for $\mathscr{X} + \mathscr{Y}$. If we can make such a choice then $\dim (\mathscr{X} \cap \mathscr{Y}) = l$, $\dim \mathscr{X} = l + m$, $\dim \mathscr{Y} = l + n$, and $\dim (\mathscr{X} + \mathscr{Y}) = l + m + n$, so we will have proved the theorem.

All the spaces we are concerned with are subspaces of the finite-dimensional space $\mathscr{V}$; so Theorem 13.5 assures us that they are all finite-dimensional.

According to Theorem 12.6, every finite-dimensional space has a basis. Hence we can choose some basis for $\mathscr{X} \cap \mathscr{Y}$ and call its members $z_1, z_2, \ldots, z_l$. Now apply Corollary 12.9 to the vector space $\mathscr{X}$ and choose $x_1, x_2, \ldots, x_m$ so that $z_1, \ldots, z_l, x_1, \ldots, x_m$ form a basis for $\mathscr{X}$. Similarly choose $y_1, y_2, \ldots, y_n$ in such a way that $z_1, \ldots, z_l, y_1, \ldots, y_n$ are a basis for $\mathscr{Y}$. All that remains is to show that

$$z_1, \ldots, z_l, x_1, \ldots, x_m, y_1, \ldots, y_n \text{ is a basis for } \mathscr{X} + \mathscr{Y}.$$

We omit the routine argument that the z's, x's, and y's together span $\mathscr{X} + \mathscr{Y}$ (see Problem 14.21).

The final step is to show that $z_1, \ldots, z_l, x_1, \ldots, x_m, y_1, \ldots, y_n$ are linearly independent, i.e., to assume

$$(13.1) \qquad \sum_i \alpha_i z_i + \sum_j \beta_j x_j + \sum_k \gamma_k y_k = 0$$

and to prove that all the α's, β's, and γ's are zero.

Let

$$(13.2) \qquad v = \sum_i \alpha_i z_i + \sum_j \beta_j x_j.$$

Since v is a linear combination of elements of the subspace $\mathcal{X}$, $v \in \mathcal{X}$. On the other hand we infer from (13.1) that $v = \sum_k (-\gamma_k) y_k$ so we also have $v \in \mathcal{Y}$. Anything which belongs both to $\mathcal{X}$ and to $\mathcal{Y}$ belongs to their intersection; so $v \in \mathcal{X} \cap \mathcal{Y}$. Since the z's are a basis for $\mathcal{X} \cap \mathcal{Y}$, there are scalars δ_i, $i = 1, 2, \ldots, l$, such that

$$(13.3) \qquad v = \sum_i \delta_i z_i.$$

Observe that both (13.2) and (13.3) give v as a linear combination of $z_1, \ldots, z_l, x_1, \ldots, x_m$. Since the z's and x's form a basis for $\mathcal{X}$, each vector in $\mathcal{X}$ can be written as a linear combination of them in one and only one way. Thus (13.2) and (13.3) must be identical so the α's are the same as the δ's and the β's are all zero.

A similar argument shows that the γ's are all zero. Finally, since both the β's and γ's are zero, (13.1) reduces to $\sum_i \alpha_i z_i = 0$, from which we get $\alpha_i = 0$ for $i = 1, 2, \ldots, l$. (Why?)

$$\text{Q.E.D.}$$

Next we introduce an extremely useful property possessed by certain pairs of subspaces. The definition is reminiscent of the definition of a basis.

DEFINITION 13.7. Two subspaces, $\mathcal{X}$ and $\mathcal{Y}$, of a vector space $\mathcal{V}$ are said to be *complementary* if, for each $z \in \mathcal{V}$, there is one and only one pair of vectors x and y such that

$$x \in \mathcal{X}, \qquad y \in \mathcal{Y}, \quad \text{and} \quad z = x + y.$$

THEOREM 13.8. *Let $\mathcal{X}$ and $\mathcal{Y}$ be subspaces of $\mathcal{V}$; $\mathcal{X}$ and $\mathcal{Y}$ are complementary if and only if*

$$\mathcal{X} \cap \mathcal{Y} = \{0\} \quad \text{and} \quad \mathcal{X} + \mathcal{Y} = \mathcal{V}.$$

PROOF. Assume that $\mathcal{X}$ and $\mathcal{Y}$ are complementary. It follows at once from Definitions 13.3 and 13.7 that $\mathcal{X} + \mathcal{Y} = \mathcal{V}$. Consider an arbitrary $z \in \mathcal{X} \cap \mathcal{Y}$. We know that $z \in \mathcal{X}$ and $z \in \mathcal{Y}$. Since $\mathcal{Y}$ is a subspace, we also have $-z \in \mathscr{Y}$. Thus 0 can be written as the sum, $z + (-z)$, of an element of $\mathscr{X}$ and an element of $\mathscr{Y}$. We also have $0 \in \mathscr{X}$, $0 \in \mathscr{Y}$, and $0 = 0 + 0$. According to Definition 13.7, the two representations, $z + (-z)$ and $0 + 0$, must be identical; so $z = 0$. This shows that the only member of $\mathscr{X} \cap \mathscr{Y}$ is 0.

Now assume that $\mathscr{X} \cap \mathscr{Y} = \{0\}$ and $\mathscr{X} + \mathscr{Y} = \mathscr{V}$. Since $\mathscr{X} + \mathscr{Y} = \mathscr{V}$, it follows that for each z there are vectors $x \in \mathscr{X}$ and $y \in \mathscr{Y}$ such that $z = x + y$. We want to prove that there is no other pair of vectors with these properties. Assume then, that $x' \in \mathscr{X}$, $y' \in \mathscr{Y}$, and that $z = x' + y'$. Then $x' + y' = x + y$ and $x' - x = y - y'$. Since $\mathscr{X}$ is a subspace and $x, x' \in \mathscr{X}$, $x' - x \in \mathscr{X}$. Similarly $y - y' \in \mathscr{Y}$. But $x' - x$ and $y - y'$ are one and the same thing and, by hypothesis, the only element which belongs both to $\mathscr{X}$ and to $\mathscr{Y}$ is zero. Thus $x' - x = y - y' = 0$.

Q.E.D.

COROLLARY 13.9. *If $\mathscr{V}$ is finite-dimensional and $\mathscr{X}$ and $\mathscr{Y}$ are complementary subspaces of $\mathscr{V}$, then*

$$\dim \mathscr{X} + \dim \mathscr{Y} = \dim \mathscr{V}.$$

The analogy between bases and complementary subspaces goes much further than the definition. In Section 12 we gave five equivalent conditions, A–E. Each of them has an analogue for subspaces and these analogous conditions are equivalent one to another. They are:

A'. $\mathscr{X}$ and $\mathscr{Y}$ are complementary.

B'. $\mathscr{X} \cap \mathscr{Y} = \{0\}$ and the only subspace of $\mathscr{V}$ which contains both $\mathscr{X}$ and $\mathscr{Y}$ is $\mathscr{V}$ itself.

C'. $\mathscr{X} \cap \mathscr{Y} = 0$ and $\dim \mathscr{X} + \dim \mathscr{Y} = \dim \mathscr{V}$.

D'. $\mathscr{X} + \mathscr{Y} = \mathscr{V}$ and $\dim \mathscr{X} + \dim \mathscr{Y} = \dim \mathscr{V}$.

E'. $\mathscr{X} \cap \mathscr{Y} = \{0\}$ and $\mathscr{X} + \mathscr{Y} = \mathscr{V}$.

The equivalence of A', C', D', and E' has already been demonstrated, although partly in camouflaged form. Problem 14.31 gives some hints for making the proof quite explicit.

The proof that B' is equivalent to the others is easy enough, but the wording in B' is new, so we give the details.

Assume that $\mathscr{X}$ and $\mathscr{Y}$ satisfy B'. If we show that $\mathscr{X} + \mathscr{Y} = \mathscr{V}$, we will know that they satisfy E'. But this is obvious! The subspace $\mathscr{X} + \mathscr{Y}$ contains $\mathscr{X}$ and also $\mathscr{Y}$ and B' says that the only subspace with this property is $\mathscr{V}$ itself.

Now assume that $\mathscr{X}$ and $\mathscr{Y}$ are complementary and that $\mathscr{Z}$ is a subspace containing both $\mathscr{X}$ and $\mathscr{Y}$. We want to show $\mathscr{Z} = \mathscr{V}$; i.e., if

$v \in \mathscr{V}$ then $v \in \mathscr{L}$. If $v \in \mathscr{V}$ then there are $x \in \mathscr{X}$, $y \in \mathscr{Y}$ such that $v = x + y$. But $\mathscr{X} \subseteq \mathscr{L}$ and $\mathscr{Y} \subseteq \mathscr{L}$; so $x, y \in \mathscr{L}$ and, $\mathscr{L}$ being a subspace, $v = x + y \in \mathscr{L}$. This shows that A′ and C′ (or A′ and E′) imply B′.

THEOREM 13.10. *Every subspace of a finite-dimensional vector space has a complement.*

PROOF. Assume that $\mathscr{X}$ is a subspace of a finite-dimensional space $\mathscr{V}$. Choose a basis $x_1, x_2, \ldots, x_m$ for $\mathscr{X}$ and apply Corollary 12.9 to choose $y_1, y_2, \ldots, y_n$ so that $x_1, \ldots, x_m, y_1, \ldots, y_n$ form a basis for $\mathscr{V}$. Let $\mathscr{Y} = \mathrm{Sp}[y_1, y_2, \ldots, y_n]$.

Obviously $\mathscr{X} + \mathscr{Y} = \mathscr{V}$, so all that must be proved is that $\mathscr{X} \cap \mathscr{Y} = \{0\}$. If $z \in \mathscr{X} \cap \mathscr{Y}$ then $z \in \mathscr{X}$ so there are scalars α_i, $i = 1, 2, \ldots, m$, such that $z = \sum_i \alpha_i x_i$. Similarly $z = \sum_j \beta_j y_j$ for some scalars $\beta_1, \beta_2, \ldots, \beta_n$. It follows that $0 = z - z = \sum_i \alpha_i x_i + \sum_j (-\beta_j) y_j$. Since the set $x_1, \ldots, x_m$, $y_1, \ldots, y_n$ is linearly independent, this implies that all the α's and β's are zero and hence that $z = 0$.

$$\text{Q.E.D.}$$

THEOREM 13.11. *If $\mathscr{X}$ and $\mathscr{Y}$ are complementary subspaces of $\mathscr{V}$ and $x_1, x_2, \ldots, x_m$ and $y_1, y_2, \ldots, y_n$ are bases for $\mathscr{X}$ and $\mathscr{Y}$ respectively, then $x_1, \ldots, x_m, y_1, \ldots, y_n$ is a basis for $\mathscr{V}$.*

PROOF. The proof is quite straightforward and we want to save it to assign as Problems 14.21 and 14.22.

A special notation for sums is often used when complementary subspaces are involved. If $\mathscr{X}$ and $\mathscr{Y}$ are complementary subspaces of $\mathscr{V}$, one writes $\mathscr{X} \oplus \mathscr{Y} = \mathscr{V}$ and says that $\mathscr{V}$ is the *direct sum* of $\mathscr{X}$ and $\mathscr{Y}$. More generally, if $\mathscr{X}_i \cap (\mathscr{X}_1 + \mathscr{X}_2 + \cdots + \mathscr{X}_{i-1}) = \{0\}$ for $i = 1, 2, \ldots, n$, one may write $\mathscr{X}_1 \oplus \mathscr{X}_2 \oplus \cdots \oplus \mathscr{X}_n = \oplus_{i=1}^n \mathscr{X}_i$ instead of $\sum_i \mathscr{X}_i$.

Section 14. Problems

NOTE: The vector spaces $\mathscr{R}^N$, $\mathscr{C}^N$, $C(-\infty, +\infty)$, $C[\alpha, \beta]$, $\mathscr{P}$, and $\mathscr{P}_n$, are defined in Section 2, but we now denote the operations in them by $+$ and $\cdot$, not by $\oplus$ and $*$.

1. Let $x_1 = (1, 1, 1, 0)$, $x_2 = (0, 0, 1, 1)$, and $x_3 = (0, 1, 1, 1)$. Show that the vectors x_1, x_2, and x_3 are linearly independent. Choose two vectors x_4 and x_5 in $\mathscr{R}^4$ so that x_1, x_2, x_3, and x_4 are linearly independent and x_1, x_2, x_3, and x_5 are linearly dependent. Prove that these sets are linearly independent and linearly dependent, respectively.

2. Let α, β, and γ be distinct real numbers and let

(14.1)
$$\begin{cases} x(\tau) = (\tau - \alpha)(\tau - \beta), \\ y(\tau) = (\tau - \alpha)(\tau - \gamma), \\ z(\tau) = (\tau - \beta)(\tau - \gamma). \end{cases}$$

Show that x, y, and z are linearly independent elements of $\mathscr{P}_2$.

3. Let x be a polynomial of degree n. Show that $x, x', x'', \ldots, x^{(n)}$ are linearly independent elements of $\mathscr{P}_n$.

4. Prove that a set consisting of a single vector is linearly dependent if and only if that vector is zero.

5. Show that $\mathrm{Sp}(\mathrm{Sp}\mathscr{A}) = \mathrm{Sp}\mathscr{A}$.

6. Give the details of the proof of Corollary 10.13. (Three or four sentences are sufficient to give the proof in painfully complete detail.)

7. Let $x = (1, 1, 0)$, $y = (2, 1, 1)$. Under what conditions does (ξ_1, ξ_2, ξ_3) lie in $\mathrm{Sp}\{x, y\}$?

8. Without using Theorem 10.12 show that every set of three vectors in $\mathrm{Sp}\{x,y\}$ is linearly dependent.

9. Let x_1, x_2, and x_3 be three vectors in some vector space. Let

$$
\begin{aligned}
y_0 &= 2x_1 - 3x_2 + 4x_3, \\
y_1 &= x_1 + x_2 - x_3, \\
y_2 &= 4x_1 + 2x_2 + x_3, \quad \text{and} \\
y_3 &= x_1 - 2x_2 + 2x_3.
\end{aligned}
$$

Apply the method used in the proof of Theorem 10.12 to find a non-trivial linear relationship among the y's.

10. Let $x_1 = (1, 0, 0, \ldots, 0)$, $x_2 = (0, 1, 0, \ldots, 0)$, and, in general, let x be the ordered N-tuple with 1 in the i-th place and 0's elsewhere.

(a) Show that every vector in $\mathscr{R}^N$ lies in $\mathrm{Sp}[x_1, x_2, \ldots, x_N]$.

(b) Which theorem says that every set of $N+1$ vectors in $\mathscr{R}^N$ is linearly dependent?

(c) Prove that $x_1, x_2, \ldots, x_N$ are linearly independent.

11. Prove Corollary 10.11.

12. DEFINITION 14.1. A *minimal generating set* in $\mathscr{V}$ is a set of vectors $x_1, x_2, \ldots, x_n$, with the properties

(i) $\mathscr{V} = \mathrm{Sp}[x_1, x_2, \ldots, x_n]$; and

(ii) no proper subset of $x_1, x_2, \ldots, x_n$, spans $\mathscr{V}$.

Prove the following theorems without using any results which appears after Section 10.

THEOREM 14.2. *Every minimal generating set is linearly independent.*

THEOREM 14.3. *If $x_1, x_2, \ldots, x_m$, and $y_1, y_2, \ldots, y_n$, are minimal generating sets of the same space, then $m = n$.*

NOTE: It is quite possible to build the theory of dimension and bases starting from minimal generating sets instead of from maximal linearly independent sets. If, on the other hand, one introduces minimal generating sets after Section 12, it follows immediately from Theorem 14.2 that a set is a minimal generating set if and only if it is a basis.

13. We know (see Problem 4.6) that the complex numbers form a real vector space. What is its dimension? Prove that your answer is correct.

14. Show that the x, y, and z defined by the equations (14.1) form a basis for $\mathscr{P}_2$.

15. Let $x_1, x_2, \ldots, x_n$ be a basis for $\mathscr{V}$ and let $y = \sum_{i=1}^{n} \alpha_i x_i$. Show that $y, x_2, \ldots, x_n$ are linearly independent if and only if $\alpha_1 \neq 0$.

16. Consider the vectors $x_1 = (1, 2, 1, 3)$ and $x_2 = (2, 1, 1, 2)$ in $\mathscr{R}^4$. Choose two vectors y_1 and y_2 so that x_1, x_2, y_1, and y_2 form a basis for $\mathscr{R}^4$. Prove that your set is a basis.

17. Prove: If a subset of $\mathscr{V}$ satisfies axioms (3.1) and (3.5), then it also satisfies axiom (3.4).

18. Prove Theorem 13.2.

19. Let $\alpha_1, \alpha_2, \ldots, \alpha_n$, be a set of real scalars. Let $\mathscr{X}$ be the set of all those vectors $x = (\xi_1, \xi_2, \ldots, \xi_n)$ in $\mathscr{R}^n$ such that $\sum_i \alpha_i \xi_i = 0$. Prove that $\mathscr{X}$ is a subspace of $\mathscr{R}^n$. Exhibit a basis for $\mathscr{X}$ under the assumption that $\alpha_n \neq 0$.

20. Figures 13.1, 13.2, 13.3a, and 13.3b illustrate four possible configurations of two subspaces in $\mathscr{R}^3$. For each of them write down:

(a) $\dim \mathscr{X}$,   (c) $\dim \mathscr{X} \cap \mathscr{Y}$,
(b) $\dim \mathscr{Y}$,   (d) $\dim \mathscr{X} + \mathscr{Y}$.

Verify Theorem 13.6 for each of these special cases.

21. Prove: If $x_1, x_2, \ldots, x_m$ is a basis for a subspace $\mathscr{X}$ and $y_1, y_2, \ldots, y_n$ is a basis for a subspace $\mathscr{Y}$, then $\mathrm{Sp}[x_1, \ldots, x_m, y_1, \ldots, y_n] = \mathscr{X} + \mathscr{Y}$.

22. Let $\mathscr{X}$ and $\mathscr{Y}$ be complementary subspaces of $\mathscr{V}$, and let $x_1, x_2, \ldots, x_m$ and $y_1, y_2, \ldots, y_n$ be bases for $\mathscr{X}$ and $\mathscr{Y}$ respectively. Show that $x_1, \ldots, x_m$, $y_1, \ldots, y_n$ are linearly independent.

NOTE: Problems 21 and 22 together provide the proof of Theorem 13.11.

23. Let $\mathscr{X}$ and $\mathscr{Y}$ be complementary subspaces of $\mathscr{V}$. Let $x_1, x_2, \ldots, x_m$ and $y_1, y_2, \ldots, y_n$ be bases for $\mathscr{X}$ and $\mathscr{Y}$ respectively, and assume that $m \leqslant n$. Let $\mathscr{Z} = \mathrm{Sp}\{y_1 + x_1, \ldots, y_m + x_m, y_{m+1}, \ldots, y_n\}$. Prove that $\mathscr{X}$ and $\mathscr{Z}$ are complementary.

24. Prove that $\mathrm{Sp}\,\mathscr{A}$ is the smallest subspace containing $\mathscr{A}$; i.e., if $\mathscr{X}$ is a subspace of $\mathscr{V}$ and $\mathscr{A} \subseteq \mathscr{X}$, then $\mathrm{Sp}\,\mathscr{A} \subseteq \mathscr{X}$.

25. Prove:

THEOREM 14.4. *If $\mathscr{X}$, $\mathscr{Y}$, and $\mathscr{Z}$ are subspaces of $\mathscr{V}$, and $\mathscr{X} \subseteq \mathscr{Z}$, $\mathscr{Y} \subseteq \mathscr{Z}$, then $\mathscr{X} + \mathscr{Y} \subseteq \mathscr{Z}$.*

NOTE: This theorem says that $\mathscr{X} + \mathscr{Y}$ is the smallest subspace containing both $\mathscr{X}$ and $\mathscr{Y}$; i.e., every *subspace* which contains both $\mathscr{X}$ and $\mathscr{Y}$ contains their sum. Similarly, the next theorem says that $\mathscr{X} \cap \mathscr{Y}$ is the largest subspace that is contained in both $\mathscr{X}$ and $\mathscr{Y}$.

26. Prove:

THEOREM 14.5. *If $\mathscr{X}$, $\mathscr{Y}$, and $\mathscr{Z}$ are subspaces of $\mathscr{V}$, and $\mathscr{Z} \subseteq \mathscr{X}$, $\mathscr{Z} \subseteq \mathscr{Y}$, then $\mathscr{Z} \subseteq \mathscr{X} \cap \mathscr{Y}$.*

27. Let T be a function whose domain is a vector space $\mathscr{V}$ and whose range is a subset of $\mathscr{V}$. Assume that T has the property that $T(\alpha x + \beta y) = \alpha T(x) + \beta T(y)$.

(a) Show that $\{x \mid T(x) = 0\}$ is a subspace of $\mathscr{V}$.

(b) Let $\mathscr{Y}$ be the range of T, i.e., $\mathscr{Y} = \{y \mid \text{for some } x \in \mathscr{V}, y = T(x)\}$. Prove that $\mathscr{Y}$ is a subspace of $\mathscr{V}$.

28. Let $\mathscr{V}$ be a vector space with an inner product, $\langle \ , \ \rangle$, which satisfies the conditions (6.3) and (6.4). Let $\mathscr{A}$ be an arbitrary subset of $\mathscr{V}$. Show that $\mathscr{Y} = \{y \mid \text{for all } x \in \mathscr{A}, \langle y, x \rangle = 0\}$ is a subspace of $\mathscr{V}$.

29. Let $\mathscr{V}$ be a vector space with an inner product, $\langle \ , \ \rangle$ which satisfies (6.3) and (6.4). Let $x_1, x_2, \ldots, x_n$ be a set of vectors in $\mathscr{V}$ such that

$$(14.2) \qquad \langle x_i, x_j \rangle = \begin{cases} 1 & \text{if } i = j \\ 0 & \text{if } i \neq j. \end{cases}$$

Prove that $x_1, x_2, \ldots, x_n$ is a linearly independent set. You may assume the validity of equation (14.3) which appears below.

30. Let $\mathscr{V}$ be a real vector space with an inner product, $\langle \ , \ \rangle$, which satisfies (6.2), (6.3), and (6.4). It can be proved by induction (and you may assume) that

$$(14.3) \qquad \left\langle \sum_{i=1}^{n} \alpha_i x_i, y \right\rangle = \sum_{i=1}^{n} \alpha_i \langle x_i, y \rangle, \quad \text{and}$$

$$\left\langle x, \sum_{i=1}^{n} \beta_i y_i \right\rangle = \sum_{i=1}^{n} \beta_i \langle x, y_i \rangle.$$

Assume that $\mathscr{X}$ is a subspace of $\mathscr{V}$, and that $\mathscr{X}$ has a basis $x_1, x_2, \ldots, x_n$ which satisfies the condition (14.2) of Problem 29. According to Problem 28, the set

$$\mathscr{Y} = \{y \mid \text{for all } x \in \mathscr{X}, \langle y, x \rangle = 0\}$$

is a subspace of $\mathscr{V}$. For each $z \in \mathscr{V}$ let

$$(14.4) \qquad Y(z) = z - \sum_{i=1}^{n} \langle z, x_i \rangle x_i.$$

(a) Show that if $z \in \mathscr{V}$ then $Y(z) \in \mathscr{Y}$.

(b) Show that $Y(\alpha x + \beta y) = \alpha Y(x) + \beta Y(y)$.

(c) Show that $Y(Y(z)) = Y(z)$.

(d) Show that $z \in \mathscr{X}$ if and only if $Y(z) = 0$.

(e) Show that $z \in \mathscr{Y}$ if and only if $Y(z) = z$.

(f) Show that $\mathscr{X} \cap \mathscr{Y} = \{0\}$.

NOTE: Equation (14.4) tells us that every $z \in \mathscr{V}$ can be written as the sum of $Y(z)$ and an element of $\mathscr{X}$ and hence, by part (a), $z \in \mathscr{X} + \mathscr{Y}$. Combining this with part (f), we see that $\mathscr{X}$ and $\mathscr{Y}$ are complementary subspaces. The subspace $\mathscr{Y}$ is called the orthogonal complement of $\mathscr{X}$ and the function Y is called the orthogonal projection of $\mathscr{V}$ on $\mathscr{Y}$.

31. Consider the conditions A' to E' of Section 13.

(a) Which theorem asserts that A' is equivalent to E'?

(b) Which results assert that A' and E' together imply both C' and D'?

(c) Write out in full a proof that C' implies E'.   HINT: if you exploit Theorems 13.5 and 13.6, four short sentences are ample.

(d) Write out in full a proof that D' implies E'.

NOTE: In the body of the text we proved that B' implies E' and that A' and E' imply B'.   The chain of implications can be shown in a diagram. Each arrow represents an established implication; the condition at its start implies the condition at its point.   Plainly, any one of the conditions implies each of the others.

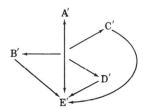

32. Prove: If $\mathscr{X}$ is a subspace of a finite-dimensional space $\mathscr{V}$ and $y \notin \mathscr{X}$, then there is a subspace $\mathscr{Y}$ of $\mathscr{V}$ which is complementary to $\mathscr{X}$ and contains y.

33. Let $q(\tau) = (\tau - 1)^2(\tau - 2)$ and let $\mathscr{V}$ consist of all rational fractions of the form $p(\tau)/q(\tau)$ where $p(\tau)$ is a polynomial of degree at most 2.   It should be obvious that $\mathscr{V}$ is a vector space.   Let

$$x_1(\tau) = 1/q(\tau), \qquad x_2(\tau) = \tau/q(\tau) \qquad \text{and} \quad x_3(\tau) = \tau^2/q(\tau);$$
$$y_1(\tau) = 1/(\tau-1)^2, \qquad y_2(\tau) = 1/(\tau-1), \quad \text{and} \quad y_3(\tau) = 1/(\tau-2).$$

(a) Rewrite y_1, y_2, and y_3, in a way which makes it obvious that they are elements of $\mathscr{V}$.

(b) Show that y_1, y_2, and y_3, are linearly independent.   HINT: consider $\lim_{\tau \to 1} (\tau - 1)^2 \{\alpha_1 y_1(\tau) + \alpha_2 y_2(\tau) + \alpha_3 y_3(\tau)\}$, etc.

NOTE: It is obvious that the x's form a basis for $\mathscr{V}$, so $\mathscr{V}$ is three dimensional.   Hence the y's form a basis also.   Consider a fraction of the form $p(\tau)/q(\tau)$ without any restriction on the degree of p.   By long division it is possible to write $p(\tau)/q(\tau)$ as the sum of a polynomial, the quotient, and a fraction of the form $r(\tau)/q(\tau)$, where the remainder, r, is a polynomial of degree less than or equal to 2.   The fact that the y's form a basis for $\mathscr{V}$ guarantees that $r(\tau)/q(\tau)$ can be written as a sum of partial fractions:

$$\frac{r(\tau)}{q(\tau)} = \frac{\alpha}{(\tau-1)^2} + \frac{\beta}{(\tau-1)} + \frac{\gamma}{(\tau-2)}.$$

The general theorem on partial fractions is given in the next problem.

34. Let $q(\tau) = (\tau - \gamma_1)^{n_1}(\tau - \gamma_2)^{n_2} \cdots (\tau - \gamma_k)^{n_k}$, where $\gamma_1, \gamma_2, \ldots, \gamma_k$, are distinct complex numbers. Let $N = n_1 + n_2 + \cdots + n_k$ and let $\mathscr{V}$ consist of all rational fractions of the form $p(\tau)/q(\tau)$, where p is a polynomial of degree strictly less than N. Let

$$y_{i,j}(\tau) = 1/(\tau - \gamma_i)^j \quad \text{for } i = 1, 2, \ldots, k; j = 1, 2, \ldots, n_i.$$

Show that the $y_{i,j}$'s form a basis for $\mathscr{V}$.

Summary

The definition of linear dependence and independence is absolutely fundamental. So is that of a basis.

For other important concepts the following check list with suggestions of the meanings may be a help.

Linear combination (trivial, non-trivial)—as the name suggests, $\sum \alpha_i x_i$.

Span—set of all linear combinations.

Maximal linearly independent subset—what the name suggests.

Subspace—what the name suggests.

$\bigcap_{i=1}^n \mathscr{A}_i$, intersection—points common to the $\mathscr{A}$'s.

$\sum_{i=1}^n \mathscr{A}_i$—set of sums, one term from each $\mathscr{A}_i$.

Complementary subspaces—every vector uniquely representable as a sum.

To follow our particular treatment or to answer examination questions, you may need to know our definition of dimension. For other purposes you must know that it is any one of the following:

> the least integer N such that every set of $N+1$ vectors is linearly dependent;
>
> or
>
> the number of elements in any particular maximal linearly independent set;
>
> or
>
> the number of elements in any particular basis.

A complete list of the important theorems and corollaries would be a recapitulation, not a summary, but incomplete statements of the majority appear below.

The vectors $x_1, x_2, \ldots, x_n$ are linearly dependent

(i) if some subset is dependent (Cor. 10.3), or

(ii) if they lie in the span of m vectors with $m < n$ (Th. 10.12).

They are independent if they are a subset of an independent set (Th. 10.2). If so, $y = \sum \alpha_i x_i$ has at most one solution (Th. 10.4). Any finite set of vectors has an independent subset with the same span

(Cor. 10.9), and this can be chosen to include any given independent subset (Th. 10.8).

Every linearly dependent set includes at least one vector which is a linear combination of the others (Cor. 10.11).

The conditions A to E of Section 12 are equivalent. Every finite-dimensional space has a basis (Th. 12.6) and a basis can be chosen so as to include any given linearly independent set (Cor. 12.8).

A subset is a subspace if and only if it satisfies axioms 3.1 and 3.5. The span of anything and the intersection and sum of subspaces are subspaces (Ths. 13.2 and 13.4).

If $\mathscr{X} \subseteq \mathscr{V}$, dim $\mathscr{X} \leqslant$ dim $\mathscr{V}$, and equality in either implies it in the other (Th. 13.5).

dim $\mathscr{X}$ + dim $\mathscr{Y}$ = dim $(\mathscr{X} + \mathscr{Y})$ + dim $(\mathscr{X} \cap \mathscr{Y})$, (Th. 13.6). The conditions A'–E' of Section 13 are equivalent.

In a finite-dimensional space every subspace has a complement (Th. 13.10).

CHAPTER IV

LINEAR TRANSFORMATIONS

In studying simultaneous linear equations you have probably learned how to solve systems like

$$\begin{cases} x - 2y + z = 5 \\ 2x + y - z = 1 \\ 2x - y + z = 3, \end{cases}$$

where the number of equations is equal to the number of unknowns. Such systems are particularly important, but they are by no means the only ones met in practical problems. The general system of simultaneous linear equations can be written*

$$\sum_{i=1}^{N} \alpha_i^j \xi^i = \eta^j, \quad \text{for } j = 1, 2, \ldots, M;$$

where the α_i^j and the η^j are given constants and the problem is to find the unknowns, $\xi^1, \xi^2, \ldots, \xi^N$.

There are two important questions about such systems of equations: (i) What is an efficient method of computing all solutions of any particular system? and (ii) What sort of solutions may we expect for any system? Although we will touch on the first question, an adequate answer to it really belongs to numerical analysis and not to the theory of vector spaces. The second question provides a natural jumping off point for the present chapter.

Section 15.   Linear Transformations

Let us look at the system

$$(15.1) \qquad \sum_{i=1}^{N} \alpha_i^j \xi^i = \eta^j, \quad \text{for } j = 1, 2, \ldots, M,$$

from the point of view of vector spaces.

* We use Greek letters for the unknowns because they are scalars, not vectors. In some of the problems you will find roman letters standing for unknown scalars.

If $(\xi^1, \xi^2, \ldots, \xi^N)$ is any element of $\mathscr{R}^N$ (everything we say applies equally well to $\mathscr{C}^N$) then

$$\left(\sum_{i=1}^{N} \alpha_i^1 \xi^i, \sum_{i=1}^{N} \alpha_i^2 \xi^i, \ldots, \sum_{i=1}^{N} \alpha_i^M \xi^i \right)$$

is an M-tuple of real numbers, that is, an element of $\mathscr{R}^M$. What we have just said is that to each $x = (\xi^1, \xi^2, \ldots, \xi^N)$ there corresponds a unique element,

$$\left(\sum_{i=1}^{N} \alpha_i^1 \xi^i, \sum_{i=1}^{N} \alpha_i^2 \xi^i, \ldots, \sum_{i=1}^{N} \alpha_i^M \xi^i \right), \text{ in } \mathscr{R}^M.$$

In other words, we have a function from $\mathscr{R}^N$ to $\mathscr{R}^M$; let us call it A. In terms of the function A the problem of solving (15.1) is the problem of finding all $x \in \mathscr{R}^N$ such that

$$(15.2) \qquad\qquad A(x) = y$$

where $y = (\eta^1, \eta^2, \ldots, \eta^M)$.

APP. F.3 FNS.

This function A has a property which is of fundamental importance throughout the remainder of this text. Changing our notation from that in (15.2), let $x = (\xi^1, \xi^2, \ldots, \xi^N)$ and $y = (\eta^1, \eta^2, \ldots, \eta^N)$ be elements of $\mathscr{R}^N$. Let

$$(15.3) \qquad\qquad \alpha x + \beta y = z = (\zeta^1, \zeta^2, \ldots, \zeta^N);$$

so, by the definition of addition and scalar multiplication in $\mathscr{R}^N$, $\zeta^i = \alpha \xi^i + \beta \eta^i$. Now let

$$(15.4) \quad \begin{cases} A(x) = \hat{x} = (\hat{\xi}^1, \hat{\xi}^2, \ldots, \hat{\xi}^M), \\ A(y) = \hat{y} = (\hat{\eta}^1, \hat{\eta}^2, \ldots, \hat{\eta}^M), \\ A(z) = \hat{z} = (\hat{\zeta}^1, \hat{\zeta}^2, \ldots, \hat{\zeta}^M), \quad \text{and} \\ \alpha\hat{x} + \beta\hat{y} = \tilde{z} = (\tilde{\zeta}^1, \tilde{\zeta}^2, \ldots, \tilde{\zeta}^M). \end{cases}$$

From the definition of A,

$$\hat{\xi}^j = \sum_{i=1}^{N} \alpha_i^j \xi^i, \qquad \hat{\eta} = \sum_{i=1}^{N} \alpha_i^j \eta^i, \quad \text{and}$$

$$(15.5) \qquad \begin{aligned} \hat{\zeta}^j &= \sum_i \alpha_i^j \zeta^i = \sum_i \alpha_i^j (\alpha \xi^i + \beta \eta^i) \\ &= \sum_i (\alpha \alpha_i^j \xi^i + \beta \alpha_i^j \eta^i) \\ &= \left(\sum_i \alpha \alpha_i^j \xi^i \right) + \left(\sum_i \beta \alpha_i^j \eta^i \right) \\ &= \alpha \sum_i \alpha_i^j \xi^i + \beta \sum_i \alpha_i^j \eta^i \\ &= \alpha \hat{\xi}^j + \beta \hat{\eta}^j = \tilde{\zeta}^j. \end{aligned}$$

APP. E.5 IND.

What we have shown is that $\hat{z} = \tilde{z}$ or, using (15.3) and (15.4),

$$A(\alpha x + \beta y) = A(z) = \hat{z} = \tilde{z} = \alpha \hat{x} + \beta \hat{y} = \alpha A(x) + \beta A(y).$$

DEFINITION 15.1.   A *linear transformation* on a vector space $\mathscr{V}$ to a vector space $\mathscr{W}$ is a function A whose domain is the whole of $\mathscr{V}$, whose range is contained in $\mathscr{W}$, and which satisfies

APP.
F.2
FNS.
(15.6) $$\qquad\qquad\qquad A(\alpha x + \beta y) = \alpha A(x) + \beta A(y)$$

for all $x, y \in \mathscr{V}$ and all scalars α and β.

The term "linear operator" is synonymous with "linear transformation," and the adjective "linear" is often omitted.   When we speak of a transformation on $\mathscr{V}$, we will mean a linear transformation on $\mathscr{V}$ to $\mathscr{V}$.

The range of a linear transformation A on $\mathscr{V}$ to $\mathscr{W}$ may be the whole of $\mathscr{W}$ or a proper subspace of $\mathscr{W}$ (see Theorem 17.3).   If the range is known to be the whole of $\mathscr{W}$, it is customary to say that A is a transformation from $\mathscr{V}$ onto $\mathscr{W}$ (or on $\mathscr{V}$ onto $\mathscr{W}$).   The phrase "a transformation into $\mathscr{W}$" is synonymous with "a transformation to $\mathscr{W}$." If the spaces are infinite-dimensional, one needs to consider also transformations whose domains are proper subsets of $\mathscr{V}$.

On applying (15.6) twice, it is easy to see that if A is a linear transformation then

$$A(\alpha_1 x_1 + \alpha_2 x_2 + \alpha_3 x_3) = A(1 \cdot [\alpha_1 x_1 + \alpha_2 x_2] + \alpha_3 x_3)$$
$$= 1 \cdot A(\alpha_1 x_1 + \alpha_2 x_2) + \alpha_3 A(x_3)$$
$$= \alpha_1 A(x_1) + \alpha_2 A(x_2) + \alpha_3 A(x_3).$$

To prove the corresponding formula for arbitrary linear combinations requires an easy induction, which we omit.   However, we often need the general result and, because it is so important, we state it as a theorem.

THEOREM 15.2.   *If A is a linear transformation on a vector space $\mathscr{V}$ to a vector space $\mathscr{W}$, then*

$$(15.7) \qquad\qquad A\left(\sum_{i=1}^{n} \alpha_i x_i \right) = \sum_{i=1}^{n} \alpha_i A(x_i)$$

for all $x_1, x_2, \ldots, x_n \in \mathscr{V}$ and all scalars $\alpha_1, \alpha_2, \ldots, \alpha_n$.

Equation (15.7) is really very simple, but it lies right at the heart of all linear algebra.   If A is a linear transformation and if y is a linear combination of $x_1, x_2, \ldots, x_n$, then to evaluate $A(y)$ take the *corresponding* linear combination of $A(x_1), A(x_2), \ldots, A(x_n)$.

You may picture a linear transformation on $\mathscr{R}^3$ to $\mathscr{R}^3$ as a deformation of the space which distorts all parts in like fashion.   A cube is deformed into a parallelepiped and any other cube of the same size and with the same orientation is deformed into a parallelepiped congruent to it. Parallel lines remain parallel. The origin stays fixed.

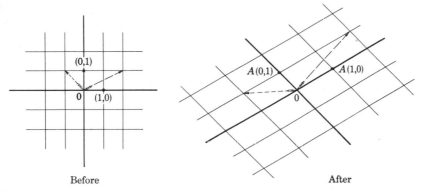

Before   After

The transformation A: $A(\xi^1, \xi^2) = (2\xi^1 - \xi^2, \xi^1 + \xi^2)$

FIGURE 15.1

Figures 15.1 and 15.2 illustrate linear transformations on $\mathscr{R}^2$ and $\mathscr{R}^3$ respectively.

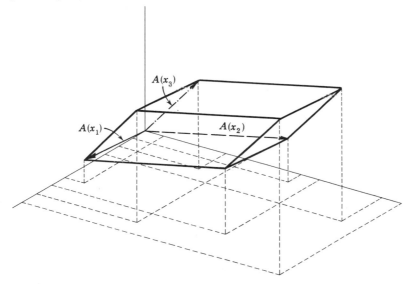

The image of the unit cube under the transformation A:

$$A(\xi^1, \xi^2, \xi^3) = (\tfrac{3}{2}\xi^1 + \tfrac{1}{4}\xi^2 + \tfrac{1}{2}\xi^3, \tfrac{1}{4}\xi^1 + 2\xi^2 + \xi^3, \tfrac{1}{4}\xi^1 + \tfrac{1}{2}\xi^2 + \xi^3)$$

FIGURE 15.2

Section 16.   The Algebra of Transformations

Linear transformations are functions and we can describe a transformation in exactly the same way that we describe a function of a real variable; that is, by a formula which tells the value of the function at each point of its domain.   To specify the function A of the preceding section we gave a formula for $A(\xi^1, \xi^2, \ldots, \xi^N)$ which is valid for all $(\xi^1, \xi^2, \ldots, \xi^N) \in \mathscr{R}^N$.   Specifically

$$A(\xi^1, \xi^2, \ldots, \xi^N) = (\sum_{i=1}^{N} \alpha_i^1 \xi^i, \sum_{i=1}^{N} \alpha_i^2 \xi^i, \ldots, \sum_{i=1}^{N} \alpha_i^M \xi^i) \in \mathscr{R}^M,$$

for $(\xi^1, \xi^2, \ldots, \xi^N) \in \mathscr{R}^N$.

In elementary calculus one learns such rules as: "The derivative of the sum of two functions is the sum of their derivatives."   Now the only objects which have derivatives are functions; so when one says "the derivative of the sum of two functions," the phrase "the sum of two functions" must be the name of some function.   Of course it is! The sum of two functions f and g is the function h defined by the formula

$$h(\tau) = f(\tau) + g(\tau)$$

whenever τ belongs both to the domain of f and to the domain of g. In fact, we used precisely this operation of adding functions back in Section 2.   The sum of two linear transformations and the product of a scalar and a linear transformation can be defined by similar formulas.

DEFINITION 16.1.   If A and B are linear transformations on a vector space $\mathscr{V}$ to a vector space $\mathscr{W}$ and if α is a scalar, then $A + B$ and $\alpha \cdot A$ are the functions on $\mathscr{V}$ to $\mathscr{W}$ defined by the formulas

APP.   (16.1) $(A + B)(x) = A(x) + B(x)$ for $x \in \mathscr{V}$, and
F.10
FNS.   (16.2) $(\alpha \cdot A)(x) = \alpha \cdot A(x)$ for $x \in \mathscr{V}$.

Notice that the symbol "$+$" is being drafted for still another job. Already we have made it stand for addition in the scalar field and for addition in vector spaces.   In equation (16.1) the "$+$" on the left-hand side is the symbol for our new operation on transformations.   Equation (16.1) will define this new operation only if we know what the right-hand side means.   This we do know; $A(x)$ and $B(x)$ are elements of $\mathscr{W}$ and the "$+$" which stands between them must be the addition symbol in $\mathscr{W}$.

Similarly the "$\cdot$" on the left of (16.2) is a new symbol, while the "$\cdot$" on the right is the familiar operation in $\mathscr{W}$.   The "$\cdot$" is often omitted.

As one might expect from their definitions, the new operations inherit the properties of the old. We shall prove only a part of the theorem describing the situation.

THEOREM 16.2. *The set of all linear transformations on a vector space $\mathscr{V}$ to a vector space $\mathscr{W}$, is, itself, a vector space.*

It is to be understood that $\mathscr{V}$ and $\mathscr{W}$ have the same scalar field and that this is to be the scalar field for the space of transformations. Also, the operations in the space of transformations are to be those given by Definition 16.1.

PARTIAL PROOF. We should verify that the set of all transformations on $\mathscr{V}$ to $\mathscr{W}$ satisfies all of the axioms for a vector space, but we will content ourselves with the proof that it satisfies (3.1) and (3.4).

PROOF OF (3.1): Let A and B be linear transformations on $\mathscr{V}$ to $\mathscr{W}$. According to Definition 16.1, $A + B$ is a function whose domain is the whole of $\mathscr{V}$ and whose range lies in $\mathscr{W}$. All we must prove is that $A + B$ is linear, i.e.,

$$(A + B)(\alpha x + \beta y) = \alpha[(A + B)(x)] + \beta[(A + B)(y)].$$

This is trivial:

(16.3)
$$
\begin{aligned}
(A + B)&(\alpha x + \beta y) \\
&= A(\alpha x + \beta y) + B(\alpha x + \beta y) && \text{[by Def. 16.1]} \\
&= \alpha A(x) + \beta A(y) + \alpha B(x) + \beta B(y) && \text{[by Def. 15.1]} \\
&= \alpha[A(x) + B(x)] + \beta[A(y) + B(y)] \\
&\qquad \text{[by (3.2), (3.3), and (3.8) applied to } \mathscr{W}] \\
&= \alpha[(A + B)(x)] + \beta[(A + B)(y)]. && \text{[by Def. 16.1]}
\end{aligned}
$$

(Here, the parenthetical explanations should be superfluous. By now, you ought to be able to look at the equation and see just what is involved at each step.)

PROOF OF (3.4): We must show that if A and B are linear transformations then there is a transformation X such that $A + X = B$. Let $X(x) = B(x) - A(x)$ for $x \in \mathscr{V}$. Note that the "$-$" in this formula stands for subtraction in the space $\mathscr{W}$. We must be careful not to assume that such operations are possible in the space of transformations; that will follow only after we show that we are dealing with a vector space. We have just exhibited an object X. It remains to show that it is a linear transformation on $\mathscr{V}$ to $\mathscr{W}$ and that it satisfies the equation $A + X = B$. The proof that X is a linear transformation is almost identical with (16.3). We omit it.

To say that two functions are equal is to say that they assign the same value to each element of their domain; so what we must show is that, for all $x \in \mathscr{V}$, $(A + X)(x) = B(x)$. This is too trivial to bother with.

Q.E.D.

It is easy to see that the zero element of this vector space is the transformation 0 such that $0(x)$ is the zero element of $\mathscr{W}$ for all $x \in \mathscr{V}$.

With real-valued functions we can define the product of f and g by the formula $(f \cdot g)(\tau) = f(\tau) \cdot g(\tau)$; but since we do not multiply together two elements of a vector space, no similar definition applies to linear transformations. There is, however, another way of combining real functions which does suggest a new operation on linear transformations. This new operation has algebraic properties which bear some resemblance to those of ordinary multiplication and the notation for it is like that for ordinary multiplication. Temporarily we will employ a non-standard notation to emphasize the fact that we are not multiplying the values of the transformations.

The operation we have in mind is the composition of functions—taking a "function of a function." If f and g are real-valued functions of a real variable, one can form a new function, h, defined by $h(\tau) = f(g(\tau))$. If A and B are linear transformations, we can, analogously,

APP.
F.2
FNS.

form the new transformation defined by $C(x) = A(B(x))$. At this point you must pay close attention to the domains and ranges of the functions. Assume that A is a linear transformation on $\mathscr{V}$ to $\mathscr{W}$ and examine the right-hand side of $C(x) = A(B(x))$. An expression of the form $A(\ldots)$ is meaningful only if the parentheses are occupied by the name of something in the domain of A. Thus we want $B(x)$ to be an element of $\mathscr{V}$. This will be the case if B is a transformation of some third space to $\mathscr{V}$. Assume that B is a linear transformation on $\mathscr{U}$ to $\mathscr{V}$. Now $A(B(x))$ is well defined so long as $x \in \mathscr{U}$ and its value, being the value of A at $B(x)$, is in $\mathscr{W}$.

DEFINITION 16.3. If B is a linear transformation on $\mathscr{U}$ to $\mathscr{V}$ and A is a linear transformation on $\mathscr{V}$ to $\mathscr{W}$, then $A \circ B$ (later denoted by $A \cdot B$ or AB) is the function on $\mathscr{U}$ to $\mathscr{W}$ defined by

$$(16.4) \qquad (A \circ B)(x) = A(B(x)) \quad \text{for } x \in \mathscr{U}.$$

A schematic diagram (Fig. 16.1) may help to clarify the roles of the different spaces. In a manner of speaking, B transforms the element x in $\mathscr{U}$ into the element $B(x)$ in $\mathscr{V}$ and this, in turn, is transformed into $A(B(x))$ by A. Note that B is applied first, even though it is written after A. This anomalous order is used because we want to be consistent with the usual functional notation. Some authors avoid the anomaly by varying the usual notation for functions, but in practice it causes little if any difficulty. You simply get in the habit of reading complicated functional equations from the innermost function to the outermost.

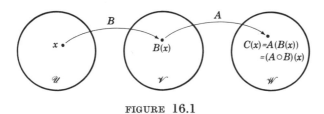

FIGURE 16.1

THEOREM 16.4. *If A and B are linear transformations on the vector spaces $\mathscr{V}$ to $\mathscr{W}$ and $\mathscr{U}$ to $\mathscr{V}$, respectively, then $A \circ B$ is a linear transformation on $\mathscr{U}$ to $\mathscr{W}$.*

PROOF. The proof is very easy, but to stress the ideas we go through it in painful detail. To keep track of the different spaces involved, we will write $\overset{u}{+}$, $\overset{v}{+}$, and $\overset{w}{+}$, for the addition operations in $\mathscr{U}$, $\mathscr{V}$, and $\mathscr{W}$, and let $\overset{u}{\cdot}$, $\overset{v}{\cdot}$, and $\overset{w}{\cdot}$ be the corresponding multiplication operations. Let $C = A \circ B$. Our object is to show that C is a linear operator, i.e., that

$$C(\alpha \overset{u}{\cdot} x \overset{u}{+} \beta \overset{u}{\cdot} y) = \alpha \overset{w}{\cdot} C(x) \overset{w}{+} \beta \overset{w}{\cdot} C(y).$$

For any $x, y \in \mathscr{U}$ and any scalars α and β we have, using the fact that A and B are themselves linear,

$$
\begin{aligned}
C(\alpha \overset{u}{\cdot} x \overset{u}{+} \beta \overset{u}{\cdot} y) &= A(B(\alpha \overset{u}{\cdot} x \overset{u}{+} \beta \overset{u}{\cdot} y)) \\
&= A(\alpha \overset{v}{\cdot} B(x) \overset{v}{+} \beta \overset{v}{\cdot} B(y)) \\
&= \alpha \overset{w}{\cdot} A(B(x)) \overset{w}{+} \beta \overset{w}{\cdot} A(B(y)) \\
&= \alpha \overset{w}{\cdot} C(x) \overset{w}{+} \beta \overset{w}{\cdot} C(y).
\end{aligned}
$$

Q.E.D.

Equally easy are the following facts, which we do not prove here.

THEOREM 16.5. *If A and B are linear transformations on $\mathscr{V}$ to $\mathscr{W}$, C is a linear transformation on $\mathscr{U}$ to $\mathscr{V}$, and D is a linear transformation on $\mathscr{W}$ to $\mathscr{X}$, then*

(16.5) $(A + B) \circ C = (A \circ C) + (B \circ C),$

(16.6) $D \circ (A + B) = (D \circ A) + (D \circ B), \quad and$

(16.7) $D \circ (A \circ C) = (D \circ A) \circ C.$

The statement of Theorem 16.5 appears complicated only because four different spaces are involved. The important part—the formulas (16.5), (16.6), and (16.7)—is simple enough. In using these formulas all that you need to check is that they are meaningful—that applying one of the transformations gives an element to which the next may be applied in turn.

If A and B are transformations on $\mathscr{U}$ to $\mathscr{V}$ and on $\mathscr{V}$ to $\mathscr{W}$, respectively, then $B{\circ}A$ is a well-defined transformation on $\mathscr{U}$ to $\mathscr{W}$, but $A{\circ}B$ is completely meaningless unless $\mathscr{W}$ happens to coincide with $\mathscr{U}$. Even if $A{\circ}B$ and $B{\circ}A$ are both meaningful, it is unusual for them to be equal. When dealing with this multiplication of transformations you must be most careful never to interchange the order of the factors in a product.

We have already mentioned the zero transformation on $\mathscr{V}$ to $\mathscr{W}$. This transformation behaves like a zero with respect to multiplication as well as with respect to addition. There are also transformations which behave rather like the number 1. These, unlike the zero transformations, are defined only as transformations on a space to the same space.

DEFINITION 16.6. If $\mathscr{V}$ and $\mathscr{W}$ are vector spaces, then the *zero transformation* on $\mathscr{V}$ to $\mathscr{W}$ is the transformation 0 (or $0_{\mathscr{V},\mathscr{W}}$ if one must be very specific) defined by

$$0(x) \; = \; 0 \in \mathscr{W} \quad \text{for all } x \in \mathscr{V},$$

and the *identity transformation* on $\mathscr{V}$ is the transformation I (or $I_{\mathscr{V}}$) defined by

$$I(x) \; = \; x \quad \text{for all } x \in \mathscr{V}.$$

THEOREM 16.7. *If A is a linear transformation from $\mathscr{V}$ to $\mathscr{W}$, then*

(16.8) $$A{\circ}I_{\mathscr{V}} \; = \; I_{\mathscr{W}}{\circ}A \; = \; A,$$

(16.9) $$A{\circ}0_{\mathscr{U},\mathscr{V}} \; = \; 0_{\mathscr{U},\mathscr{W}}, \quad and$$

(16.10) $$0_{\mathscr{W},\mathscr{X}}{\circ}A \; = \; 0_{\mathscr{V},\mathscr{X}}.$$

We omit the proof, which consists merely of looking to see exactly what each of the equations says. Note that, once again, we have formulas which look obvious. If we omit the subscripts and write "$\cdot$" instead of "$\circ$" they are $A \cdot I = I \cdot A = A$, $A \cdot 0 = 0$, and $0 \cdot A = 0$. The subscripts are included to ensure that each formula is meaningful. Looking at the schematic picture, Fig. 16.2, we see that a factor which appears before A (and hence acts *after* A) must be a transformation whose domain is $\mathscr{W}$, while a factor which appears after A must have its range in $\mathscr{V}$.

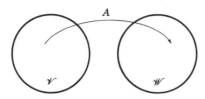

FIGURE 16.2

DEFINITION 16.8.   If A is a linear transformation on $\mathscr{V}$ to $\mathscr{W}$, B is said to be the *inverse* of A if B is a transformation on $\mathscr{W}$ to $\mathscr{V}$ such that

$$(16.11) \qquad\qquad A \circ B = I_{\mathscr{W}}, \quad \text{and}$$

$$(16.12) \qquad\qquad B \circ A = I_{\mathscr{V}}.$$

A transformation B satisfying (16.11) is called a *right inverse* of A, one satisfying (16.12) is called a *left inverse* of A.   The transformation A is said to be *invertible* if it has a (two-sided) inverse.

The use of the phrase "*the* inverse of A" in this definition is not really proper because we do not yet know that there can be at most one inverse.   As a matter of fact some transformations have many left inverses and others have many right inverses, but the following theorem shows that the use of the definite article is appropriate when we are speaking of genuine—that is, two-sided—inverses.

THEOREM 16.9.   *A linear transformation has at most one inverse.*

PROOF.   Assume that A is a linear transformation on $\mathscr{V}$ to $\mathscr{W}$ and that B and C are both inverses of A.   Then

$$
\begin{aligned}
B &= B \circ I_{\mathscr{W}} & \text{[by (16.8)]} \\
&= B \circ (A \circ C) & \text{[by (16.11)]} \\
&= (B \circ A) \circ C & \text{[by (16.7)]} \\
&= I_{\mathscr{V}} \circ C & \text{[by (16.12)]} \\
&= C. & \text{[by (16.8)]}
\end{aligned}
$$

Q.E.D.

In the proof we have not used the assumption that B and C are two-sided inverses, but only the weaker assumption that B is a left and C a right inverse of A.   Thus we have really proved the following corollary.

COROLLARY 16.10.   *If B is a left inverse of the transformation A, and C is a right inverse of A, then B = C, A is invertible, and its inverse is B.*

If A is invertible, the usual notation for the inverse of A is A^{-1}.

Consider such an expression as "$A\alpha Bx$" where, for simplicity, we will assume that A and B are transformations on $\mathcal{V}$ to itself.   As it stands "$A\alpha Bx$" has no meaning.   By inserting parentheses and an "$\circ$" in it we can obtain three meaningful expressions: $(A \circ (\alpha \cdot B))(x)$, $A((\alpha \cdot B)(x))$, and $A(\alpha \cdot (B(x)))$.   Fortunately, these are all equal so it is natural to let $A\alpha Bx$ stand for the common value of the three expressions.   Other compound expressions are treated similarly.   In particular, if A is a linear transformation we usually write just Ax instead of $A(x)$.

This convention dovetails nicely with the convention first forming products and then taking sums.   Thus $ABx + CBy$ means any one of the equal vectors $A(B(x)) + C(B(y))$, $(A \circ B)(x) + C(B(y))$, $A(B(x)) + (C \circ B)(y)$, or $(A \circ B)(x) + (C \circ B)(y)$.   It does not mean either of the vectors $A(B(x) + [(C \circ B)(y)])$ or $(A \circ B)(x + C(B(y)))$.

These conventions are extraordinarily helpful.   If one is very careful never to interchange the order of factors and to make sure that all the expressions used are meaningful, then almost any formula that looks correct really is valid.

As you would expect, we will often write A^2 for $A \circ A$, A^3 for $A \circ A \circ A$, etc.   We may also define A^0 to be I.   It is easy to prove that if m and n are natural numbers, then

(16.13) $$A^m A^n = A^{m+n}.$$

If A is invertible and one defines A^{-n} to be $(A^{-1})^n$, then (16.13) is valid for all integer values of m and n.

Section 17.   Simultaneous Linear Equations: General Theory

We now return to the problem of solving the system of equations

(17.1) $$\sum_{i=1}^{N} \alpha_i^j \xi^i = \eta^j, \quad j = 1, 2, \ldots, M.$$

In Section 15 we saw that this was a special case of the apparently more general problem of solving an equation of the form

(17.2) $$Ax = y$$

where A is a linear transformation on a vector space $\mathcal{V}$ to a vector space $\mathcal{W}$, y is a given element of $\mathcal{W}$, and we are to find those vectors x in $\mathcal{V}$ which satisfy (17.2).

Our problem is, first, to give a general description of the set consisting of all solutions and, second, to devise an efficient method for computing these solutions.

We begin by looking at the homogeneous equation

(17.3) $$Ax = 0.$$

DEFINITION 17.1. The set of all solutions of equation (17.3) is called the *null space* of A, and is denoted by $\mathcal{N}(A)$.

In work dealing with linear transformations on vector spaces the term "null space" is standard, but many authors prefer the word "kernel" because it is used for similar objects in other contexts. There is no generally accepted symbol for the null space of A, but "$\mathcal{N}(A)$" is not uncommon.

In a formula,

$$\mathcal{N}(A) = \{x \mid Ax = 0\}.$$

In words, $\mathcal{N}(A)$ is the set of vectors which are annihilated when A acts upon them. Geometrically $\mathcal{N}(A)$ consists of those vectors which

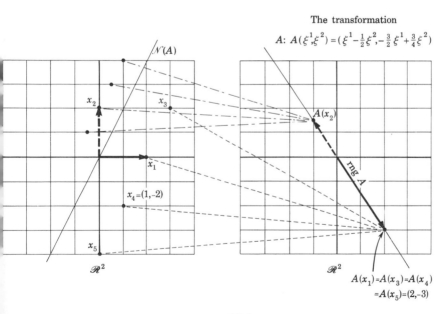

The transformation

$$A: A(\xi^1,\xi^2) = (\xi^1 - \tfrac{1}{2}\xi^2, -\tfrac{3}{2}\xi^1 + \tfrac{3}{4}\xi^2)$$

FIGURE 17.1

are compressed to zero under the action of A. Figure 17.1 illustrates a transformation on $\mathscr{R}^2$. The line $\{(\xi^1, \xi^2) \mid \xi^2 = 2\xi^1\}$ is $\mathcal{N}(A)$. Points on it go to zero; other points are transformed to points somewhere on the line

$$\operatorname{rng} A = \{(\xi^1, \xi^2) \mid 3\xi^1 + 2\xi^2 = 0\}$$

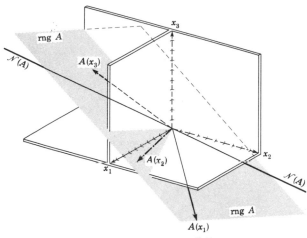

The transformation A:

$$A(\xi^1, \xi^2, \xi^3) = (.9\xi^1 + 1.0\xi^2 + .4\xi^3, .9\xi^1 + .3\xi^2 - .6\xi^3, -.4\xi^1 + .1\xi^2 + .6\xi^3)$$

FIGURE 17.2

It is harder to visualize transformations on $\mathscr{R}^3$, but Fig. 17.2 illustrates one. It is very easy to visualize certain special transformations. For instance, if

$$A(\xi^1, \xi^2, \xi^3) = (\xi^1, \xi^2, 0),$$

then A simply projects each vector vertically onto the plane $\operatorname{rng} A = \{(\xi^1, \xi^2, \xi^3) \mid \xi^3 = 0\}$. Its null space is the vertical axis (see Fig. 17.3).

For most linear transformations from one space to another space *of the same dimension* the null space consists only of the zero vector. In a sense, Fig. 15.2 illustrates the typical situation—parallelepipeds are distorted, but not squashed flat—and Fig. 17.2 illustrates a pathological case.

THEOREM 17.2. *If A is a linear transformation on $\mathscr{V}$ to $\mathscr{W}$, then $\mathscr{N}(A)$ is a subspace of $\mathscr{V}$.*

PROOF   See Problem 14.27.

APP. F.2
FNS.
APP. C.3
SETS

We next observe a triviality. The range of A, $\operatorname{rng} A$, is the set $\{z \mid \text{for some } x, z = A(x)\}$. To say that (17.2) has a solution, is just another way of saying that $y \in \operatorname{rng} A$. Now we state without proof a slight generalization of the second half of Problem 14.27.

THEOREM 17.3. *If A is a linear transformation on $\mathscr{V}$ to $\mathscr{W}$, then rng A is a subspace of $\mathscr{W}$.*

Although we are more interested in its corollaries, the following theorem is one of the. fundamental results in the theory of finite dimensional vector spaces.

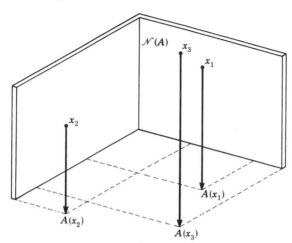

FIGURE 17.3

THEOREM 17.4. *If A is a linear transformation on a finite dimensional vector space $\mathscr{V}$ to a vector space $\mathscr{W}$, then*

$$\dim \mathscr{N}(A) + \dim \text{rng } A = \dim \mathscr{V}.$$

PROOF. By Theorem 13.10, the subspace $\mathscr{N}(A)$ has a complement. Choose one such complement and call it $\mathscr{M}$. In the proof of that theorem we chose $x_1, \ldots, x_m, y_1, \ldots, y_n$ in such a way that the x's formed a basis for the first subspace (here $\mathscr{N}(A)$) and the y's formed a basis for the second subspace (here $\mathscr{M}$) while the x's and y's together formed a basis for $\mathscr{V}$. Let $z_i = A(y_i)$ for $i = 1, 2, \ldots, n$. If we show that the z's form a basis for rng A, we will have $\dim \mathscr{N}(A) = m$, $\dim \text{rng } A = n$, and $\dim \mathscr{V} = m + n$, which will prove the theorem.

To show that the z's form a basis for rng A we show that they are linearly independent and that they span rng A.

To show linear independence, assume that $\sum_i \alpha_i z_i = 0$. Then

$$A(\sum_i \alpha_i y_i) = \sum_i \alpha_i A(y_i) = \sum_i \alpha_i z_i = 0$$

APP.
D.8
PRF.

so $\sum_i \alpha_i y_i \in \mathscr{N}(A)$. Since the y's are in the subspace $\mathscr{M}$, we also have $\sum_i \alpha_i y_i \in \mathscr{M}$. However, the only element which complementary subspaces have in common is 0. Thus $\sum_i \alpha_i y_i = 0$ and, since the y's form a basis for $\mathcal{M}$, it follows that $\alpha_1 = \alpha_2 = \cdots = \alpha_n = 0$. Thus the z's are linearly independent.

To show that the z's span rng A, consider an arbitrary $y \in$ rng A. From the definition of the range we know that there is an $x \in \mathcal{V}$ such that $y = Ax$. Since $x_1, \ldots, x_m, y_1, \ldots, y_n$ form a basis for $\mathcal{V}$, we can choose $\alpha_1, \ldots, \alpha_m, \beta_1, \ldots, \beta_n$ so

$$x = \sum_{i=1}^{m} \alpha_i x_i + \sum_{j=1}^{n} \beta_j y_j.$$

Finally, since $x_1, \ldots, x_m \in \mathcal{N}(A)$,

$$y = Ax = A(\sum_{i=1}^{m} \alpha_i x_i + \sum_{j=1}^{n} \beta_j y_j)$$

$$= \sum_{i=1}^{m} \alpha_i A(x_i) + \sum_{j=1}^{n} \beta_j A(y_j) = 0 + \sum_{j=1}^{n} \beta_j z_j.$$

Q.E.D.

COROLLARY 17.5. *Let A be a linear transformation on a finite-dimensional space $\mathcal{V}$ to a space $\mathcal{W}$ and let $\mathcal{M}$ be a complement of $\mathcal{N}(A)$. Let B be the transformation on $\mathcal{M}$ to rng A defined by $B(x) = A(x)$ for $x \in \mathcal{M}$. Then B has an inverse.*

PROOF. Let $y_i, z_i, i = 1, 2, \ldots, n$, be chosen as in the proof of the theorem. For each $z \in$ rng A there is a uniquely determined set of scalars $\alpha_i, i = 1, 2, \ldots, n$, such that $z = \sum_i \alpha_i z_i$. Let $C(z) = \sum_i \alpha_i y_i$. It is a routine exercise to verify that C is linear and that $C = B^{-1}$.

Q.E.D.

The function B, which is just like A except that the domain has been cut down to $\mathcal{M}$, is called the restriction of A to $\mathcal{M}$ and is often denoted by $A \mid \mathcal{M}$.

Surprisingly, Corollary 17.5 tells all about the solutions of $Ax = y$. The meaning of the corollary is revealed by a picture. Assume that A is a linear transformation on a three-dimensional space $\mathcal{V}$ and assume that rng A is the whole of a two-dimensional space $\mathcal{W}$. According to Theorem 17.4, $\mathcal{N}(A)$ is a one-dimensional subspace of $\mathcal{V}$. Look at Fig. 17.4. Any plane which does not contain the line $\mathcal{N}(A)$ will serve as $\mathcal{M}$. Underneath $\mathcal{V}$ we picture the plane $\mathcal{W} =$ rng A. Corollary 17.5 says that if we look only at $\mathcal{M}$, each point of $\mathcal{W}$ "comes from" exactly one point. More precisely: for each $z \in \mathcal{W}$ there is one and only one point in $\mathcal{M}$, namely $B^{-1}(z)$, such that A assigns to that point the value z.

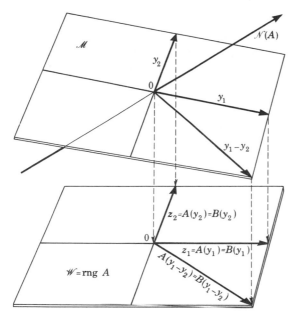

FIGURE 17.4

The same spaces are illustrated again in Fig. 17.5. Now we ask: What vectors x satisfy the equation $Ax=y$? Certainly $x_0 = B^{-1}(y)$ satisfies this equation, but so do many other vectors. If $Ax=y$ then $A(x-x_0) = Ax - Ax_0 = y - y = 0$. This shows that if x is a solution then $x - x_0 \in \mathcal{N}(A)$. Conversely if $x - x_0 \in \mathcal{N}(A)$ then

$$Ax = A(x - x_0 + x_0) = A(x - x_0) + A(x_0) = 0 + y$$

and x is a solution.

Although this discussion was suggested by Fig. 17.5, the argument is perfectly general and provides a proof of the following theorem.

THEOREM 17.6. *If $\mathcal{M}$ is a complement of $\mathcal{N}(A)$ and B is the function on $\mathcal{M}$ to rng A defined by*

$$Bx = Ax \quad \text{for } x \in \mathcal{M},$$

then for each $y \in$ rng A the set of all solutions of $Ax=y$ is

$$\{x \mid x - B^{-1}(y) \in \mathcal{N}(A)\}.$$

Theorem 17.6 not only provides the "general solution" of equation (17.2) but even describes how the solution varies with y. For a *fixed* $y \in$ rng A we find one solution, x_0, and a basis $x_1, x_2, \ldots, x_m$, for $\mathcal{N}(A)$.

We need to know that there is a subspace $\mathcal{M}$ complementary to $\mathcal{N}(A)$ and containing x_0 (see Problem 14.32), but we do not need explicit APP. formulas either for $\mathcal{M}$ or for B. Since $x_0 \in \mathcal{M} = \text{dmn } B$, we have F.6 $x_0 = B^{-1}(Bx_0) = B^{-1}(Ax_0) = B^{-1}(y)$. By Theorem 17.6, x is a solution FNS. if and only if $x - x_0 \in \mathcal{N}(A)$, i.e., since $x_1, x_2, \ldots, x_m$ is a basis for $\mathcal{N}(A)$ if and only if there are scalars $\alpha_1, \alpha_2, \ldots, \alpha_m$ such that $x = x_0 + \sum_i \alpha_i x_i$. This proves that

$$x = x_0 + \sum_i \alpha_i x_i$$

is the general solution of (17.2) in the following sense. For each choice of $\alpha_1, \alpha_2, \ldots, \alpha_m$, the corresponding x is a solution of (17.2) and for

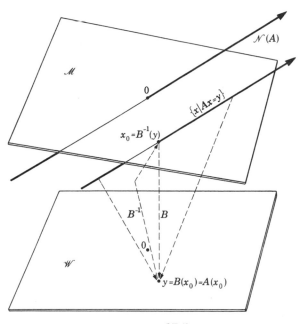

FIGURE 17.5

each x that satisfies (17.2) there are scalars $\alpha_1, \alpha_2, \ldots, \alpha_m$ such that $x = x_0 + \sum_i \alpha_i x_i$. Another way of phrasing this conclusion is to say that the set of all solutions is $\{x_0\} + \mathcal{N}(A)$. If we want the solutions for different values of y, we choose an $\mathcal{M}$, find B, and observe that, for each $y \in \text{rng } A$, the general solution is

$$x = B^{-1}(y) + \sum_i \alpha_i x_i.$$

A particularly important case is that where $\mathcal{V}$ and $\mathcal{W}$ have the same dimension.

COROLLARY 17.7. *Assume that $\mathscr{V}$ and $\mathscr{W}$ are vector spaces of the same dimension. If A is a linear transformation on $\mathscr{V}$ to $\mathscr{W}$, then the following conditions are equivalent:*

(i) *A has an inverse,*

(ii) *$\mathscr{N}(A) = \{0\}$, and*

(iii) *rng $A = \mathscr{W}$.*

Under the same assumptions the following are equivalent:

(iv) *A does not have an inverse;*

(v) *$\mathscr{N}(A) \neq \{0\}$;*

(vi) *rng $A \neq \mathscr{W}$;*

(vii) *there is an $x \neq 0$ such that $Ax = 0$.*

Section 18.   Simultaneous Linear Equations: Computation

The general theory of the preceding section does not provide us with explicit solutions for particular systems of simultaneous linear equations. For the numerical calculation of solutions we turn again to the system (17.1).

Our object is to find a basis for $\mathscr{N}(A)$, a suitable complement $\mathscr{M}$, and to calculate the corresponding B^{-1}. To achieve this we replace (17.1) by a simpler system whose solutions are precisely the same as those of the original system. The replacement is made in a series of routine steps which we now describe.

It should be clear that if we have a system of equations, any one of the following simple changes gives a system with precisely the same set of solutions.

  I. Interchange two of the equations.

 II. Multiply any one of the equations by a non-zero scalar.

III. If the j-th equation is $\sum_i \alpha_i^j \xi^i = \eta^j$ and the k-th equation is $\sum_i \alpha_i^k \xi^i = \eta^k$ and if ρ is a scalar, leave all equations except the k-th unchanged and replace the k-th by

$$\sum_i (\alpha_i^k - \rho \alpha_i^j)\xi^i \; = \; \eta^k - \rho\eta^j.$$

A change of type III is usually described by saying "subtract ρ times the j-th equation from the k-th equation."

The application of successive steps of types I, II, and III may be tedious, but it is more difficult in theory than in practice. For this reason we combine a description of the general procedure with a specific example.

Consider the system

$$\begin{cases} \quad\quad -2\xi^2 + \xi^3 - \xi^4 = \eta^1, \\ 2\xi^1 - 2\xi^2 + \xi^3 + \xi^4 = \eta^2, \\ 3\xi^1 - \xi^2 + 4\xi^3 - 2\xi^4 = \eta^3. \end{cases}$$

The process of solution runs as follows.

(1) Find the smallest i such that ξ^i appears (with non-zero coefficient) in some equation. If this is not the first equation, interchange it with the first. Here $i = 1$ and our system becomes:

$$\begin{cases} 2\xi^1 - 2\xi^2 + \xi^3 + \xi^4 = \eta^2, \\ \quad\quad -2\xi^2 + \xi^3 - \xi^4 = \eta^1, \\ 3\xi^1 - \xi^2 + 4\xi^3 - 2\xi^4 = \eta^3. \end{cases}$$

(2) Divide the (new) first equation by the coefficient of ξ^i. We get:

$$\begin{cases} \xi^1 - \xi^2 + (1/2)\xi^3 + (1/2)\xi^4 = (1/2)\eta^2, \\ \quad -2\xi^2 + \xi^3 - \xi^4 = \eta^1, \\ 3\xi^1 - \xi^2 + 4\xi^3 - 2\xi^4 = \eta^3. \end{cases}$$

(3) Multiply the first equation by the coefficient of ξ^i in the second equation and subtract this multiple from the second equation. In our system the coefficient of ξ^1 in the second equation is zero so this step leaves the system unchanged.

(3′) Repeat step (3) using the third equation instead of the second. In our case we obtain:

$$\begin{cases} \xi^1 - \xi^2 + (1/2)\xi^3 + (1/2)\xi^4 = (1/2)\eta^2, \\ \quad -2\xi^2 + \xi^3 - \xi^4 = \eta^1, \\ \quad +2\xi^2 + (5/2)\xi^3 - (7/2)\xi^4 = (-3/2)\eta^2 + \eta^3. \end{cases}$$

(3″) Repeat this process for the 4th, 5th, ... equations. In the general case one gets a system which looks like:

$$(18.1) \quad \begin{cases} 0\cdot\xi^1 + \cdots + 0\cdot\xi^{i-1} + \xi^i + \beta^1_{i+1}\xi^{i+1} + \cdots + \beta^1_N\xi^N = \cdots, \\ 0\cdot\xi^1 + \cdots + 0\cdot\xi^{i-1} + 0\cdot\xi^i + \beta^2_{i+1}\xi^{i+1} + \cdots + \beta^2_N\xi^N = \cdots, \\ \quad\quad \cdot\quad\cdot\quad\cdot\quad\cdot\quad\cdot\quad\cdot \\ 0\cdot\xi^1 + \cdots + 0\cdot\xi^{i-1} + 0\cdot\xi^i + \beta^M_{i+1}\xi^{i+1} + \cdots + \beta^M_N\xi^N = \cdots. \end{cases}$$

Now repeat the whole process leaving the first equation alone. Thus step (1) becomes: find the least i such that ξ^i appears (with non-zero coefficient) in some equation below the first. If this equation is not the second, interchange it with the second. Etc., etc., etc.

With our system we obtain:

$$\left\{ \begin{array}{l} \xi^1 - \xi^2 + (1/2)\xi^3 + (1/2)\xi^4 = (1/2)\eta^2, \\ \xi^2 + (-1/2)\xi^3 + (1/2)\xi^4 = (-1/2)\eta^1, \\ 2\xi^2 + (5/2)\xi^3 + (-7/2)\xi^4 = (-3/2)\eta^2 + \eta^3, \end{array} \right.$$

and then:

$$\left\{ \begin{array}{l} \xi^1 - \xi^2 + (1/2)\xi^3 + (1/2)\xi^4 = (1/2)\eta^2, \\ \xi^2 + (-1/2)\xi^3 + (1/2)\xi^4 = (-1/2)\eta^1, \\ (7/2)\xi^3 + (-9/2)\xi^4 = \eta^1 + (-3/2)\eta^2 + \eta^3. \end{array} \right.$$

We next repeat the process, leaving the first two equations alone, and so on. For the particular system we are looking at, there is only one more step. We make a change of type II in the third equation and get:

$$(18.2) \left\{ \begin{array}{l} \xi^1 - \xi^2 + (1/2)\xi^3 + (1/2)\xi^4 = (1/2)\eta^2 \quad , \\ \xi^2 + (-1/2)\xi^3 + (1/2)\xi^4 = (-1/2)\eta^1 \quad , \\ \xi^3 + (-9/7)\xi^4 = (2/7)\eta^1 + (-3/7)\eta^2 + (2/7)\eta^3. \end{array} \right.$$

If there were more equations we would continue, leaving the first three equations unchanged, and so on, until finally we would have a system which looked like (18.3) (p. 88).

For $j = 1, 2, \ldots, k$, the j-th equation is of the form

$$\xi^{i_j} + \sum_{l=i_j+1}^{n} \gamma_{l}^{j}\xi^l = \cdots$$

where $i_1 < i_2 < \cdots < i_k$, and the last $M - k$ equations are of the form $0 = \cdots$. Moreover, in the process we get an explicit form for the right-hand sides as well. At each stage all of these right-hand sides are linear combinations of the original η's.

We may go one step further and eliminate the ξ^{i_j} term from the equations which precede the j-th as well as from those which follow it. This is achieved by applying steps of type III.

$$
\begin{aligned}
0\cdot\xi^1 + \cdots + 0\cdot\xi^{t_1-1} + \xi^{t_1} + \gamma^1_{i_1+1}\xi^{t_1+1} + \cdots & + \gamma^1_N\xi^N = \cdots \\[2pt]
0\cdot\xi^1 + \cdots + 0\cdot\xi^{t_1-1} + 0\cdot\xi^{t_1} + 0\cdot\xi^{t_1+1} + \cdots + 0\cdot\xi^{t_2-1} + \xi^{t_2} + \gamma^2_{i_2+1}\xi^{t_2+1} + \cdots & + \gamma^2_N\xi^N = \cdots \\[2pt]
&\qquad\vdots \\[2pt]
0\cdot\xi^1 + \cdots + 0\cdot\xi^{t_1-1} + 0\cdot\xi^{t_1} + \cdots + 0\cdot\xi^{t_2} + \cdots + 0\cdot\xi^{t_k-1} + \xi^{t_k} + \gamma^k_{i_k+1}\xi^{t_k+1} + \cdots & + \gamma^k_N\xi^N = \cdots \\[2pt]
&\qquad\vdots \\[2pt]
0\cdot\xi^1 + 0\cdot\xi^2 + \cdots & + 0\cdot\xi^N = \cdots \\[2pt]
0\cdot\xi^1 + 0\cdot\xi^2 + \cdots & + 0\cdot\xi^N = \cdots
\end{aligned}
$$

(18.3)

Performing two such steps at once, we can eliminate ξ^3 from the first two equations in (18.2) and obtain:

$$
\left\{
\begin{aligned}
&\xi^1 - \xi^2 + \quad + [(1/2) - (-9/14)]\xi^4 \\
&\qquad\qquad = (-1/7)\eta^1 + [(1/2) + (3/14)]\eta^2 + (-1/7)\eta^3, \\
&\xi^2 + \quad + [(1/2) + (-9/14)]\xi^4 \\
&\qquad\qquad = [(-1/2) + (1/7)]\eta^1 + (-3/14)\eta^2 + (1/7)\eta^3, \\
&\xi^3 + \qquad\qquad (-9/7)\xi^4 \\
&\qquad\qquad = \qquad\qquad (2/7)\eta^1 + (-3/7)\eta^2 + (2/7)\eta^3.
\end{aligned}
\right.
$$

or

$$
\left\{
\begin{aligned}
\xi^1 - \xi^2 + \quad + (8/7)\xi^4 &= (-1/7)\eta^1 + \quad (5/7)\eta^2 + (-1/7)\eta^3, \\
\xi^2 + \quad + (-1/7)\xi^4 &= (-5/14)\eta^1 + (-3/14)\eta^2 + \quad (1/7)\eta^3, \\
\xi^3 + (-9/7)\xi^4 &= \quad (2/7)\eta^1 + \quad (-3/7)\eta^2 + \quad (2/7)\eta^3.
\end{aligned}
\right.
$$

Finally, elimination of ξ^2 from the first equation yields:

$$
(18.4) \quad
\left\{
\begin{aligned}
\xi^1 \qquad\quad + \qquad \xi^4 &= \quad (-1/2)\eta^1 + \quad (1/2)\eta^2, \\
\xi^2 \qquad + (-1/7)\xi^4 &= (-5/14)\eta^1 + (-3/14)\eta^2 + (1/7)\eta^3, \\
\xi^3 + (-9/7)\xi^4 &= \quad (2/7)\eta^1 + \quad (-3/7)\eta^2 + (2/7)\eta^3.
\end{aligned}
\right.
$$

In the general case there are certain special indices which we have called i_j ($j = 1, 2, \ldots, k$) and ξ^{i_j} appears only in the j-th equation. (In the example $k = 3$ and $i_1 = 1$, $i_2 = 2$, and $i_3 = 3$.) There is no reason why these special indices should be consecutive. You will observe that in (18.3) we expect that $\xi^{i_1 + 1}, \ldots, \xi^{i_2 - 1}$ will appear in the first equation, etc. If it happens that $i_2 = i_1 + 1$ there will be no such terms. The general description is simplified if we assume that all the special indices come first, i.e., $i_1 = 1$, $i_2 = 2$, $\ldots$, $i_k = k$. When this does not happen, the necessary modifications are quite obvious. (One way to handle the situation is to renumber the ξ's so that the special ones do come first.)

For simplicity, then, assume that (18.3) assumes the form

$$
(18.5) \quad
\left\{
\begin{aligned}
&\xi^j + \sum_{i=k+1}^{N} \gamma_i^j \xi^i = \sum_{i=1}^{M} \delta_i^j \eta^i \quad \text{for } j = 1, 2, \ldots, k \\
&0 = \sum_{i=1}^{M} \delta_i^j \eta^i \quad \text{for } j = k+1, k+2, \ldots, M.
\end{aligned}
\right.
$$

It is now easy to read off the general solution of the equivalent systems (17.1) and (18.5). There is a solution if and only if

$$
(18.6) \quad \sum_{i=1}^{M} \delta_i^j \eta^i = 0 \quad \text{for } j = k+1, k+2, \ldots, M.
$$

If (18.6) is satisfied, then the totality of solutions is obtained by giving $\xi^{k+1}, \xi^{k+2}, \ldots, \xi^N$ arbitrary values and setting

$$(18.7) \qquad \xi^j = \sum_{i=1}^M \delta_i^j \eta^i - \sum_{i=k+1}^N \gamma_i^j \xi^i \quad \text{for } j = 1, 2, \ldots, k.$$

It may make things clearer if we replace the "arbitrary constants," $\xi^{k+1}, \xi^{k+2}, \ldots, \xi^N$, by some other symbols, say by $\rho^{k+1}, \rho^{k+2}, \ldots, \rho^N$. From (18.7) we see that the general solution of the equivalent systems (17.1) and (18.5) is given by the following equation:

$$(18.8) \begin{cases} \xi^1 = \delta_1^1 \eta^1 + \delta_2^1 \eta^2 + \cdots + \delta_M^1 \eta^M - \gamma_{k+1}^1 \rho^{k+1} - \gamma_{k+2}^1 \rho^{k+2} - \cdots - \gamma_N^1 \rho^N, \\ \xi^2 = \delta_1^2 \eta^1 + \delta_2^2 \eta^2 + \cdots + \delta_M^2 \eta^M - \gamma_{k+1}^2 \rho^{k+1} - \gamma_{k+2}^2 \rho^{k+2} - \cdots - \gamma_N^2 \rho^N, \\ \vdots \qquad \vdots \qquad \vdots \qquad\quad \vdots \qquad\quad \vdots \qquad\quad \vdots \qquad\qquad \vdots \\ \xi^k = \delta_1^k \eta^1 + \delta_2^k \eta^2 + \cdots + \delta_M^k \eta^M - \gamma_{k+1}^k \rho^{k+1} - \gamma_{k+2}^k \rho^{k+2} - \cdots - \gamma_N^2 \rho^N, \\ \xi^{k+1} = \quad 0 \quad + \quad 0 \quad + \cdots + \quad 0 \quad + \quad \rho^{k+1} \quad + \quad 0 \quad + \cdots + \quad 0 \;, \\ \xi^{k+2} = \quad 0 \quad + \quad 0 \quad + \cdots + \quad 0 \quad + \quad 0 \quad + \quad \rho^{k+2} \quad + \cdots + \quad 0 \;, \\ \vdots \qquad \vdots \quad \vdots \qquad\quad \vdots \qquad\quad \vdots \qquad\quad \vdots \qquad\qquad \vdots \\ \xi^N = \quad 0 \quad + \quad 0 \quad + \cdots + \quad 0 \quad + \quad 0 \quad + \quad 0 \quad + \cdots + \rho^N \;. \end{cases}$$

It will be easier to remember this solution if we write the elements of $\mathscr{R}^N$ as columns of N numbers instead of as rows. The left-hand side of (18.8) is the column

$$x = \begin{bmatrix} \xi^1 \\ \xi^2 \\ \vdots \\ \xi^k \\ \xi^{k+1} \\ \xi^{k+2} \\ \vdots \\ \xi^N \end{bmatrix}.$$

Such a column, regarded as an element of $\mathscr{R}^N$ is called a *column vector*.

The right-hand side is a sum of columns and you will note that each column contains a common factor: η^1 in the 1st, η^2 in the 2nd, up to η^M in the M-th. In the $M+1$-st column the common factor is ρ^{k+1}, in the $M+2$-nd it is ρ^{k+2}, and so on. The vector space $\mathscr{R}^N$ is made to order for this situation. We add elements of $\mathscr{R}^N$ by adding corresponding entries in the columns and to multiply an element of $\mathscr{R}^N$ by a scalar we multiply each entry by that scalar. Thus the right-hand side of (18.8) is the sum of the columns:

$$\begin{bmatrix} \delta_1^1 \eta^1 \\ \delta_1^2 \eta^1 \\ \vdots \\ \delta_1^k \eta^1 \\ 0 \\ 0 \\ \vdots \\ 0 \end{bmatrix} = \eta^1 \begin{bmatrix} \delta_1^1 \\ \delta_1^2 \\ \vdots \\ \delta_1^k \\ 0 \\ 0 \\ \vdots \\ 0 \end{bmatrix}, \ \ldots, \ \begin{bmatrix} \delta_M^1 \eta^M \\ \delta_M^2 \eta^M \\ \vdots \\ \delta_M^k \eta^M \\ 0 \\ 0 \\ \vdots \\ 0 \end{bmatrix} = \eta^M \begin{bmatrix} \delta_M^1 \\ \delta_M^2 \\ \vdots \\ \delta_M^k \\ 0 \\ 0 \\ \vdots \\ 0 \end{bmatrix},$$

$$\begin{bmatrix} -\gamma_{k+1}^1 \rho^{k+1} \\ -\gamma_{k+1}^2 \rho^{k+1} \\ \vdots \\ -\gamma_{k+1}^k \rho^{k+1} \\ \rho^{k+1} \\ 0 \\ \vdots \\ 0 \end{bmatrix} = \rho^{k+1} \begin{bmatrix} -\gamma_{k+1}^1 \\ -\gamma_{k+1}^2 \\ \vdots \\ -\gamma_{k+1}^k \\ 1 \\ 0 \\ \vdots \\ 0 \end{bmatrix}, \ \ldots, \ \begin{bmatrix} -\gamma_N^1 \rho^N \\ -\gamma_N^2 \rho^N \\ \vdots \\ -\gamma_N^k \rho^N \\ 0 \\ 0 \\ \vdots \\ \rho^N \end{bmatrix} = \rho^N \begin{bmatrix} -\gamma_N^1 \\ -\gamma_N^2 \\ \vdots \\ -\gamma_N^k \\ 0 \\ 0 \\ \vdots \\ 1 \end{bmatrix}.$$

It is now easy to give the prescription for writing down the general solution:

> For $i = 1, 2, \ldots, M$, let d_i be the column vector with δ_i^j in the j-th place, $j = 1, 2, \ldots, k$, and with 0 in all places below the k-th. For $i = k+1, k+2, \ldots, N$, let c_i be the column vector with $-\gamma_i^j$ in the j-th place, $+1$ in the i-th place, and 0's elsewhere. The general solution of (17.1) is

$$(18.9) \qquad x = \sum_{i=1}^{M} \eta^i d_i + \sum_{i=k+1}^{N} \rho^i c_i,$$

> where $\rho^{k+1}, \rho^{k+2}, \ldots, \rho^n$, are arbitrary constants.

The last sentence is an abbreviated way of making two assertions: (1) if x is a solution of (17.1), then there is a way of choosing the ρ's so that x is given by (18.9); and (2) no matter how the scalars ρ^{k+1}, $\rho^{k+2}, \ldots, \rho^N$, are chosen, the corresponding x, calculated from (18.9), is a solution of (17.1).

Examine (18.4). You will see that in our example $k = 3$, $M = 3$, $N = 4$, and

$$d_1 = \begin{bmatrix} -1/2 \\ -5/14 \\ 2/7 \\ 0 \end{bmatrix}, \quad d_2 = \begin{bmatrix} 1/2 \\ -3/14 \\ -3/7 \\ 0 \end{bmatrix}, \quad d_3 = \begin{bmatrix} 0 \\ 1/7 \\ 2/7 \\ 0 \end{bmatrix}, \quad c_4 = \begin{bmatrix} -1 \\ +1/7 \\ +9/7 \\ 1 \end{bmatrix}.$$

The general solution is

$$
x = \begin{bmatrix} \xi^1 \\ \xi^2 \\ \xi^3 \\ \xi^4 \end{bmatrix} = \eta^1 \begin{bmatrix} -1/2 \\ -5/14 \\ 2/7 \\ 0 \end{bmatrix} + \eta^2 \begin{bmatrix} 1/2 \\ -3/14 \\ -3/7 \\ 0 \end{bmatrix} + \eta^3 \begin{bmatrix} 0 \\ 1/7 \\ 2/7 \\ 0 \end{bmatrix} + \rho^4 \begin{bmatrix} -1 \\ 1/7 \\ 1/7 \\ 1 \end{bmatrix}
$$

$$
= \begin{bmatrix} (-1/2)\eta^1 + \quad (1/2)\eta^2 + \quad\quad - \quad\quad \rho^4 \\ (-5/14)\eta^1 + (-3/14)\eta^2 + (1/7)\eta^3 + (1/7)\rho^4 \\ (2/7)\eta^1 + \quad (-3/7)\eta^2 + (2/7)\eta^3 + (9/7)\rho^4 \\ \rho^4 \end{bmatrix},
$$

where ρ^4 is an arbitrary constant.

This completes the process of solution, but many comments are in order.

For any but the simplest systems this long and tedious process is about the best available. It is well adapted to high-speed computers, although slight modifications are desirable to minimize the so-called rounding-off errors. Standard programs for it, or some very similar process, are available on all large computers. In applying it to small systems a human being can use intelligence to make a few short cuts— such things as rearranging the order of the steps to make the arithmetic a little easier, and performing several steps of type III at once. More rarely, you may even omit or combine some steps of types I and II.

We have given an example wherein we study the solution for all possible values of y. If one is seeking the solution for a single given y, it may happen that, at some early stage of the process, one obtains a system containing an equation of the form $0 = \cdots$ where the $\cdots$ is not zero. Here one stops, knowing that the system has no solution.

Of course, the general solution which we have now found explicitly is the same as that described long ago in Theorem 17.6. Let A be the linear transformation which assigns to each

$$
x = \begin{bmatrix} \xi^1 \\ \xi^2 \\ \vdots \\ \xi^N \end{bmatrix} \in \mathscr{R}^N \quad \text{the value} \quad A(x) = \begin{bmatrix} \sum_{i=1}^{N} \alpha_i^1 \xi^i \\ \sum_{i=1}^{N} \alpha_i^2 \xi^i \\ \vdots \\ \sum_{i=1}^{N} \alpha_1^M \xi^i \end{bmatrix} \in \mathscr{R}^M.
$$

A column vector $y = \begin{bmatrix} \eta^1 \\ \eta^2 \\ \vdots \\ \eta^M \end{bmatrix} \in \mathscr{R}^M$ lies in rng A if and only if it satisfies

equation (18.6). For such a $y \in$ rng A we can set $B^{-1}(y) = \sum_{i=1}^{M} \eta^i d_i$. The vectors $c_{k+1}, c_{k+2}, \ldots, c_N$, are a basis of the null space of A.

Late in our work, it was a slight help to think of $\mathscr{R}^N$ as the set of all columns of N real numbers. As a matter of fact, this is usually the more convenient way of looking at $\mathscr{R}^N$ and we adopt it hereafter.

Finally, it is silly to carry along the ξ's throughout the computation. The rectangular array

$$\begin{bmatrix} \alpha_1^1 & \alpha_2^1 & \cdots & \alpha_N^1 \\ \alpha_1^2 & \alpha_2^2 & \cdots & \alpha_N^2 \\ \vdots & \vdots & & \vdots \\ \alpha_1^M & \alpha_2^M & \cdots & \alpha_N^M \end{bmatrix}$$

is called the matrix of the system (17.1) and the array

$$\begin{bmatrix} \alpha_1^1 & \alpha_2^1 & \cdots & \alpha_N^1 & \eta^1 \\ \alpha_1^2 & \alpha_2^2 & \cdots & \alpha_N^2 & \eta^2 \\ \vdots & \vdots & & \vdots & \vdots \\ \alpha_1^M & \alpha_2^M & \cdots & \alpha_N^M & \eta^M \end{bmatrix}$$

is called the augmented matrix of the system. The amount of writing to be done is cut enormously if we perform the operations of types I, II, and III on the augmented matrix rather than on the equations. After the last such step you may write down the corresponding system of equations if you wish, but you can, if you prefer, simply read off the general solution from the matrix. The operations of types I, II, and III, regarded as operations on matrices, are called elementary row operations. Two matrices which can be obtained from each other by a series of such operations are said to be row equivalent. If $[\alpha]$ and $[\beta]$ are matrices, we will write "$[\alpha] \leftrightarrow [\beta]$" to mean "$[\alpha]$ and $[\beta]$ are row equivalent." This terminology suggests that if $[\alpha]$ can be obtained from $[\beta]$ by a series of elementary row operations, then $[\beta]$ can be obtained from $[\alpha]$ by another series of such operations. This you can easily verify if it is not already obvious to you.

Let us solve our particular example in this way, taking now the case where the η's are given constants. Let $\eta^1 = 2$, $\eta^2 = 2$, $\eta^3 = 1$. The augmented matrix is

$$\begin{bmatrix} 0 & -2 & 1 & -1 & 2 \\ 2 & -2 & 1 & 1 & 2 \\ 3 & -1 & 4 & -2 & 1 \end{bmatrix}$$

$$\leftrightarrow \begin{bmatrix} 2 & -2 & 1 & 1 & 2 \\ 0 & -2 & 1 & -1 & 2 \\ 3 & -1 & 4 & -2 & 1 \end{bmatrix}$$ (type I)

$$\leftrightarrow \begin{bmatrix} 1 & -1 & 1/2 & 1/2 & 1 \\ 0 & -2 & 1 & -1 & 2 \\ 0 & 2 & 5/2 & -7/2 & -2 \end{bmatrix}$$ (types II and III, care is needed)

$$\leftrightarrow \begin{bmatrix} 1 & -1 & 1/2 & 1/2 & 1 \\ 0 & 1 & -1/2 & 1/2 & -1 \\ 0 & 0 & 7/2 & -9/2 & 0 \end{bmatrix}$$ (easiest if type III, adding 2nd and 3rd equations, is used before type II, great care is required)

$$\leftrightarrow \begin{bmatrix} 1 & -1 & 1/2 & 1/2 & 1 \\ 0 & 1 & -1/2 & 1/2 & -1 \\ 0 & 0 & 1 & -9/7 & 0 \end{bmatrix}$$ (type II)

$$\leftrightarrow \begin{bmatrix} 1 & 0 & 0 & 1 & 0 \\ 0 & 1 & -1/2 & 1/2 & -1 \\ 0 & 0 & 1 & -9/7 & 0 \end{bmatrix}$$ (type III, but the order of steps is not the same as that used with the equations)

$$\leftrightarrow \begin{bmatrix} 1 & 0 & 0 & 1 & 0 \\ 0 & 1 & 0 & -1/7 & -1 \\ 0 & 0 & 1 & -9/7 & 0 \end{bmatrix}.$$ (type III)

Since $k = 3$ and $N = 4 = k + 1$, we must place one 0 below the last column to get $\sum_{i=1}^{M} \eta^i d_i$. There is a single c and it is obtained by reversing the signs in the fourth column and placing a 1 in the fourth line. The general solution is

$$x = \begin{bmatrix} \xi^1 \\ \xi^2 \\ \xi^3 \\ \xi^4 \end{bmatrix} = \begin{bmatrix} 0 \\ -1 \\ 0 \\ 0 \end{bmatrix} + \rho^4 \begin{bmatrix} -1 \\ 1/7 \\ 9/7 \\ 1 \end{bmatrix}.$$

The row operations on the matrices reflect precisely the operations on the equations. Every system of simultaneous linear equations can be transformed to an equivalent system of a particularly simple type. The corresponding elementary row operations on the matrix transform it to a matrix in the so-called "echelon form" (see opposite page). In an echelon matrix each row consists of a sequence of 0's followed by a 1, after which come other entries. In the first row there need not be any 0's to start with, and the last few rows may consist entirely of 0's. In each successive row the initial sequence of 0's is longer than that in

ECHELON FORM

$$\begin{bmatrix}
\alpha_n^1 & \alpha_n^2 & \alpha_n^3 & \cdot\ \cdot\ \cdot & \alpha_n^l & 0 & \cdot\ \cdot\ \cdot & 0 \\
\alpha_{k_l+1}^1 & \alpha_{k_l+1}^2 & \alpha_{k_l+1}^3 & \cdot\ \cdot\ \cdot & \alpha_{k_l+1}^l & 0 & \cdot\ \cdot\ \cdot & 0 \\
0 & 0 & 0 & \cdot\ \cdot\ \cdot & 1 & 0 & \cdot\ \cdot\ \cdot & 0 \\
\alpha_{k_l-1}^1 & \alpha_{k_l-1}^2 & \alpha_{k_l-1}^3 & \cdot\ \cdot\ \cdot & 0 & 0 & \cdot\ \cdot\ \cdot & 0 \\
\alpha_{k_3+1}^1 & \alpha_{k_3+1}^2 & \alpha_{k_3+1}^3 & \cdot\ \cdot\ \cdot & 0 & 0 & \cdot\ \cdot\ \cdot & 0 \\
0 & 0 & 1 & \cdot\ \cdot\ \cdot & 0 & 0 & \cdot\ \cdot\ \cdot & 0 \\
\alpha_{k_3-1}^1 & \alpha_{k_3-1}^2 & 0 & \cdot\ \cdot\ \cdot & 0 & 0 & \cdot\ \cdot\ \cdot & 0 \\
\alpha_{k_2+1}^1 & \alpha_{k_2+1}^2 & 0 & \cdot\ \cdot\ \cdot & 0 & 0 & \cdot\ \cdot\ \cdot & 0 \\
0 & 1 & 0 & \cdot\ \cdot\ \cdot & 0 & 0 & \cdot\ \cdot\ \cdot & 0 \\
\alpha_{k_2-1}^1 & 0 & 0 & \cdot\ \cdot\ \cdot & 0 & 0 & \cdot\ \cdot\ \cdot & 0 \\
\alpha_{k_1+1}^1 & 0 & 0 & \cdot\ \cdot\ \cdot & 0 & 0 & \cdot\ \cdot\ \cdot & 0 \\
1 & 0 & 0 & \cdot\ \cdot\ \cdot & 0 & 0 & \cdot\ \cdot\ \cdot & 0 \\
0 & 0 & 0 & \cdot\ \cdot\ \cdot & 0 & 0 & \cdot\ \cdot\ \cdot & 0 \\
0 & 0 & 0 & \cdot\ \cdot\ \cdot & 0 & 0 & \cdot\ \cdot\ \cdot & 0
\end{bmatrix}$$

the previous row. If a column contains the initial 1 of some row, then all its other entries are 0.

Formally: a matrix

$$\begin{bmatrix}
\alpha_1^1 & \alpha_2^1 & \cdots & \alpha_N^1 \\
\alpha_1^2 & \alpha_2^2 & \cdots & \alpha_N^2 \\
\vdots & \vdots & & \vdots \\
\alpha_1^M & \alpha_2^M & \cdots & \alpha_N^M
\end{bmatrix}$$

is in echelon form if and only if there is an integer $l \leqslant M$ and a sequence of integers $1 \leqslant k_1 < k_2 < \cdots < k_l \leqslant N$ such that

$$\alpha_j^i = 0 \quad \text{if } j < k_i,$$

$$\alpha_{k_i}^i = 1,$$

$$\alpha_{k_i}^j = 0 \quad \text{if } j \neq i, \quad \text{and}$$

$$\alpha_j^i = 0 \quad \text{if } i > l.$$

Section 19.   Matrices

In Section 17 we studied the system of linear equations

$$\sum_{i=1}^{N} \alpha_i^j \xi^i = \eta^j, \quad j = 1, 2, \ldots, M,$$

by introducing the linear transformation A which assigns to each

$$x = \begin{bmatrix} \xi^1 \\ \xi^2 \\ \vdots \\ \xi^N \end{bmatrix} \in \mathscr{R}^N \text{ the value}$$

(19.1)
$$A(x) = \begin{bmatrix} \displaystyle\sum_{i=1}^{N} \alpha_i^1 \xi^i \\ \displaystyle\sum_{i=1}^{N} \alpha_i^2 \xi^i \\ \vdots \\ \displaystyle\sum_{i=1}^{N} \alpha_i^M \xi^i \end{bmatrix} \in \mathscr{R}^M.$$

In Section 18 we introduced the matrix of the system:

$$[\alpha] = \begin{bmatrix} \alpha_1^1 & \alpha_2^1 & \cdots & \alpha_N^1 \\ \alpha_1^2 & \alpha_2^2 & \cdots & \alpha_N^2 \\ \vdots & \vdots & & \vdots \\ \alpha_1^M & \alpha_2^M & \cdots & \alpha_N^M \end{bmatrix}.$$

In the present section we forget about the system of equations and study directly the relation between the linear transformation and the matrix.

As soon as we are given the matrix $[\alpha]$ we can use (19.1) to define the function A on $\mathscr{R}^N$ to $\mathscr{R}^M$.   In the other direction, it can be proved that every linear transformation on $\mathscr{R}^N$ to $\mathscr{R}^M$ has the form given in

(19.1) so each transformation determines a corresponding matrix. We will go further and associate a matrix with every linear transformation from one finite-dimensional vector space to another. These matrices are essential when we reach a point where numerical calculation is required; but they are clumsy and it is usually wise to think and work in terms of the linear transformations just as long as possible.

There is another disadvantage in working with the matrices rather than with the transformations themselves. There is no unique correspondence between the matrix and the transformation. Before we can introduce the matrix we need bases for the spaces involved, and the matrix we associate with the transformation depends on which bases we choose.

It will help us to keep the indices straight if we always write as subscripts the indices of the vectors forming a basis. We will soon introduce certain scalars, called coordinates, and their indices will be written as superscripts. These conventions are by no means universal. Most commonly all indices are written as subscripts, and in the very next chapter we will want to reverse our own custom for certain spaces.

DEFINITION 19.1. If $x_1, x_2, \ldots, x_N$, is a basis for a vector space $\mathscr{V}$, then for each y in $\mathscr{V}$, the scalars $\eta^1, \eta^2, \ldots, \eta^N$ such that $y = \sum_i \eta^i x_i$ are called the *coordinates* of y relative to the basis $x_1, x_2, \ldots, x_N$.

To visualize the meaning of coordinates think of $\mathscr{R}^2$. The vectors

$$x_1 = \begin{bmatrix} 1 \\ 0 \end{bmatrix} \quad \text{and} \quad x_2 = \begin{bmatrix} 0 \\ 1 \end{bmatrix}$$

form the simplest possible basis for $\mathscr{R}^2$. If

$$x = \begin{bmatrix} \xi^1 \\ \xi^2 \end{bmatrix}$$

is any vector in $\mathscr{R}^2$ then

$$x = \xi^1 x_1 + \xi^2 x_2.$$

In the terminology of elementary analytic geometry the coordinates of the point x are ξ^1 and ξ^2. Referring to Definition 19.1, we see that ξ^1 and ξ^2 are also the coordinates of the vector x relative to the basis x_1, x_2. Of course, x has quite different coordinates relative to other bases. If

$$y_1 = \begin{bmatrix} 1 \\ -2 \end{bmatrix} \quad \text{and} \quad y_2 = \begin{bmatrix} 2 \\ 2 \end{bmatrix},$$

then to find the coordinates of $\begin{bmatrix} 3 \\ 2 \end{bmatrix}$ relative to y_1, y_2 we must find η^1 and η^2 so

$$\begin{bmatrix} 3 \\ 2 \end{bmatrix} = \eta^1 y_1 + \eta^2 y_2 = \eta^1 \begin{bmatrix} 1 \\ -2 \end{bmatrix} + \eta^2 \begin{bmatrix} 2 \\ 2 \end{bmatrix} = \begin{bmatrix} \eta^1 + 2\eta^2 \\ -2\eta^1 + 2\eta^2 \end{bmatrix}.$$

The unique solution of this equation is $\eta^1 = 1/3$, $\eta^2 = 4/3$; so the coordinates of $\begin{bmatrix} 3 \\ 2 \end{bmatrix}$ relative to this new basis are 1/3 and 4/3. Obviously, most problems in $\mathscr{R}^N$ will be easiest if we use the *natural basis*:

$$x_1 = \begin{bmatrix} 1 \\ 0 \\ 0 \\ \vdots \\ 0 \end{bmatrix}, \quad x_2 = \begin{bmatrix} 0 \\ 1 \\ 0 \\ \vdots \\ 0 \end{bmatrix}, \quad x_3 = \begin{bmatrix} 0 \\ 0 \\ 1 \\ \vdots \\ 0 \end{bmatrix}, \quad \ldots, \quad x_N = \begin{bmatrix} 0 \\ 0 \\ 0 \\ \vdots \\ 1 \end{bmatrix}.$$

Bases occur so frequently in our work that it will be a great convenience to have a short notation for "the basis $x_1, x_2, \ldots, x_N$." Let us write simply "the basis $x]$" or just "$x]$". If we wish to stress the fact that there are exactly N vectors in the basis $x]$ and that they are numbered from 1 to N, we may write "$x]_1^N$".

When we speak of the coordinates of y we will not bother to add "relative to the basis $x]$" if there is no doubt about the basis.

Consider a linear transformation A on $\mathscr{V}$ to $\mathscr{W}$ and assume that $x]_1^M$ and $y]_1^N$ are bases for $\mathscr{V}$ and for $\mathscr{W}$ respectively. Each $x \in \mathscr{V}$ has certain coordinates, $\xi^1, \xi^2, \ldots, \xi^M$, relative to $x]$ and each $y \in \mathscr{W}$ has coordinates relative to $y]$. From all points of view except the typographical, it is more convenient to write these coordinates in columns rather than in rows.

For each $i = 1, 2, \ldots, M$, $A(x_i) \in \mathscr{W}$ and hence has certain coordinates, say $\begin{bmatrix} \alpha_i^1 \\ \alpha_i^2 \\ \vdots \\ \alpha_i^N \end{bmatrix}$, relative to $y]$. There is one such column for each $i = 1, 2, \ldots, M$, and if we stand them together we get a matrix:

$$\begin{bmatrix} \alpha_1^1 & \alpha_2^1 & \cdots & \alpha_M^1 \\ \alpha_1^2 & \alpha_2^2 & \cdots & \alpha_M^2 \\ \vdots & \vdots & & \vdots \\ \alpha_1^N & \alpha_2^N & \cdots & \alpha_m^N \end{bmatrix}.$$

This process associates with each transformation A a certain matrix which we will denote by $[A]$ or, when we wish to emphasize the fact that the matrix depends not only on the transformation but also on the particular bases used, by $[A; x], y]$.

How do we use $[A]$ to study A? Let us find the relationship between the coordinates of Ax and those of x. If

$$x = \sum_{i=1}^{M} \xi^i x_i \quad \text{and} \quad Ax = y = \sum_{j=1}^{N} \eta^j y_j$$

then

(19.2) $$\sum_{j} \eta^j y_j = Ax = A(\sum_{i} \xi^i x_i) = \sum_{i} \xi^i A(x_i).$$

By the definition of $[A; x], y]$, the coordinates of Ax_i relative to $y]$ are

$$\begin{bmatrix} \alpha_i^1 \\ \alpha_i^2 \\ \vdots \\ \alpha_i^N \end{bmatrix}$$

or, by Definition 19.1, $Ax_i = \sum_j \alpha_i^j y_j$. Thus equation (19.2) becomes

(19.3) $$\sum_{j} \eta^j y_j = \sum_{i} \xi^i (\sum_{j} \alpha_i^j y_j)$$

$$= \sum_{i} \sum_{j} \xi^i \alpha_i^j y_j$$

$$= \sum_{j} (\sum_{i} \xi^i \alpha_i^j y_j)$$

$$= \sum_{j} (\sum_{i} \xi^i \alpha_i^j y_j.$$

APP.
E.8
IND.

Since the y's form a basis for $\mathcal{W}$, two linear combinations of them are equal if and only if the corresponding coefficients are equal. Thus we must have

(19.4) $$\eta^j = \sum_{i} \alpha_i^j \xi^i,$$

which is the desired formula for the coordinates, $\eta^1, \eta^2, \ldots, \eta^N$, of $y = A(x)$ in terms of the coordinates, $\xi^1, \xi^2, \ldots, \xi^M$, of x.

We can equally well go in the opposite direction. If we are given the matrix

$$\begin{bmatrix} \alpha_1^1 & \alpha_2^1 & \cdots & \alpha_M^1 \\ \alpha_1^2 & \alpha_2^2 & \cdots & \alpha_M^2 \\ \vdots & \vdots & & \vdots \\ \alpha_1^N & \alpha_2^N & \cdots & \alpha_M^N \end{bmatrix},$$

the basis $x]_1^M$ for the M-dimensional space $\mathcal{V}$, and the basis $y]_1^N$ for the N-dimensional space $\mathcal{W}$, then we can define a linear transformation on $\mathcal{V}$ to $\mathcal{W}$ by the formula

$$A(x) = A(\sum_i \xi^i x_i) = \sum_j \eta^j y_j$$

where the η's are given by (19.4). Note that x uniquely determines its coordinates, $\xi^1, \xi^2, \ldots, \xi^M$, and these uniquely determine the η's so this formula really defines a function. We do not bother with the routine proof that this function is a linear transformation.

We summarize in a long definition and a short theorem. The proof of the theorem is implicit in preceding discussion.

DEFINITION 19.2. Let $x]_1^M$ and $y]_1^N$ be bases for finite-dimensional vector spaces $\mathcal{V}$ and $\mathcal{W}$. If A is a linear transformation on $\mathcal{V}$ to $\mathcal{W}$, then the matrix, $[A]$ or $[A; x], y]]$, *associated with* A is the rectangular array

$$\begin{bmatrix} \alpha_1^1 & \alpha_2^1 & \ldots & \alpha_M^1 \\ \alpha_1^2 & \alpha_2^2 & \ldots & \alpha_M^2 \\ \vdots & \vdots & & \vdots \\ \alpha_1^N & \alpha_2^N & \ldots & \alpha_M^N \end{bmatrix},$$

where α_i^j is the j-th coordinate of Ax_i relative to the basis $y]$. The transformation B which is *associated with the matrix*

$$\begin{bmatrix} \beta_1^1 & \beta_2^1 & \ldots & \beta_M^1 \\ \beta_1^2 & \beta_2^2 & \ldots & \beta_M^2 \\ \vdots & \vdots & & \vdots \\ \beta_1^N & \beta_2^N & \ldots & \beta_M^N \end{bmatrix}$$

by the bases $x]$ and $y]$ is defined by

$$B(\sum_{i=1}^M \xi^i x_i) = \sum_{j=1}^N (\sum_{i=1}^M \beta_i^j \xi^i) y_j.$$

THEOREM 19.3. *If* $[A]$ *is the matrix associated with the transformation* A, *then the transformation associated with* $[A]$ *is* A, *and conversely.*

There is another important theorem which is suggested by the discussion.

THEOREM 19.4. *If* $x]_1^N$ *is a basis for a vector space* $\mathcal{V}$ *and* $y_1, y_2,$ $\ldots, y_N$, *are any given elements of a vector space* $\mathcal{W}$, *then there is one and only one linear transformation* A *such that* $Ax_i = y_i$ *for* $i = 1, 2,$ $\ldots, N$.

PROOF. Each vector $x \in \mathscr{V}$ uniquely determines a set of coordinates $\xi^1, \xi^2, \ldots, \xi^N$, relative to $x]$. Use these to define the function A by the formula

$$A(x) = \sum_i \xi^i y_i.$$

It is a routine exercise (see Problem 20.28) to verify that A is a linear transformation, and it should be obvious that $Ax_i = y_i$. It is even easier to show that if A is a linear transformation and $Ax_i = y_i$, then A must be given by the formula

$$Ax = \sum_i \xi^i y_i,$$

where the ξ's are the coordinates of x relative to $x]$.

Q.E.D.

This theorem is a convenience because it frequently happens that it is easier to tell the value of a transformation at each element of a basis than to give a complete formula for it.

Having taken care of these preliminaries, we now ask how matrices are related to the operations with transformations. What are the matrices $[A + B]$, $[\rho A]$, and $[AB]$? We want a brief notation for the matrix with α_i^j in the j-th place in the i-th column; $[\alpha_i^j]$ is an obvious candidate, but the indices inside the bracket turn out to be superfluous. We will write simply $[\alpha]$ for a matrix with the element α_i^j in the place where the j-th row and i-th column cross. When it is not clear from the context how many rows and columns there are, we may write $[\alpha]_m^n$ to suggest that the subscripts—corresponding to the columns—run from 1 to m and the superscripts—corresponding to the rows—run from 1 to n.

THEOREM 19.5. *If $[\alpha]$ and $[\beta]$ are the matrices associated with the transformations A and B and if $[\gamma]$ and $[\delta]$ are the matrices associated with $A + B$ and with ρA, respectively, then $\gamma_i^j = \alpha_i^j + \beta_i^j$, and $\delta_i^j = \rho \alpha_i^j$.*

PROOF. The proof consists of little more than looking to see just what the theorem says. We have two vector spaces, call them $\mathscr{V}$ and $\mathscr{W}$, and two transformations, A and B, on $\mathscr{V}$ to $\mathscr{W}$. Furthermore, the theorem does not make any sense until the spaces are provided with bases. It is phrased as it is in the hopeful belief that all readers will take it for granted that the various matrices will be computed using the same bases. Let the basis for $\mathscr{V}$ be $x]_1^M$ and that for $\mathscr{W}$ be $y]_1^N$.

By Definition 19.2, γ_i^j is the j-th coordinate of $(A+B)(x_i)$. That is to say (see Definition 19.1)

$$\sum_j \gamma_i^j y_j = (A+B)(x_i).$$

Similarly

$$\sum_j \alpha_i^j y_j = A(x_i) \quad \text{and} \quad \sum_j \beta_i^j y_j = B(x_i).$$

Now the definition of $A+B$ tells us that

$$(A+B)(x_i) = A(x_i) + B(x_i)$$

so

$$\sum_j \gamma_i^j y_j = \sum_j \alpha_i^j y_j + \sum_j \beta_i^j y_j = \sum_j (\alpha_i^j + \beta_i^j) y_j.$$

Since the y's form a basis for $\mathcal{W}$, the coefficients on the two sides of the equation must be the same: i.e., $\gamma_i^j = \alpha_i^j + \beta_i^j$.

A similar examination of the meaning of the symbols shows that $\delta_i^j = \rho \alpha_i^j$.

Q.E.D.

The question about $[AB]$ is less trivial. Here we will give the proof first and then state the theorem.

To begin with we need three vector spaces—$\mathcal{U}$, $\mathcal{V}$, and $\mathcal{W}$. We assume that B is a transformation on $\mathcal{U}$ to $\mathcal{V}$ and that A is a transformation on $\mathcal{V}$ to $\mathcal{W}$. Next we assume that $x]_1^L$, $y]_1^M$, and $z]_1^N$, are bases for $\mathcal{U}$, $\mathcal{V}$, and $\mathcal{W}$, respectively.

Our object is to calculate the coordinates of $(AB)(x_i)$ relative to the basis $z]$. Call them γ_i^k so, by definition,

$$\sum_{k=1}^{N} \gamma_i^k z_k = (AB)(x_i).$$

Let $[A] = [\alpha]_M^N$ and $[B] = [\beta]_L^M$. Then

$$\sum_{k=1}^{N} \gamma_i^k z_k = (AB)(x_i)$$
$$= A(B(x_i))$$
$$= A\left(\sum_{j=1}^{M} \beta_i^j y_j\right)$$
$$= \sum_{j=1}^{M} \beta_i^j A(y_j)$$
$$= \sum_{j=1}^{M} \beta_i^j \left(\sum_{k=1}^{N} \alpha_j^k z_k\right)$$

$$= \sum_{j=1}^{M} \sum_{k=1}^{N} (\beta_i^j \alpha_j^k z_k)$$

$$= \sum_{k=1}^{N} \sum_{j=1}^{M} (\beta_i^j \alpha_j^k z_k)$$

$$= \sum_{k=1}^{N} (\sum_{j=1}^{M} \beta_i^j \alpha_j^k) z_k.$$

Again, the fact that z] is a basis guarantees that the coefficients are equal, so

$$\gamma_i^k = \sum_{j=1}^{M} \beta_i^j \alpha_j^k = \sum_{j=1}^{M} \alpha_j^k \beta_i^j.$$

This proves:

THEOREM 19.6. *If A is a linear transformation on $\mathscr{V}$ to $\mathscr{W}$, B is a linear transformation on $\mathscr{U}$ to $\mathscr{V}$, $[A]=[\alpha]_M^N$, $[B]=[\beta]_L^M$, and $[AB]=[\gamma]$, then*

$$\gamma_i^k = \sum_{j=1}^{M} \alpha_j^k \beta_i^j, \quad for \ i = 1, 2, \dots, L; k = 1, 2, \dots, N.$$

Theorems 19.5 and 19.6 motivate the following definition.

DEFINITION 19.7. If $[\alpha]$ and $[\beta]$ are $m \times n$ matrices (i.e., matrices with m rows and n columns), then

$$[\alpha]+[\beta] = [\gamma], \quad \text{where } \gamma_i^j = \alpha_i^j + \beta_i^j,$$

and $$\rho[\alpha] = [\delta], \quad \text{where } \delta_i^j = \rho\alpha_i^j.$$

If $[\alpha]$ is an $l \times m$ matrix and $[\beta]$ is an $m \times n$ matrix then $[\alpha][\beta]$ is the $l \times n$ matrix $[\epsilon]$ where

$$\epsilon_i^k = \sum_{j=1}^{m} \alpha_j^k \beta_i^j.$$

Note that the product of two matrices is defined only if the number of columns in the first factor is equal to the number of rows in the second factor. The number of rows in the product is the same as the number of rows in the first factor; the number of columns in the product is the same as the number of columns in the second factor.

In computing, the following verbal description is easier to use than the formula $\epsilon_i^k = \sum_j \alpha_j^k \beta_i^j$. The entry in the k-th row and i-th column of the product is a sum of products. The entries in the k-th row of the first factor are multiplied, each by the corresponding entry in the i-th

column of the second factor, and these products are added together.
Schematically:

$$
\begin{array}{c} i\text{-th} \\ \text{column} \end{array}
$$

$$
\begin{array}{c} k\text{-th} \\ \text{row} \end{array}
\left[\; \ldots\ldots\ldots \epsilon_i^k \ldots\ldots \; \right]
= \left[\; \underrightarrow{k\text{-th row of } [\alpha]} \; \right]
\left[\; \begin{array}{c} i\text{-th} \\ \text{col-} \\ \text{umn} \\ \text{of} \\ [\beta] \end{array} \right]
$$

Definition 19.7 simply says that the matrix operations correspond exactly to the transformation operations: i.e., $[A][B]=[AB]$, $[A+B]=[A]+[B]$, and $\rho[A]=[\rho A]$. An immediate consequence is that all the algebraic results of Section 16 are equally valid for the matrix operations (see Problem 20.34).

Of course, those results in Section 16 which involve the zero, identity, and inverse transformations cannot be carried over to matrices until we introduce zero, identity, and inverse matrices.

DEFINITION 19.8. A *zero matrix* is a matrix all of whose entries are zero. An *identity matrix* is a square matrix with 1's on its main diagonal and 0's elsewhere. If $[\alpha]$ is an $m \times n$ matrix, we say that $[\beta]$ is a *left inverse* for $[\alpha]$ if $[\beta]$ is an $n \times m$ matrix such that $[\beta][\alpha]$ is the $n \times n$ identity matrix; it is a *right inverse* for $[\alpha]$ if it is an $n \times m$ matrix such that $[\alpha][\beta]$ is the $m \times m$ identity matrix. We say that $[\beta]$ is an *inverse* of $[\alpha]$ if it is both a right inverse and a left inverse of $[\alpha]$.

The terms "square matrix" and "main diagonal" should be self explanatory, but the definition of an identity matrix can be given a more explicit, if less vivid, form. An identity matrix is an $n \times n$ matrix $[\alpha]$ such that $\alpha_i^i = 1$ and $\alpha_i^j = 0$ if $i \neq j$.

The specification of the size of the inverse is really unnecessary. If the product of two matrices is an identity matrix, then the first must have as many columns as the second has rows (why?) and the number of rows in the first and columns in the second must both be equal to the number of rows and columns in the identity matrix.

It can be shown (see Problem 20.36) that only square matrices, and not all of them, can have inverses.

From now on we will assume that matrices have all the algebraic properties which we need.

The troublesome fact that the matrix associated with a given transformation depends on the bases used has its compensations.

When one must compute with matrices, it is often possible to choose the basis or bases so that the matrices assume a particularly simple form. Many of the classical problems of matrix theory can be rephrased as "choose a basis (or bases) so that the matrix $[A]$ assumes the form ...." The translation of the problem from one about matrices alone to one about transformations, bases, and matrices may involve conceptual difficulties, but the rephrased problem is usually far easier than the original problem in pure matrix theory.

We have already solved the easiest of such problems:

> If A is a linear transformation on a vector space $\mathscr{V}$ to a vector space $\mathscr{W}$ how should we choose a basis $x]$ for $\mathscr{V}$ and a basis $y]$ for $\mathscr{W}$ in order to make $[A; x], y]]$ particularly simple?

In Theorem 17.4 we are given a completely arbitrary linear transformation A on one finite-dimensional space $\mathscr{V}$ to another $\mathscr{W}$. Let us rearrange and rename the basis $x_1, \ldots, x_m, y_1, \ldots, y_n$ which appears in the proof of that theorem. Let

$$u_i = \begin{cases} y_i & \text{for } i = 1, 2, \ldots, n, \\ x_{i-n} & \text{for } i = n+1, n+2, \ldots, n+m. \end{cases}$$

Thus $u_1, u_2, \ldots, u_{n+m}$ is just another name for the basis $y_1, \ldots, y_n$, $x_1, \ldots, x_m$. Moreover, we chose the x's, y's, and z's, so that

$$A(u_i) = A(y_i) = z_i \qquad \text{for } i = 1, 2, \ldots, n;$$

$$A(u_i) = A(x_{i-n}) = 0 \quad \text{for } i = n+1, n+2, \ldots, n+m.$$

Let $v_i = z_i$ for $i = 1, 2, \ldots, n$, and use Corollary 12.9 to choose v_{n+1}, $v_{n+2}, \ldots, v_p$, in such a way that $v]_1^p$ is a basis for $\mathscr{W}$. Let $[\alpha]$ be the matrix of A relative to the bases $u]$ and $v]$.

Now

$$\sum_{j=1}^{p} \alpha_i^j v_j = A(u_i) = \begin{cases} v_i & \text{if } i = 1, 2, \ldots, n, \\ 0 & \text{if } i = n+1, n+2, \ldots, n+m. \end{cases}$$

It follows that

$$\alpha_i^j = \begin{cases} 1 & \text{if } 1 \leqslant i = j \leqslant n, \\ 0 & \text{otherwise.} \end{cases}$$

Thus $[A; u], v]]$ is the matrix with 1's in the first n places on the main diagonal and 0's elsewhere. For instance, if $\mathscr{V}$ is 7-dimensional, $\mathscr{W}$ is 5-dimensional, and rng A is 3-dimensional, then

$$[A] = \begin{bmatrix} 1 & 0 & 0 & 0 & 0 & 0 & 0 \\ 0 & 1 & 0 & 0 & 0 & 0 & 0 \\ 0 & 0 & 1 & 0 & 0 & 0 & 0 \\ 0 & 0 & 0 & 0 & 0 & 0 & 0 \\ 0 & 0 & 0 & 0 & 0 & 0 & 0 \end{bmatrix}.$$

We can achieve this very simple form only because we are free to choose the bases in both $\mathscr{V}$ and $\mathscr{W}$. When we are dealing with a transformation A on a space and to the *same* space, we usually want matrices of the form $[A; x], x]]$, not ones of the form $[A; x], y]]$.

Section 20. Problems

1. Let A and B be the transformations on $\mathscr{R}^4$ to $\mathscr{R}^3$ defined by

$$A(\xi^1, \xi^2, \xi^3, \xi^4) = (2\xi^1 - 3\xi^2, \xi^1 + \xi^2 + \xi^3, \xi^2 - \xi^3 + \xi^4)$$

and $B(\xi^1, \xi^2, \xi^3, \xi^4) = (\xi^2 - \xi^3, \xi^3 - \xi^4, \xi^4 - \xi^1),$

and let C be the transformation on $\mathscr{R}^3$ to $\mathscr{R}^4$ defined by

$$C(\xi^1, \xi^2, \xi^3) = (\xi^1 + \xi^2, \xi^1 + 2\xi^3, \xi^2 - \xi^3, \xi^1 + \xi^2 + \xi^3).$$

Calculate those of the following which are meaningful:

(a) $A(1, -1, 2, 3)$,

(b) $A(2, 3, 0, 1)$,

(c) $A(2 \cdot (1, -1, 2, 3) - (2, 3, 0, 1))$,

(d) $2A(1, -1, 2, 3) - A(2, 3, 0, 1)$,

(e) $A(B(1, 2, 3, 4) + C(1, 2, 3))$,

(f) $A(1, 2, 3)$,

(g) $B(1, 2, 3)$,

(h) $C(1, 2, 3)$,

(i) $A(B(1, 2, 3) + C(1, 2, 3))$,

(j) $C(A(1, 2, 3, 4) + B(1, 2, 3, 4))$,

(k) $C(1, 2, 3) + B(1, 2, 3, 4)$,

(l) $C((1, 2, 3) + B(1, 2, 3, 4))$,

(m) $B(1, 1, 1, 1)$,

(n) $C(B(1, 1, 1, 1))$,

(o) $B(C(1, 1, 1, 1))$,

(p) $B(A(2, 3, 0, 1))$,

(q) $B(C(A(2, 3, 0, 1)))$,

(r) $A(C(B(2, 3, 0, 1)))$.

2. Show that the set of all linear transformations on a vector space $\mathscr{V}$ to a vector space $\mathscr{W}$ satisfies axioms (3.6), (3.8), and (3.9).

3. Verify the equations (16.5), (16.6), and (16.7), of Theorem 16.5.

4. Let A and B be the linear transformations on $\mathscr{R}^3$ to $\mathscr{R}^3$ defined by

$$A(\xi^1, \xi^2, \xi^3) = (\xi^1 + 2\xi^2 - \xi^3, -\xi^1 + \xi^2, 2\xi^1 + \xi^2)$$

and $B(\xi^1, \xi^2, \xi^3) = (-\xi^1 + \xi^2 + \xi^3, 2\xi^1 - \xi^3, \xi^1 + \xi^2 - 2\xi^3).$

Calculate:

   (a) $(A+B)(\xi^1, \xi^2, \xi^3)$,
   (b) $(A \circ B)(\xi^1, \xi^2, \xi^3)$,
   (c) $(B \circ A)(\xi^1, \xi^2, \xi^3)$.

5. Prove that if O is the zero transformation on $\mathcal{V}$ to $\mathcal{W}$ and A is any linear transformation on $\mathcal{W}$ to $\mathcal{U}$ then $A \circ O$ is the zero transformation on $\mathcal{V}$ to $\mathcal{U}$.

6. For $x \in \mathcal{P}_n$ let $T(x)$ be the element of $\mathcal{P}_n$ defined by the formula

$$(T(x))(\tau) = x(\tau+1).$$

   (a) Show that T is a linear transformation on $\mathcal{P}_n$ to $\mathcal{P}_n$.
   (b) Show that rng T is the whole of $\mathcal{P}_n$.

7. Let $C^2(-\infty, +\infty)$ be the subspace of $C(-\infty, +\infty)$ consisting of all functions in $C(-\infty, +\infty)$ which have everywhere continuous second derivatives.

   (a) For $x \in C^2(-\infty, +\infty)$ let

$$L(x) = x'' + 3x' + 2x.$$

Show that L is a linear transformation on $C^2(-\infty, +\infty)$ to $C(-\infty, +\infty)$.

   (b) Let a and b be given elements of $C(-\infty, +\infty)$. For each $x \in C^2(-\infty, +\infty)$, let $M(x)$ be the element $y \in C(-\infty, +\infty)$ defined by the formula

$$y(\tau) = x''(\tau) + a(\tau)x'(\tau) + b(\tau)x(\tau).$$

Show that M is a linear transformation.

8. (a) Prove:

THEOREM 20.1. *If A is a linear transformation on $\mathcal{V}$ to $\mathcal{W}$ and if Ax_1, $Ax_2, \ldots, Ax_n$, are linearly independent, then so are $x_1, x_2, \ldots, x_n$.*

   (b) Give an example to show that the converse of Theorem 20.1 is false.

9. For $x \in \mathcal{P}$ let Mx and Dx be defined by

$$(Mx)(\tau) = \tau \cdot x(\tau) \quad \text{and} \quad (Dx)(\tau) = x'(\tau).$$

   (a) Show that M and D are linear transformations.
   (b) Show that

(20.1)　　　　　　　　　　$$DM - MD = I.$$

NOTE: Formulas like (20.1) play an important role in quantum mechanics.

10. Let $\mathcal{X}$ and $\mathcal{Y}$ be complementary subspaces of $\mathcal{V}$. For each $z \in \mathcal{V}$ there are uniquely determined vectors $x \in \mathcal{X}$ and $y \in \mathcal{Y}$ such that $z = x + y$. Since z determines x and y uniquely, we are really dealing with functions. There are two functions, X and Y, such that

$$X(z) \in \mathcal{X}, \qquad Y(z) \in \mathcal{Y}, \quad \text{and} \quad z = X(z) + Y(z),$$

for all $z \in \mathcal{V}$. Prove that X is a linear transformation.

NOTE: This useful transformation X is commonly called the projection along $\mathscr{Y}$ onto $\mathscr{X}$. To see the reason for this name, draw a picture of two complementary one-dimensional subspaces of $\mathscr{R}^2$. Pick a vector z on neither of the subspaces and mark $X(z)$ and $Y(z)$ on your illustration.

11. Let E be a linear transformation on $\mathscr{V}$ to $\mathscr{V}$ and assume that $EE = E$. Prove that $\mathscr{N}(E)$ and rng E are complementary subspaces of $\mathscr{V}$.

NOTE: In this case E is the projection along $\mathscr{N}(E)$ onto rng E.

12. Let A be a linear transformation on $\mathscr{V}$ to $\mathscr{W}$. Using nothing but the definitions of dimension and of range and Theorem 15.2, prove

$$\dim (\text{rng } A) \leqslant \dim \mathscr{V}.$$

13. In equation (16.3) the symbol "$+$" appears fourteen times and has three different meanings. Explain the three meanings and copy the formula indicating the meaning of "$+$" at each of its occurrences.

14. Let D be the linear transformation which assigns to each $x \in \mathscr{P}_n$ its derivative x'. What is the null space of D? What is its range?

15. Prove:

THEOREM 20.2. *If A is a linear transformation on $\mathscr{V}$ to $\mathscr{V}$ and if $\mathscr{N}(A) = \mathscr{N}(A^2)$, then $\mathscr{N}(A)$ and rng A are complementary subspaces.*

16. Solve:

$$\left\{ \begin{array}{l} x + 2y - 3z + w = -6 \\ 2x - 3y + z + 2w = 16 \\ x - y + 2z - w = 4 \\ 3x + 7y - 6z - w = -26. \end{array} \right.$$

17. Solve:

$$\left\{ \begin{array}{l} 2x + y - z + w = 2 \\ x - 2y + z \quad\;\; = 4 \\ 3y - 2z + 2w = -1 \\ 3x + 2y \quad\;\; + w = 2. \end{array} \right.$$

18. Solve:

$$\left\{ \begin{array}{l} x + y - 2z + w = 5 \\ x + 2y + z - 3w = 2 \\ 2x + y - z + 3w = -1. \end{array} \right.$$

19. Solve:

$$\left\{ \begin{array}{l} x + y - z - w = 1 \\ 2x + y + z + 2w = -1 \\ 3x + 2y - z + w = 2 \\ x + 2y - 5z - 5w = 3. \end{array} \right.$$

20. Solve:

$$\left\{ \begin{array}{l} x + 2y - z = 1 \\ x - y + 3z = 10 \\ 2x + y + 2z = 11 \\ x - 4y + 7z = 19. \end{array} \right.$$

21. Assume that

$$[A] = \begin{bmatrix} 1 & 2 & 1 \\ -1 & 3 & 2 \\ 0 & -1 & 4 \end{bmatrix}, \qquad [B] = \begin{bmatrix} 1 & 0 & -1 & 2 \\ 3 & 1 & -2 & 4 \\ 0 & 2 & -3 & 1 \end{bmatrix},$$

$$[C] = \begin{bmatrix} 1 \\ 2 \\ 3 \end{bmatrix}, \quad \text{and} \quad [D] = \begin{bmatrix} 1 & 2 & 1 \\ -1 & 3 & 4 \end{bmatrix}.$$

Calculate those of the following which are meaningful:

(a) $[AB]$, (e) $[DA]$, (i) $[BAD]$,
(b) $[BA]$, (f) $[DC]$, (j) $[DAB]$,
(c) $[ABC]$, (g) $[AC]$, (k) $[AD]$,
(d) $[ABD]$, (h) $[CA]$, (l) $[BC]$.

22. Consider the system of equations

$$x - 3y + 2z = \alpha$$
$$2x - 4y - 3z = \beta$$
$$x + 3y - 7z = \gamma$$
$$2x - 3y - 5z = \delta.$$

(a) What relation must α, β, γ, and δ, satisfy in order that the system may have a solution?

(b) If α, β, γ, and δ, satisfy this relation what is the solution?

23. (a) Solve the system of linear equations:

$$\left\{ \begin{array}{l} 2x + y - 2z = a \\ 6x + 2y - z = b \\ 5x + y + 3z = c. \end{array} \right.$$

(b) The solution in part (a) can be written in the form

$$\begin{bmatrix} x \\ y \\ z \end{bmatrix} = \begin{bmatrix} \alpha_1^1 a + \alpha_2^1 b + \alpha_3^1 c \\ \alpha_1^2 a + \alpha_2^2 b + \alpha_3^2 c \\ \alpha_1^3 a + \alpha_2^3 b + \alpha_3^3 c \end{bmatrix} = \begin{bmatrix} \alpha_1^1 & \alpha_2^1 & \alpha_3^1 \\ \alpha_1^2 & \alpha_2^2 & \alpha_3^2 \\ \alpha_1^3 & \alpha_2^3 & \alpha_3^3 \end{bmatrix} \cdot \begin{bmatrix} a \\ b \\ c \end{bmatrix}.$$

Write down the matrix

$$[\alpha] = \begin{bmatrix} \alpha_1^1 & \alpha_2^1 & \alpha_3^1 \\ \alpha_1^2 & \alpha_2^2 & \alpha_3^2 \\ \alpha_1^3 & \alpha_2^3 & \alpha_3^3 \end{bmatrix}$$

and calculate

$$\begin{bmatrix} 2 & 1 & -2 \\ 6 & 2 & -1 \\ 5 & 1 & 3 \end{bmatrix} \cdot [\alpha].$$

24. Assume that $[\alpha]$ and $[\beta]$ are $n \times n$ matrices and that $[\alpha][\beta]$ is the $n \times n$ identity matrix. Use the formula for the product of matrices to show that

$$\begin{bmatrix} \xi^1 \\ \xi^2 \\ \vdots \\ \xi^n \end{bmatrix} = [\beta] \cdot \begin{bmatrix} \eta^1 \\ \eta^2 \\ \vdots \\ \eta^n \end{bmatrix}$$

is a solution of the system

$$\begin{cases} \alpha_1^1\xi^1 + \alpha_2^1\xi^2 + \cdots + \alpha_n^1\xi^n = \eta^1 \\ \alpha_1^2\xi^1 + \alpha_2^2\xi^2 + \cdots + \alpha_n^2\xi^n = \eta^2 \\ \quad\vdots \qquad\quad \vdots \qquad\qquad\quad \vdots \qquad \vdots \\ \alpha_1^n\xi^1 + \alpha_2^n\xi^2 + \cdots + \alpha_n^n\xi^n = \eta^n. \end{cases}$$

25. The vectors $x_1 = \begin{bmatrix} 2 \\ 1 \end{bmatrix}$ and $x_2 = \begin{bmatrix} -1 \\ 3 \end{bmatrix}$ form a basis for $\mathscr{R}^2$.

(a) What is the vector whose coordinates relative to x_1 and x_2 are 3, -2?

(b) What are the coordinates of $\begin{bmatrix} 4 \\ -5 \end{bmatrix}$ relative to the basis $x]_1^2$?

26. Let x_1, x_2, x_3, be the natural basis for $\mathscr{R}^3$ and let

$$y = \begin{bmatrix} 1 \\ 2 \\ 3 \end{bmatrix}, \quad z = \begin{bmatrix} 1 \\ 1 \\ 1 \end{bmatrix}.$$

What are the coordinates of z relative to the basis x_1, x_2, x_3? What are its coordinates relative to x_1, x_2, y?

NOTE: The 1st and 2nd coordinates of z change when we change the 3rd vector in the basis, even though the 1st and 2nd basis vectors are unchanged.

27. Let x_1, x_2, x_3, be the natural basis for $\mathscr{R}^3$ and let

$$y_1 = \begin{bmatrix} 1 \\ 1 \\ 1 \end{bmatrix}, \quad y_2 = \begin{bmatrix} 1 \\ 0 \\ 1 \end{bmatrix}, \quad y_3 = \begin{bmatrix} 1 \\ 1 \\ 0 \end{bmatrix}.$$

Which of the following sets of vectors are bases for $\mathscr{R}^3$:

(a) x_1, x_2, y_1;   (c) x_1, x_2, y_3;

(b) x_1, y_1, y_2;   (d) x_1, y_2, y_3?

Let

$$u = \begin{bmatrix} 1 \\ 2 \\ 3 \end{bmatrix} \quad \text{and} \quad v = \begin{bmatrix} -1 \\ 0 \\ -2 \end{bmatrix}.$$

(e) Consider, in turn, each of the sets of vectors in parts (a), (b), (c), and (d). If it is a basis, calculate—mentally if possible—the coordinates of u and v with respect to that basis.

28. If $x]_1^n$ is a basis for a vector space $\mathscr{V}$, we can define n functions $C^1, C^2, \ldots, C^n$ on $\mathscr{V}$ to its scalar field by letting $C^i(x)$ be the i-th coordinate of x relative to $x]$.

(a) Prove that C^i is a linear transformation.

(b) Prove that if A is a linear transformation on $\mathscr{V}$ to some space $\mathscr{W}$, then

$$Ax = \sum_i C^i(x) \cdot A(x_i).$$

(c) Prove that if $y_1, y_2, \ldots, y_n$, are any given vectors in another space $\mathscr{W}$, and B is defined by the formula

$$B(x) = \sum_i C^i(x) y_i,$$

then B is a linear transformation from $\mathscr{V}$ to $\mathscr{W}$. Calculate $B(x_j)$.

29. Let $x]_1^N$ be a basis for a vector space $\mathscr{V}$. Remember that (Theorem 19.4) you know all about a linear transformation as soon as you know its values at the elements of a basis. Thus we can define a linear transformation C^i on $\mathscr{V}$ to its scalar field by saying that

$$C^i(x_j) = \begin{cases} 1 & \text{if } i = j, \\ 0 & \text{if } i \neq j. \end{cases}$$

Show that $C^1(y), C^2(y), \ldots, C^n(y)$, are the coordinates of y relative to $x]$.

30. Let A be the linear transformation on $\mathscr{P}_3$ to $\mathscr{P}_3$ defined by

$$(Ax)(\tau) = \tau x'(\tau) + x(\tau).$$

What is the matrix of A relative to the basis $x]_0^3$ where

$$x_0(\tau) = 1, \qquad x_1(\tau) = \tau, \qquad x_2(\tau) = \tau^2, \quad \text{and} \quad x_3(\tau) = \tau^3?$$

31. Let $x]_1^3$ be the natural basis for $\mathscr{R}^3$ and let A be the linear transformation on $\mathscr{R}^3$ to $\mathscr{R}^2$ such that

$$Ax_1 = \begin{bmatrix} 2 \\ 3 \end{bmatrix}, \qquad Ax_2 = \begin{bmatrix} 1 \\ 2 \end{bmatrix}, \quad \text{and} \quad Ax_3 = \begin{bmatrix} 1 \\ -4 \end{bmatrix}.$$

(a) What is

$$A\begin{bmatrix} 1 \\ -2 \\ -1 \end{bmatrix}?$$

(b) If $y]_1^2$ is the natural basis for $\mathscr{R}^2$, what is the matrix $[A; x], y]$?

(c) If $z_1 = \begin{bmatrix} 2 \\ 3 \end{bmatrix}$ and $z_2 = \begin{bmatrix} 1 \\ 2 \end{bmatrix}$, what is $[A; x], z]$?

32. Let

$$[A] = \begin{bmatrix} 1 & 2 \\ -1 & 3 \end{bmatrix}$$

and calculate $[A^2 - 4A + 5I]$. Here I is the identity transformation; its matrix (see Problem 35) is

$$\begin{bmatrix} 1 & 0 \\ 0 & 1 \end{bmatrix}.$$

33. Let

$$[A] = \begin{bmatrix} 0 & 0 & 0 & 0 \\ 1 & 0 & 0 & 0 \\ 0 & 1 & 0 & 0 \\ 0 & 0 & 1 & 0 \end{bmatrix}.$$

Calculate $[A^2]$, $[A^3]$, and $[A^4]$.

34. (a) Exploit the correspondence between matrices and transformations and Theorem 16.5 to prove that, for any matrices $[\alpha]$, $[\beta]$, and $[\gamma]$, with the right number of rows and columns,

$$[\alpha]([\beta][\gamma]) = ([\alpha][\beta])[\gamma].$$

(b) Prove the same result directly from Definition 19.7.

35. Let $I = I_{\mathscr{V}}$ be the identity transformation defined in Definition 16.6. Show that, for every basis $x]$ in $\mathscr{V}$,

$$[I; x], x]] = \begin{bmatrix} 1 & 0 & \ldots & 0 \\ 0 & 1 & \ldots & 0 \\ \vdots & \vdots & & \vdots \\ 0 & 0 & \ldots & 1 \end{bmatrix}.$$

36. Assume that $[\alpha]$ is an $m \times n$ matrix and that $[\beta]$ is an $n \times m$ matrix such that $[\alpha][\beta]$ is the $m \times m$ identity matrix and $[\beta][\alpha]$ is the $n \times n$ identity matrix. Show that $m = n$. HINT: introduce suitable transformations and apply either Theorem 17.4 or Problem 20.12.

37. Let A be the transformation on $\mathscr{R}^2$ to $\mathscr{R}^2$ defined by

$$A\left(\begin{bmatrix} \xi \\ \eta \end{bmatrix} \right) = \begin{bmatrix} 2\xi \\ -\eta \end{bmatrix}.$$

Let

$$x_1 = \begin{bmatrix} 1 \\ 2 \end{bmatrix} \quad \text{and} \quad x_2 = \begin{bmatrix} 2 \\ 1 \end{bmatrix}.$$

Calculate $[A; x], x]]$.

38. Let A be a linear transformation on $\mathscr{R}^2$ to $\mathscr{R}^2$ whose matrix is

$$[A] = \begin{bmatrix} 9 & 12 \\ 40 & 13 \end{bmatrix}.$$

(Unless there is an explicit statement to the contrary, matrices of transformations on $\mathscr{R}^m$ to $\mathscr{R}^n$ are always given in terms of the natural basis.)

(a) Find a non-zero vector $y_1 = \begin{bmatrix} \eta_1^1 \\ \eta_1^2 \end{bmatrix}$

such that $Ay_1 = 33y_1$.

(b) Find a non-zero vector $y_2 = \begin{bmatrix} \eta_2^1 \\ \eta_2^2 \end{bmatrix}$

such that $Ay_2 = -11y_2$.

(c) What is the matrix $[A; y], y]]$?

(d) What are the matrices $[\beta]=[I; x], y]]$ and $[\gamma]=[I; y], x]]$, where x] is the natural basis?

(e) Compute $[\beta][\gamma]$, $[\gamma][\beta]$, and $[\beta][A][\gamma]$.

39. Let A and B be linear transformations on an N-dimensional space $\mathscr{V}$ to itself and assume that $AB=I$. Let $x]_1^N$ be a basis for $\mathscr{V}$ and let $y_i = Bx_i$, for $i=1, 2, \ldots, N$.

(a) Show that the y_i are linearly independent. Hence $y]_1^N$ is a basis for $\mathscr{V}$.

(b) By considering BAy_i, show that $BA=I$.

(c) Consider two sets of scalars, α_j^i and β_j^i, where $i, j=1, 2, \ldots, N$, and assume that the α's and β's satisfy the conditions

$$\sum_{k=1}^N \alpha_k^i\beta_j^k = \begin{cases}1 & \text{if } i = j, \\ 0 & \text{if } i \neq j.\end{cases}$$

By introducing suitable transformations on $\mathscr{R}^N$ to $\mathscr{R}^N$ and applying part (b), prove that the α's and β's must satisfy the conditions

$$\sum_{k=1}^N \alpha_i^k\beta_k^j = \begin{cases}1 & \text{if } i = j, \\ 0 & \text{if } i \neq j.\end{cases}$$

40. Let A be a linear transformation on a vector space $\mathscr{V}$ and let $x]_1^N$ be a basis for $\mathscr{V}$. Show that if $Ax_1, Ax_2, \ldots, Ax_N$ is a basis for $\mathscr{V}$, then A has an inverse.

NOTE: Problems 39 and 40 contain three very useful results which we now restate as formal theorems.

THEOREM 20.3. *Let A be a linear transformation on $\mathscr{V}$ to $\mathscr{V}$. If A is invertible, then for all $x_1, x_2, \ldots, x_N$, if $x]_1^N$, is a basis for $\mathscr{V}$, so is $Ax]_1^N$. Conversely, if, for some $x_1, x_2, \ldots, x_N$, $Ax]_1^N$ is a base for $\mathscr{V}$, then A is invertible.*

THEOREM 20.4. *Let $\mathscr{V}$ be a finite-dimensional vector space. If a linear transformation on $\mathscr{V}$ to $\mathscr{V}$ has a right inverse, then it is invertible.*

THEOREM 20.5. *If, for $i, j=1, 2, \ldots, N$,*

$$\sum_{k=1}^N \alpha_k^i\beta_j^k = \begin{cases}1 & \text{when } i = j, \\ 0 & \text{when } i \neq j,\end{cases}$$

then

$$\sum_{k=1}^N \alpha_i^k\beta_k^j = \begin{cases}1 & \text{when } i = j, \\ 0 & \text{when } i \neq j.\end{cases}$$

41. Show that if $[\alpha]$ is an $n \times n$ matrix which has an inverse then there is a basis $y_1, y_2, \ldots, y_n$, for $\mathscr{R}^n$ such that

$$[\alpha] = [I; x], y]],$$

where $x]_1^n$ is the natural basis for $\mathscr{R}^n$.

42. Every solution of the differential equation

$$x''(\tau) - 3x'(\tau) + 2x(\tau) = 0$$

is a function of the form

$$x(\tau) = \alpha e^{\tau} + \beta e^{2\tau},$$

for suitably chosen constants α and β. Consider a particular solution x and let $\xi^1 = x(0)$, $\xi^2 = x'(0)$.

(a) Express the corresponding α and β in terms of ξ^1 and ξ^2.

(b) In terms of ξ^1 and ξ^2, what are the vectors

$$\begin{bmatrix} x(\log 2) \\ x'(\log 2) \end{bmatrix} \quad \text{and} \quad \begin{bmatrix} x(\tau) \\ x'(\tau) \end{bmatrix} ?$$

(c) Find a matrix $[\alpha(\tau)]$ such that

$$\begin{bmatrix} x(\tau) \\ x'(\tau) \end{bmatrix} = [\alpha(\tau)] \begin{bmatrix} x(0) \\ x'(0) \end{bmatrix}.$$

(d) Let $[\alpha'(\tau)]$ be the matrix whose elements are the derivatives, with respect to τ, of the corresponding elements of $[\alpha(\tau)]$. Calculate $[\alpha'(\tau)]$.

(e) Calculate

$$\begin{bmatrix} 0 & 1 \\ -2 & 3 \end{bmatrix} [\alpha(\tau)].$$

43. Let $\mathscr{V}$ be a vector space and let A be a linear transformation on $\mathscr{V}$ to $\mathscr{V}$. Let x and y be given vectors in $\mathscr{V}$ and assume that

$$Ax = \lambda x \quad \text{and} \quad Ay = \lambda y + \kappa x.$$

Let α and β be scalars and, for each real number τ, let

$$z(\tau) = e^{\lambda \tau} [(\alpha + \beta \kappa \tau) x + \beta y].$$

Assuming that the differentiation formulas of elementary calculus are valid for vector valued functions, calculate $z'(\tau)$ and show that

$$z'(\tau) = Az(\tau).$$

44. Let $\mathscr{V}$ be a real vector space and let $\mathscr{W}$ consist of all ordered pairs of elements of $\mathscr{V}$. If we define $+$ and $\cdot$ in $\mathscr{W}$ by

$$(x_1, y_1) + (x_2, y_2) = (x_1 + x_2, y_1 + y_2)$$

and

$$(\alpha + i\beta) \cdot (x, y) = (\alpha x - \beta y, \beta x + \alpha y),$$

it is known that $\mathscr{W}$ is a complex vector space (see Problem 4.12). Let A be a linear transformation on $\mathscr{V}$ to $\mathscr{V}$.

(a) Show that if

(20.2) $$(Ax, Ay) = (\lambda + i\mu)(x, y)$$

then

(20.3) $$[A^2 - 2\lambda A + (\lambda^2 + \mu^2)I]x = 0.$$

(b) Conversely, show that if $\mu \neq 0$, x satisfies (20.3), and

$$y = -\mu^{-1}(A - \lambda I)x$$

then (20.2) is satisfied.

(c) Show that if the ordinary differentiation formulas are valid for vector valued functions and

$$z(\tau) = e^{\lambda \tau}[(\cos \mu\tau)x - (\sin \mu\tau)y]$$

then, assuming that x and y satisfy (20.2),

$$z'(\tau) = Az(\tau).$$

Summary

The critically important idea is *linearity*. A linear transformation is a function A such that

$$A\left(\sum_{i=1}^{n} \alpha^i x_i\right) = \sum_{i=1}^{n} \alpha^i A(x_i).$$

Sums and scalar multiples of transformations are *defined* by a very similar formula. If $A_1, A_2, \ldots, A_n$, are transformations, then so is $\sum_{i=1}^{n} \alpha^i A_i$ and its value at x is

$$\left(\sum_{i=1}^{n} \alpha^i A_i\right)(x) = \sum_{i=1}^{n} \alpha^i A_i(x).$$

By now, the algebra of transformations should be familiar. Remember, in particular, $(AB)(x) = A(B(x))$ and that AB is not the same as BA. Zeros, identities, and inverses should present no difficulties.

The *coordinates* of a vector are the coefficients when the vector is expressed as a linear combination of basis vectors. The same vector has different coordinates with respect to different bases.

The *matrix* of a linear transformation A is an array whose i-th column consists of the coordinates of the image of the i-th basis vector. Of course, the matrix depends on the bases used.

The solution of simultaneous linear equations is of great practical importance, but we will not use it often in later chapters.

In addition to the theorems about the algebra of transformations and matrices, you must know that

$$\dim \mathcal{N}(A) + \dim (\text{rng } A) = \dim \mathcal{V}.$$

Remember that if $x]_1^n$ is a basis, you know a linear transformation A as soon as you know $Ax_1, Ax_2, \ldots, Ax_n$.

A linear transformation A between spaces of the same (finite) dimension has an inverse if and only if the equation $Ax = 0$ has no solution except $x = 0$.

CHAPTER V

THE DUAL SPACE; MULTILINEAR FORMS; DETERMINANTS

The main object of this chapter is to derive a number of classical theorems about determinants, but we follow a roundabout route. The simplest proofs of the theorems involve new concepts. If our sole aim were to prove the theorems, the effort of mastering the new abstractions would hardly be justified, for the traditional proofs are not much longer than those given here. In recent years, however, it has become clear that these new concepts are, in fact, more useful than determinants themselves. Even if determinants had never been invented, the rest of the material in the chapter would still be of tremendous importance.

We have seen that the linear transformations on one vector space to another form a vector space. If we take the second vector space to be just the scalar field itself, we get a new vector space which is intimately related to the one we started with. This new space is very useful indeed and is called the *dual* of the original space.

Linear transformations from a single vector space to its scalar field are sufficient for many purposes, but in other parts of mathematics, and its applications, one needs functions of several variables. Section 22 is devoted to a particularly important class of functions of several variables: multilinear forms.

With the aid of multilinear forms—which are not especially easy—and a bit of fancy footwork, most of the properties of determinants are derived with little effort.

In Section 24, we see how the determinant of a transformation is related to a matrix of the transformation. Here, finally, we prove many of the standard theorems about determinants.

Section 21.   Linear Functionals and the Dual Space

In Problem 4.6 you showed that the complex numbers are a real vector space. It is just as easy to show that they are a complex vector

116

space. Similarly the real numbers are a real vector space. These two are the simplest vector spaces there are, and the study of linear transformations from a more complicated vector space into one of these simple spaces has many applications.

It is customary to use a special terminology for this special type of linear transformation.

DEFINITION 21.1. A *linear functional* on a vector space $\mathscr{V}$ is a linear transformation on $\mathscr{V}$ to its scalar field. The vector space consisting of all linear functionals on $\mathscr{V}$ is called the *dual space* of $\mathscr{V}$ and is denoted by $\tilde{\mathscr{V}}$.

Linear functionals are often called linear forms, and the dual space is often called the conjugate space. The term adjoint space is used more rarely. The notation $\tilde{\mathscr{V}}$ for the dual space is unusual. The common notations are $\mathscr{V}^*$ or $\mathscr{V}'$. We use the tilde "$\sim$" because the "$*$" and "$'$" would get in the way of superscripts, which will soon appear in droves.

We will use lower case letters with a tilde to designate elements of $\tilde{\mathscr{V}}$, but there is no unique element of $\tilde{\mathscr{V}}$ associated with an $x \in \mathscr{V}$ and $\tilde{x}$ stands for any element of $\tilde{\mathscr{V}}$. There is no special connection between x and $\tilde{x}$. If another alphabet were readily available we would use it instead of simply putting tildes on the italic alphabet.

For the dual space it is sometimes convenient to reverse the customs of Section 19. We will index the elements of a basis for $\tilde{\mathscr{V}}$ by superscripts. The corresponding coordinates will be indexed by subscripts.

Which functionals are the simplest in terms of their values on the elements, $x_1, x_2, \ldots, x_N$, of some basis for $\mathscr{V}$? The simplest is, of course, the zero functional, 0. Next in simplicity are the functionals which assign 0 to all but one of the x's and assign 1 to that particular x. Let

$$(21.1) \qquad \tilde{y}^j(x_i) = \begin{cases} 0 & \text{if } i \neq j, \\ 1 & \text{if } i = j. \end{cases}$$

We will soon show that $\tilde{y}^1, \tilde{y}^2, \ldots, \tilde{y}^N$ form a basis for $\tilde{\mathscr{V}}$, but before doing so we introduce the standard notation for the right-hand side of (21.1).

NOTATION. Hereafter δ_i^j will stand for 1 if $i = j$ and for 0 if $i \neq j$.

The symbol δ_i^j which is also written δ_{ij} and δ^{ij}, is called the Kronecker* delta.

---

* Named for the distinguished German mathematician Leopold Kronecker (1823–1891).

THEOREM 21.2.   *If $x]_1^N$ is a basis for $\mathscr{V}$, then there is one and only one basis $\tilde{y}]_1^N$ for $\tilde{\mathscr{V}}$ which satisfies the condition that*

(21.2) $$\tilde{y}^j(x_i) = \delta_i^j, \quad \text{for } i, j = 1, 2, \ldots, N.$$

PROOF.   The easiest way to specify a transformation is to tell its values at each vector in a basis.   Equation (21.2) does just that.   It tells the value of $\tilde{y}^j$ at $x_1, x_2, \ldots, x_N$.   Since these values are scalars— i.e., 0 and 1—$\tilde{y}^j$ is linear transformation on $\mathscr{V}$ to its scalar field, i.e., $\tilde{y}^j \in \tilde{\mathscr{V}}$ for $j = 1, 2, \ldots, N$.

We have just seen that there is one and only one set of $\tilde{y}$'s which fulfill (21.2), so all that remains is to show that it is a basis.   To do so we show that the $\tilde{y}$'s are linearly independent and that they span $\tilde{\mathscr{V}}$.

To show that $\tilde{y}^1, \tilde{y}^2, \ldots, \tilde{y}^N$ are linearly independent we must show that the condition $\sum_j \alpha_j \tilde{y}^j = 0$ implies that $\alpha_j = 0$ for each j.   Assume, then, that $\sum_j \alpha_j \tilde{y}^j = 0$, i.e., $\sum_j \alpha_j \tilde{y}^j$ is the zero *functional*, and hence $(\sum_j \alpha_j \tilde{y}^j)(x) = 0$ for every $x \in \mathscr{V}$.   Now, by Definition 16.1, the value of a linear combination of transformations is computed by taking the *corresponding* combination of their values.   Thus, by its very definition, $\sum_j \alpha_j \tilde{y}^j$ is the function which assigns to x the value $\sum_j \alpha_j \tilde{y}^j(x)$.   In particular $\sum_j \alpha_j \tilde{y}^j(x_i) = 0$ for $i = 1, 2, \ldots, N$.   Hence, by (21.2),

(21.3) $$\sum_j \alpha_j \delta_i^j = 0.$$

As j runs from 1 to N, δ_i^j is zero except when $j = i$, in which case it is 1. Thus the sum in (21.3) has only one non-zero term and that term is just α_i.   Thus $\alpha_i = 0$ for $i = 1, 2, \ldots, N$.

To show that the $\tilde{y}$'s span $\tilde{\mathscr{V}}$ we consider an arbitrary $\tilde{z} \in \tilde{\mathscr{V}}$ and show how to choose $\beta_1, \beta_2, \ldots, \beta_N$ so $\tilde{z} = \sum_j \beta_j \tilde{y}^j$.   The choice is easy: let $\beta_j = \tilde{z}(x_j)$.   The reason for it will appear in the computation.

To say that $\tilde{z} = \sum_j \beta_j \tilde{y}^j$ is to say that $z(x) = (\sum_j \beta_j y^j)(x)$ for each $x \in \mathscr{V}$.   To prove this for any particular x, we let $\xi^1, \xi^2, \ldots, \xi^N$ be its coordinates, so that

(21.4) $$x = \sum_i \xi^i x_i.$$

Now compute

(21.5) $$\left(\sum_j \beta_j \tilde{y}^j\right)(x) = \sum_j \beta_j \tilde{y}^j(x)$$

$$= \sum_j \beta_j \tilde{y}^j\left(\sum_i \xi^i x_i\right)$$

$$= \sum_j \beta_j\left(\sum_i \xi^i \tilde{y}^j(x_i)\right)$$

$$= \sum_j \beta_j \left(\sum_i \xi^i \delta_i^j \right)$$

$$= \sum_j \beta_j \xi^j$$

$$= \sum_j \xi^j \beta_j$$

$$= \sum_j \xi^j \tilde{z}(x_j)$$

$$= \tilde{z} \left(\sum_j \xi^j x_j \right)$$

$$= \tilde{z}(x)$$

Q.E.D.

The individual steps in (21.5) are easy enough, but one often needs to make such computations quickly and surely. You should examine each step and make sure you know which definition, theorem, or previous equation justifies it. See Problem 25.1.

COROLLARY 21.3. *If $\mathscr{V}$ is a finite-dimensional vector space, then so is $\tilde{\mathscr{V}}$ and* dim $\tilde{\mathscr{V}} =$ dim $\mathscr{V}$.

COROLLARY 21.4. *If $\mathscr{X}$ is any proper subspace of a finite-dimensional vector space $\mathscr{V}$ and $y \notin \mathscr{X}$, then there is a $\tilde{y} \in \tilde{\mathscr{V}}$ such that*

$$\tilde{y}(x) = 0 \quad \text{for all } x \in \mathscr{X}$$

and $\qquad\qquad \tilde{y}(y) = 1.$

PROOF. See Problem 25.3.

Before giving the next corollary we introduce a name for the basis $\tilde{y}^1, \tilde{y}^2, \ldots, \tilde{y}^N$.

DEFINITION 21.5. *If $x]_1^N$ is a basis for a vector space $\mathscr{V}$, then the basis for $\tilde{\mathscr{V}}$, $y]_1^N$, defined by (21.2) is called the *basis dual to* $x]$.*

For reasons which may become apparent in Chapter VII, a pair consisting of a basis and its dual is often called a bi-orthonormal system.

COROLLARY 21.6. *If $x]_1^N$ is a basis for $\mathscr{V}$ and $\tilde{y}]_1^N$ is the dual basis for $\tilde{\mathscr{V}}$, then for all $z \in \mathscr{V}$*

(21.6) $$z = \sum_{i=1}^N \tilde{y}^i(z) x_i,$$

and for all $\tilde{z} \in \tilde{\mathscr{V}}$

(21.7) $$\tilde{z} = \sum_{i=1}^N \tilde{z}(x_i) \tilde{y}^i.$$

We omit the proof because (21.7) is just (21.5) and the verification of (21.6) makes a fine easy problem—Problem 25.5.

Remember that (21.6) says that $\tilde{y}^i(z)$ are the coordinates of z relative to $x]$ and (21.7) says that $\tilde{z}(x_i)$ are the coordinates of $\tilde{z}$ relative to $\tilde{y}]$. For future reference, we reformulate this using the same letter for both bases.

If $x]_1^N$ and $\tilde{x}]_1^N$ are dual bases, then for any $z \in \mathscr{V}$, the i-th coordinate of z is $\tilde{x}^i(z)$, and for any $\tilde{z} \in \tilde{\mathscr{V}}$, the i-th coordinate of $\tilde{z}$ is $\tilde{z}(x_i)$.

COROLLARY 21.7.   *If $\mathscr{V}$ is a vector space and $\tilde{z}(x) = \tilde{z}(y)$ for all $\tilde{z} \in \tilde{\mathscr{V}}$, then $x = y$.*

In many problems concerning differential equations one obtains analogues of bi-orthonormal pairs of bases. The spaces involved are infinite-dimensional, so one cannot use Theorem 21.2, or its corollaries; but the corresponding results in these infinite-dimensional cases are tremendously important for both pure and applied mathematics. The sort of reasoning used on equation (21.3)—replacing $\sum_j \alpha_j \delta_i^j$ by α_i—is particularly helpful.

We now turn to the relationships between dual spaces, transformations, and matrices.

We have seen that the space $\mathscr{V}$ determines a corresponding dual space $\tilde{\mathscr{V}}$, but that there is no natural correspondence which assigns to each $x \in \mathscr{V}$ a corresponding element of $\tilde{\mathscr{V}}$. With transformations we again have a natural correspondence. Corresponding to each linear transformation A there is another linear transformation, denoted by $\tilde{A}$ and defined by

APP.
F.11
FNS.
(21.8) $(\tilde{A}\tilde{y})(x) = \tilde{y}(Ax).$

Before we formalize the definition implicit in (21.8) we need to examine that formula in some detail. Assume that A is a transformation on $\mathscr{V}$ to $\mathscr{W}$. If (21.8) is to define the new object $\tilde{A}$ which appears in its left-hand side, it must do so in terms of objects we already know.

When is the right-hand side meaningful? Since A is a transformation on $\mathscr{V}$ to $\mathscr{W}$, Ax is meaningful only if $x \in \mathscr{V}$ and, in that case, $Ax \in \mathscr{W}$. If $Ax \in \mathscr{W}$ then $\tilde{y}(Ax)$ is a well-defined scalar, provided $\tilde{y} \in \tilde{\mathscr{W}}$. The left-hand side of (21.8) appears to be some function, $\tilde{A}\tilde{y}$, acting on x. In fact this equation defines $\tilde{A}\tilde{y}$ in precisely the usual way. It tells us the value, $(\tilde{A}\tilde{y})(x)$, of the function, $\tilde{A}\tilde{y}$, at each $x \in \mathscr{V}$.

We have just observed that $\tilde{A}\tilde{y}$ is a function on $\mathscr{V}$ to its scalar field and it is natural to hope that it is linear, i.e., an element of $\tilde{\mathscr{V}}$. If $\tilde{A}\tilde{y}$ is an element of $\tilde{\mathscr{V}}$ for each $\tilde{y} \in \tilde{\mathscr{W}}$, then $\tilde{A}$ itself is a function: it assigns to each $\tilde{y} \in \tilde{\mathscr{W}}$ the element $\tilde{A}\tilde{y}$ in $\tilde{\mathscr{V}}$. Again we hope for, and expect, linearity.

Obviously two theorems are needed before the definition. Fortunately the proofs are easy and provide an excellent check on your understanding of the notations. We will leave them for you.

THEOREM 21.8. *If A is a linear transformation on $\mathscr{V}$ to $\mathscr{W}$ and if $\tilde{y} \in \tilde{\mathscr{W}}$, then the function $\tilde{z}$ defined by*

$$(21.9) \qquad\qquad \tilde{z}(x) = \tilde{y}(Ax) \quad \text{for } x \in \mathscr{V}$$

is an element of $\tilde{\mathscr{V}}$.

THEOREM 21.9. *If A is a linear transformation on $\mathscr{V}$ to $\mathscr{W}$ and if $\tilde{A}$ is the function which assigns to each $\tilde{y} \in \tilde{\mathscr{W}}$ the $\tilde{z} \in \tilde{\mathscr{W}}$ defined by (21.9), then $\tilde{A}$ is a linear transformation.*

DEFINITION 21.10. If A is a linear transformation on $\mathscr{V}$ to $\mathscr{W}$, then its *dual* $\tilde{A}$ is the linear transformation on $\tilde{\mathscr{W}}$ to $\tilde{\mathscr{V}}$ such that

$$(21.10) \qquad\qquad (\tilde{A}\tilde{y})(x) = \tilde{y}(Ax) \quad \text{for all } x \in \mathscr{V}, \tilde{y} \in \tilde{\mathscr{W}}.$$

———————

Note that the dual goes, so to speak, in the opposite direction from the original transformation.

The dual transformation is often called the adjoint, but the term "adjoint transformation" has two other common uses—one intimately related to the dual, the other wholly unrelated.

When we turn to matrices there is one minor inconvenience in our notations. If you have been particularly observant, you will have noticed that since the beginning of Section 19, we have summed over an index if and only if it occurred both as a subscript and as a superscript. The apparently arbitrary decision to write the indices for a basis in the dual space as superscripts was motivated by a desire to preserve this useful mnemonic. To maintain this helpful feature of our notation when we study matrices, we agree that in a matrix associated with a transformation on dual spaces, the subscript will refer to the row and the superscript to the column.

THEOREM 21.11. *Assume that*
    (i) *A is a transformation on one finite-dimensional vector space $\mathscr{V}$ to another $\mathscr{W}$;*
    (ii) *$x]_1^M$ and $y]_1^N$ are bases for $\mathscr{V}$ and $\mathscr{W}$, respectively;*
    (iii) *$\tilde{x}]_1^M$ and $\tilde{y}]_1^N$ are the corresponding dual bases for $\tilde{\mathscr{V}}$ and $\tilde{\mathscr{W}}$;*

(iv) *the matrices* $[A; x], y]]$ *and* $[\tilde{A}; \tilde{y}], \tilde{x}]]$ *are*

$$\begin{bmatrix} \alpha_1^1 & \alpha_2^1 & \dots & \alpha_M^1 \\ \alpha_1^2 & \alpha_2^2 & \dots & \alpha_M^2 \\ \vdots & \vdots & & \vdots \\ \alpha_1^N & \alpha_2^N & \dots & \alpha_M^N \end{bmatrix}$$

and

$$\begin{bmatrix} \beta_1^1 & \beta_1^2 & \dots & \beta_1^N \\ \beta_2^1 & \beta_2^2 & \dots & \beta_2^N \\ \vdots & \vdots & & \vdots \\ \beta_M^1 & \beta_M^2 & \dots & \alpha_M^N \end{bmatrix}$$

respectively.
Then

$$\alpha_i^j = \beta_i^j.$$

PROOF. β_i^j is the element in the i-th row and the j-th column of $[\tilde{A}; \tilde{y}], \tilde{x}]]$ or, by Definition 19.2, the i-th coordinate of $\tilde{A}\tilde{y}^j$ (relative to $\tilde{x}]$). But, by (21.7), the i-th coordinate of $\tilde{A}\tilde{y}^j$ is $\tilde{A}\tilde{y}^j(x_i)$, so, using the definition of $\tilde{A}$,

$$\beta_i^j = \tilde{A}\tilde{y}^j(x_i) = \tilde{y}^j(Ax_i).$$

On the other hand, by (21.6), $\tilde{y}^j(Ax_i)$ is the j-th coordinate (relative to $y]$) of Ax_i. Again by Definition 19.2, this is the element in the j-th row and the i-th column of $[A; x], y]]$, namely α_i^j. Thus

$$\beta_i^j = y^j(Ax_i) = \alpha_i^j.$$

$$\text{Q.E.D.}$$

This theorem says that the matrix of $\tilde{A}$ is obtained from that of A by interchanging rows for columns. In matrix theory two matrices obtainable from one another by such an interchange are called the transposes of one another.

We now return to the algebra of transformations. The proofs are not difficult and we give one only as a sample.

THEOREM 21.12. *If A and B are linear transformations on a vector space $\mathcal{V}$ to a vector space $\mathcal{W}$ and α is a scalar then*

(21.11) $$(\widetilde{A+B}) = \tilde{A} + \tilde{B},$$

and

(21.12) $$\widetilde{(\alpha A)} = \alpha(\tilde{A}).$$

THEOREM 21.13. *If O is the zero linear transformation on $\mathscr{V}$ to $\mathscr{W}$ then $\tilde{O}$ is the zero linear transformation $\tilde{\mathscr{W}}$ to $\tilde{\mathscr{V}}$. If I is the identity transformation on $\mathscr{V}$ to $\mathscr{V}$ then $\tilde{I}$ is the identity transformation on $\tilde{\mathscr{V}}$ to $\tilde{\mathscr{V}}$.*

THEOREM 21.14. *If A and B are linear transformations on $\mathscr{V}$ to $\mathscr{W}$ and on $\mathscr{U}$ to $\mathscr{V}$, respectively, then $(\widetilde{AB}) = \tilde{B}\tilde{A}$.*

PROOF. To see what must be proved simply look at Definition 21.10. Let $C = AB$. Then $\tilde{C} = (\widetilde{AB})$ is defined to be *the* transformation such that $(\tilde{C}\tilde{z})(x) = \tilde{z}(Cx)$ for all $x \in \mathscr{U}$, $\tilde{z} \in \tilde{\mathscr{W}}$. What we must show is that $\tilde{B}\tilde{A}$ fulfills this equation: i.e., we must prove

$$((\tilde{B}\tilde{A})\tilde{z})(x) = \tilde{z}(Cx) = \tilde{z}((AB)x).$$

But this is easy. For any $x \in \mathscr{U}$, $\tilde{z} \in \tilde{\mathscr{W}}$, we have

$$((\tilde{B}\tilde{A})\tilde{z})(x) = (\tilde{B}(\tilde{A}\tilde{z}))(x) = (\tilde{A}\tilde{z})(Bx)$$
$$= \tilde{z}(A(Bx)) = \tilde{z}((AB)x).$$

Q.E.D.

Section 22.   Multilinear Forms

In our study of transformations we have stressed the transformations from one space to another. A part of the material in this and later sections is significant when dealing with more than one vector space, but for our present purpose it is sufficient to consider the simpler case where all the vectors belong to a single space. In the remainder of this book we will almost always assume that we are dealing with a single vector space $\mathscr{V}$ over a particular scalar field $\mathscr{F}$. The letter N will always denote the dimension of $\mathscr{V}$.

In Section 5 we observed that in $\mathscr{R}^2$ two vectors, $x = \begin{bmatrix} \xi^1 \\ \xi^2 \end{bmatrix}$ and $y = \begin{bmatrix} \eta^1 \\ \eta^2 \end{bmatrix}$, are linearly dependent if and only if $\xi^1\eta^2 - \xi^2\eta^1 = 0$. We now look for the N-dimensional analogue of the function φ which assigns to the pair (x,y) the value

(22.1) $$\varphi(x,y) = \xi^1\eta^2 - \xi^2\eta^1.$$

In our search for this analogue we will meet other quantities of comparable importance, but we touch on them only briefly.

Looking at (22.1) you will see that if y is thought of as a fixed vector, then *as a function of x alone*, φ is a linear functional. Similarly φ is a linear function of y alone.

DEFINITION 22.1. A *bilinear form* on $\mathscr{V}$ is a function φ of two variables such that for all $x, x', y, y' \in \mathscr{V}$ and all $\alpha, \alpha' \in \mathscr{F}$

(22.2) $$\varphi(x,y) \in \mathscr{F},$$

(22.3) $$\varphi(\alpha x + \alpha' x', y) = \alpha\varphi(x,y) + \alpha'\varphi(x',y), \quad \text{and}$$

(22.4) $$\varphi(x,\alpha y + \alpha' y') = \alpha\varphi(x,y) + \alpha'\varphi(x,y').$$

Bilinear forms are often called bilinear functionals or 2-forms.

It is easy to get the first generalization. We simply allow for an arbitrary number of variables. When we start talking about functions of several variables, the notations become complicated and the formulas long. Once you get used to the notations, the ideas are relatively simple. In this section we will be talking of scalar-valued functions of n vector-valued variables, but our attention will be focused on just one or two of the variables. Only once will we have to look at all of the variables simultaneously. What we need is some device to indicate which variables to look at and which to neglect.

The next definition is typical. We have a function φ of n variables $x_1, x_2, \ldots, x_n$, and we want to say what happens when we change the i-th variable, keeping the others fixed. The notation

$$\varphi(x_1, \ldots, x_{i-1}, \alpha y + \beta z, x_{i+1}, \ldots, x_n)$$

is intended to direct your eye to the spot where the action is taking place. When you compare this with

$$\alpha\varphi(x_1, \ldots, x_{i-1}, y, x_{i+1}, \ldots, x_n) + \beta\varphi(x_1, \ldots, x_{i-1}, z, x_{i+1}, \ldots, x_n)$$

you are supposed to note that all the entries, $x_1, \ldots, x_{i-1}$ and $x_{i+1}, \ldots, x_n$, remain unchanged and then to concentrate on those entries which are different in different places. With practice you will not find this difficult. Even such a formula as (22.9) is quite tractable as soon as you realize that you need to look only at two places: that between x_{i-1} and x_{i+1} and that between x_{j-1} and x_{j+1}.

As you are well aware, the phrase "for all x and y" is usually to be understood before such a formula as $\varphi(x,y) = -\varphi(y,x)$. With such a phrase the letters x and y are just dummies; replacing them with other letters does not change the meaning. Strictly speaking, the term "variable" should be employed only for symbols used in this way. When one wishes to speak of $\varphi(1, -3)$ the 1 and the -3 are obviously not variables and common sense forbids us to speak of the "1" as the first variable. We need some non-committal term to refer to the x in $\varphi(x,y)$ and to the 1 in $\varphi(1, -3)$. The usual word is "argument" and we will speak of the arguments of various functions, whether these be variables in the strict sense or constants.

APP.
B.3
VAR

DEFINITION 22.2. An *n-linear functional*, or *n-form*, on $\mathcal{V}$ is a function, φ, of n vector variables, such that for all $x_1, x_2, \ldots, x_n, y, z \in \mathcal{V}$ and all $\alpha, \beta \in \mathcal{F}$,

$$(22.5) \qquad \varphi(x_1, x_2, \ldots, x_n) \in \mathcal{F} \text{ and}$$

$$(22.6) \qquad \varphi(x_1, \ldots, x_{i-1}, \alpha y + \beta z, x_{i+1}, \ldots, x_n)$$

$$= \alpha \varphi(x_1, \ldots, x_{i-1}, y, x_{i+1}, \ldots, x_n)$$

$$+ \beta \varphi(x_1, \ldots, x_{i-1}, z, x_{i+1}, \ldots, x_n)$$

for $1 = 1, 2, \ldots, n$.

By induction, (22.6) implies the more general formula:

$$(22.7) \qquad \varphi(x_1, \ldots, x_{i-1}, \sum_{j=1}^{k} \alpha_j y_j, x_{i+1}, \ldots, x_n)$$

$$= \sum_{j=1}^{k} \alpha_j \varphi(x_1, \ldots, x_{i-1}, y_j, x_{i+1}, \ldots, x_n).$$

Note that a 1-form is just a linear functional.

We will use the letters φ, ψ, and θ, to stand for n-forms.

Under a thin disguise, and using the alias "tensor," the n-forms are an indispensable tool of both physicist and mathematician.

Looking again at equation (22.1), we see that interchanging the roles of x and y changes the sign of $\varphi(x,y)$. Expressing this by a formula:

$$(22.8) \qquad \varphi(x,y) = -\varphi(y,x).$$

Such a bilinear form, which changes sign when one interchanges its arguments, is called an antisymmetric or alternating form.

We might, equally well, consider symmetric forms, i.e., those which satisfy $\varphi(x,y) = +\varphi(y,x)$. Symmetric forms are indeed important, but we will not need them here.

It is convenient to look at alternating forms from two points of view and, at first, to use two different names.

DEFINITION 22.3. An *n*-form is *antisymmetric with respect to its i-th and j-th arguments* if, for all $x_1, x_2, \ldots, x_n \in \mathcal{V}$,

$$(22.9) \qquad \varphi(x_1, \ldots, x_{i-1}, x_i, x_{i+1}, \ldots, x_{j-1}, x_j, x_{j+1}, \ldots, x_n)$$

$$= -\varphi(x_1, \ldots, x_{i-1}, x_j, x_{i+1}, \ldots, x_{j-1}, x_i, x_{j+1}, \ldots, x_n).$$

It is *antisymmetric* if it is antisymmetric with respect to every pair of arguments.

DEFINITION 22.4.   An n-form *alternates with respect to its i-th and j-th arguments* if

$$(22.10) \quad \varphi(x_1, \ldots, x_{i-1}, x_i, x_{i+1}, \ldots, x_{j-1}, x_j, x_{j+1}, \ldots, x_n) = 0$$

whenever x_i and x_j are equal.   It is *alternating* if it alternates with respect to every pair of arguments.

We first show that if a form is alternating with respect to a pair of arguments, then it is antisymmetric with respect to those arguments, and conversely.*   This will show that the two concepts, alternation and antisymmetry, are equivalent; but we want to go one step further. We will show that if an n-form alternates on every pair of *adjacent* arguments, then it is an alternating form, i.e., it is alternating with respect to every pair of arguments.

THEOREM 22.5.   *If an n-form alternates with respect to its i-th and j-th arguments, then it is antisymmetric with respect to those arguments.*

PROOF.   Let φ be an n-form which alternates with respect to its i-th and j-th arguments, and let $x_1, x_2, \ldots, x_n$, be arbitrary elements of $\mathcal{V}$. We know that φ vanishes whenever its i-th and j-th arguments are equal.   Let both of them be $x_i + x_j$ and compute, using (22.6) twice. For simplicity we exhibit just the 1st, i-th, j-th, and n-th, arguments in each function.   Thus

$$
\begin{aligned}
0 &= \varphi(x_1, \ldots, x_i + x_j, \ldots, x_i + x_j, \ldots, x_n) \\
&= \varphi(x_1, \ldots, \quad x_i, \ldots, \quad x_i + x_j, \ldots, x_n) \\
&\quad + \varphi(x_1, \ldots, x_j, \ldots, x_i + x_j, \ldots, x_n) \\
&= \varphi(x_1, \ldots, \quad x_i, \ldots, \quad x_i, \ldots, x_n) \\
&\quad + \varphi(x_1, \ldots, \quad x_i, \ldots, \quad x_j, \ldots, x_n) \\
&\quad + \varphi(x_1, \ldots, \quad x_j, \ldots, \quad x_i, \ldots, x_n) \\
&\quad + \varphi(x_1, \ldots, \quad x_j, \ldots, \quad x_j, \ldots, x_n).
\end{aligned}
$$

Examine the right-hand side.   The first term has x_i both in the i-th and in the j-th place.   Since φ alternates with respect to these arguments, this term is zero.   Similarly the fourth term vanishes.   Hence the second term is the negative of the third; but to say that these are negatives of one another is to say that φ satisfies equation (22.9).

Q.E.D.

THEOREM 22.6.   *If an n-form is antisymmetric with respect to its i-th and j-th arguments, then it alternates with respect to those arguments.*

---

*Mathematicians often consider scalar fields other than the real or complex field For certain rather peculiar fields the proof of the converse is invalid.   For such fields antisymmetry does not imply alternation.

PROOF. Assume that φ is an n-form which is antisymmetric with respect to its i-th and j-th arguments. We want to show that the condition $x_i = x_j$ implies that

(22.11) $\varphi(x_1, \ldots, x_{i-1}, x_i, x_{i+1}, \ldots, x_{j-1}, x_j, x_{j+1}, \ldots, x_n) = 0.$

Assume, then, that $x_i = x_j$ and remember that φ is antisymmetric (with respect to its i-th and j-th arguments), so

(22.12) $\varphi(x_1, \ldots, x_{i-1}, x_i, x_{i+1}, \ldots, x_{j-1}, x_j, x_{j+1}, \ldots, x_n)$

     $= -\varphi(x_1, \ldots, x_{i-1}, x_j, x_{i+1}, \ldots, x_{j-1}, x_i, x_{j+1}, \ldots, x_n).$

Since $x_i = x_j$ the arguments of φ on the right-hand side of (22.12) are identical with those on the left-hand side. Thus (22.12) really says that $\varphi(x_1, x_2, \ldots, x_n)$ is its own negative. The only scalar which is its own negative is zero; so this implies (22.11).

Q.E.D.

THEOREM 22.7. *If an n-form φ alternates with respect to every pair of adjacent arguments, then it is an alternating form.*

PROOF. The proof really is easy, but the key equation may look terribly complicated. We are given the n-form φ which alternates with respect to adjacent arguments. Since alternation implies antisymmetry, interchanging adjacent arguments just changes the sign. Our object is to prove that φ vanishes whenever any pair of arguments are equal. To do so, we assume that $x_j = x_k$ and show that

$$\varphi(x_1, \ldots, x_{j-1}, x_j, x_{j+1}, \ldots, x_{k-1}, x_k, x_{k+1}, \ldots, x_n) = 0.$$

We simply move x_k towards x_j one step at a time, using antisymmetry at each step. (The signs given are correct, but play no role in the argument.) After $k-j-1$ steps, x_k has become the $(j+1)$-th argument. At this point we can invoke alternation. Thus

$\varphi(x_1, \ldots, x_{j-1}, x_j, x_{j+1}, \ldots, x_{k-2}, x_{k-1}, x_k, x_{k+1}, \ldots, x_n)$

   $= -\varphi(x_1, \ldots, x_{j-1}, x_j, x_{j+1}, \ldots, x_{k-2}, x_k, x_{k-1}, x_{k+1}, \ldots, x_n)$

   $= +\varphi(x_1, \ldots, x_{j-1}, x_j, x_{j+1}, \ldots, x_k, x_{k-2}, x_{k-1}, x_{k+1}, \ldots, x_n)$

   $= \ldots$

   $= (-1)^{k-1-i}\varphi(x_1, \ldots, x_{j-1}, x_j, x_{j+1}, \ldots, x_{i-1}, x_i, x_k, \ldots,$
                                  $x_{k-2}, x_{k-1}, x_{k+1}, \ldots, x_n)$

   $= (-1)^{(k-1)-(i-1)}\varphi(x_1, \ldots, x_{j-1}, x_j, x_{j+1}, \ldots, x_{i-1}, x_k, x_i, \ldots,$
                                  $x_{k-2}, x_{k-1}, x_{k+1}, \ldots, x_n)$

   $= \ldots$

   $= (-1)^{(k-1)-(j+1)}\varphi(x_1, \ldots, x_{j-1}, x_j, x_{j+1}, x_k, \ldots,$
                                  $x_{k-2}, x_{k-1}, x_{k+1}, \ldots, x_n)$

$$= (-1)^{k-j-1}\varphi(x_1, \ldots, x_{j-1}, x_j, x_k, x_{j+1}, \ldots,$$
$$x_{k-2}, x_{k-1}, x_{k+1}, \ldots, x_n)$$
$$= 0$$

Q.E.D.

Our object is to study alternating forms and, in particular, the so-called alternating forms of *maximal degree*; that is, alternating N-forms where N is the dimension of the space. We first need a couple of results about forms in general.

DEFINITION 22.8.   If φ and ψ are n-forms and $\alpha \in \mathscr{F}$, then $\varphi + \psi$ and $\alpha\varphi$ are defined by the formulas

(22.13) $(\varphi + \psi)(x_1, x_2, \ldots, x_n) = \varphi(x_1, x_2, \ldots, x_n) + \psi(x_1, x_2, \ldots, x_n)$

and

(22.14) $(\alpha\varphi)(x_1, x_2, \ldots, x_n) = \alpha\varphi(x_1, x_2, \ldots, x_n).$

We state our first result without giving the proof, which is almost identical with that of Theorem 16.2.

THEOREM 22.9.   *The set of all n-forms is a vector space and the set of all alternating n-forms is a subspace of it.*

THEOREM 22.10.   *If φ is an m-form and ψ is an n-form, then the function θ defined by*

$$\theta(x_1, \ldots, x_m, y_1, \ldots, y_n) = \varphi(x_1, \ldots, x_m)\psi(y_1, \ldots, y_n)$$

is an $m+n$ form.

PROOF.   All we need to show is that θ is linear in each of its arguments. For this theorem it should be clear that all the arguments are on an equal footing. If we can show that θ is linear in its first argument then we could show that it is linear in any other argument. It is nice to work with the first argument because it is easy to keep your eye on the place where the action is going on. In the following equation you can forget all about $x_2, \ldots, x_m, y_1, \ldots, y_n$.
For any $u, v, x_2, \ldots, x_m, y_1, \ldots, y_n \in \mathscr{V}$ and any $\alpha, \beta \in \mathscr{F}$ we have

$\theta(\alpha u + \beta v, x_2, \ldots, x_m, y_1, \ldots, y_n)$
$\quad = \varphi(\alpha u + \beta v, x_2, \ldots, x_m)\psi(y_1, \ldots, y_n)$
$\quad = [\alpha\varphi(u, x_2, \ldots, x_m) + \beta\varphi(v, x_2, \ldots, x_m)]\psi(y_1, \ldots, y_n)$
$\quad = \alpha\varphi(u, x_2, \ldots, x_m)\psi(y_1, \ldots, y_n) + \beta\varphi(v, x_2, \ldots, x_m)\psi(y_1, \ldots, y_n)$
$\quad = \alpha\theta(u, x_2, \ldots, x_m, y_1, \ldots, y_n) + \beta\theta(v, x_2, \ldots, x_m, y_1, \ldots, y_n).$

Q.E.D.

Unfortunately this process of generating new forms by multiplying the values of old forms does not generate alternating forms even if the original forms are alternating. However, a more complicated construction does yield alternating forms. We give only a special case of an important operation which combines alternating forms to get a new alternating form. The idea is to use Theorem 22.10 to get new forms and to add and subtract these forms in such a way as to get an alternating form.

DEFINITION 22.11. If φ is an alternating n-form and ψ is a 1-form, then the *exterior product** of ψ and φ is the $n+1$ form $\psi \wedge \varphi$ defined by

$$(22.15) \quad (\psi \wedge \varphi)(x_1, x_2, \ldots, x_{n+1})$$

$$= \sum_{i=1}^{n+1} (-1)^{i-1} \psi(x_i) \varphi(x_1, \ldots, x_{i-1}, x_{i+1}, \ldots, x_{n+1}).$$

The expression "$\psi \wedge \varphi$" is often read "psi wedge phi." Strictly speaking, this definition is premature because it takes for granted the unverified fact that $\psi \wedge \varphi$ is an $n+1$ form. This should be obvious, because Theorem 22.10 says that each product on the right-hand side of (22.15) is an $n+1$ form and Theorem 22.9 assures us that the sum is again such a form.

THEOREM 22.12. *If φ is an alternating n-form and ψ is a 1-form then $\psi \wedge \varphi$ is an alternating $n+1$ form.*

PROOF. Theorem 22.7 was designed for just this proof. All we need to do is to consider an arbitrary j between 1 and n, assume that $x_j = x_{j+1}$ and show that $(\psi \wedge \varphi)(x_1, x_2, \ldots, x_{n+1}) = 0$. Now by definition,

$$(22.16) \quad (\psi \wedge \varphi)(x_1, x_2, \ldots, x_{n+1})$$

$$= \sum_{i=1}^{n+1} (-1)^{i-1} \psi(x_i) \varphi(x_1, \ldots, x_{i-1}, x_{i+1}, \ldots, x_{n+1}),$$

and every term in the sum except those for $i=j$ and for $i=j+1$ contains φ with the equal arguments x_j and x_{j+1}. Since φ is an alternating

---

* Hermann Günther Grassmann (1809–1877) introduced and exploited exterior products in his book *Die lineale Ausdehnungslehre*, Leipzig, 1844. Their advantages have become widely recognized only recently.
  Unfortunately, two mutually incompatible definitions of the exterior product are in common use. Some authors would insert a factor $1/(n+1)$ on the right-hand side of equation (22.15).

form, this implies that the sum contains only two non-zero terms. These are

$$(-1)^{j-1}\psi(x_j)\varphi(x_1, \ldots, x_{j-1}, x_{j+1}, \ldots, x_n)$$
$$+(-1)^{j+1-1}\psi(x_{j+1})\varphi(x_1, \ldots, x_j, x_{j+2}, \ldots, x_n).$$

They have opposite signs and are otherwise identical, because $x_j = x_{j+1}$. Hence the sum is zero.

Q.E.D.

The operation of forming exterior products provides us with new alternating forms, but for all we know, these new forms might be the identically zero form. We need to know that there are non-zero alternating n-forms if $1 \leqslant n \leqslant N$. The case $n = 1$ is very special. Definition 22.3 says that an n-form is antisymmetric if ("and only if" understood) the condition $1 \leqslant i < j \leqslant n$ implies equation (22.9). In other words, to say that φ is antisymmetric is to say that we never have both $1 \leqslant i < j \leqslant n$ and the denial of (22.9). For the case $n = 1$ we cannot have $1 \leqslant i < j \leqslant n$ so we cannot possibly have both $1 \leqslant i < j \leqslant n$ and anything else. In particular we cannot have both $1 \leqslant i < j \leqslant n$ and the denial of (22.9), so every 1-form is antisymmetric ($=$ alternating).

This sort of legalistic chicanery—proving that $\cdots$ implies $///$ by showing that $\cdots$ can never occur—is not uncommon in mathematics. It may seem troublesome when first met, but it is not really far from everyday usage. (For further discussion see Alfred Tarski, *Introduction to Logic*, Oxford University Press, New York, 1950.) If it worries you, you can reassure yourself about the existence of alternating n-forms for $2 \leqslant n \leqslant N$ by working Problem 25.22.

If we admit that all 1-forms are alternating, we see that the vector space of alternating 1-forms is just $\tilde{\mathscr{V}}$ and hence there are lots of alternating 1-forms. This will provide the starting point for an inductive proof that there are non-trivial n-forms for $n = 1, 2, \ldots, N$.

THEOREM 22.13. *If $\mathscr{V}$ is an N-dimensional vector space and $1 \leqslant n \leqslant N$, then there is at least one non-zero alternating n-form.*

PROOF. We know that there are plenty of non-zero 1-forms and we proceed inductively. All we need to show is that if $k < N$ and there is a non-zero alternating k-form, then there is an alternating $k + 1$ form which does not vanish identically.

Assume then that φ is a non-zero alternating k-form and that $k < N$. Since φ is not identically zero, there are vectors $x_1, x_2, \ldots, x_k$ such that

$$(22.17) \qquad \varphi(x_1, x_2, \ldots, x_k) \neq 0.$$

Since $k < N$, the vectors $x_1, x_2, \ldots, x_k$ cannot span the whole of $\mathscr{V}$

and we may choose a vector x_{k+1} not in $\text{Sp}(x_1, x_2, \ldots, x_k)$. According to Corollary 21.4 this guarantees that there is a linear functional, or 1-form, ψ such that

(22.18) $$\psi(x) = 0 \quad \text{for } x \in \text{Sp}(x_1, x_2, \ldots, x_k) \text{ and}$$
(22.19) $$\psi(x_{k+1}) = 1.$$

Let $\theta = \psi \wedge \varphi$. We know that θ is an alternating $k+1$ form and want to show that it is not identically zero. Now

$$\theta(x_1, x_2, \ldots, x_{k+1}) = (\psi \wedge \varphi)(x_1, x_2, \ldots, x_{k+1})$$
$$= \sum_{i=1}^{k+1} (-1)^{i-1} \psi(x_i) \varphi(x_1, \ldots, x_{i-1}, x_{i+1}, \ldots, x_{k+1}).$$

According to (22.18) all terms in the sum, except the last, are zero. We thus have, by (22.19), and (22.17),

$$\theta(x_1, x_2, \ldots, x_{k+1}) = (-1)^{k+1-1} \psi(x_{k+1}) \varphi(x_1, \ldots, x_k)$$
$$= (-1)^k \varphi(x_1, \ldots, x_k)$$
$$\neq 0.$$

Q.E.D.

We now turn to the relation between alternating forms and linear dependence.

THEOREM 22.14. *If φ is an alternating n-form and if $x_1, x_2, \ldots, x_n$ are linearly dependent, then $\varphi(x_1, x_2, \ldots, x_n) = 0$.*

PROOF. Assume that $x_1, x_2, \ldots, x_n$ are linearly dependent. Corollary 10.11 tells us that every linearly dependent set contains one vector which is a linear combination of the others, say $x_j = \sum_{i \neq j} \alpha^i x_i$. Then

$$\varphi(x_1, \ldots, x_{j-1}, x_j, x_{j+1}, \ldots, x_n)$$
$$= \varphi(x_1, \ldots, x_{j-1}, \sum_{i \neq j} \alpha^i x_i, x_{j+1}, \ldots, x_n)$$
$$= \sum_{i \neq j} \alpha^i \varphi(x_1, \ldots, x_{j-1}, x_i, x_{j+1}, \ldots, x_n)$$
$$= \alpha^1 \varphi(x_1, \ldots, x_{j-1}, x_1, x_{j+1}, \ldots, x_n)$$
$$+ \cdots$$
$$+ \alpha^{j-1} \varphi(x_1, \ldots, x_{j-1}, x_{j-1}, x_{j+1}, \ldots, x_n)$$
$$+ \alpha^{j+1} \varphi(x_1, \ldots, x_{j-1}, x_{j+1}, x_{j+1}, \ldots, x_n)$$
$$+ \cdots$$
$$+ \alpha^n \varphi(x_1, \ldots, x_{j-1}, x_n, x_{j+1}, \ldots, x_n).$$

By Definition 22.4 all the terms in the last sum are zero.

Q.E.D.

COROLLARY 22.15.   *If φ is an alternating n-form and $\varphi(x_1, x_2, \ldots, x_n)$ $\neq 0$, then $x_1, x_2, \ldots, x_n$ are linearly independent.*

COROLLARY 22.16.   *If φ is an alternating n-form and $n > N = \dim \mathscr{V}$, then φ is the identically zero n-form.*

THEOREM 22.17.   *If φ is an alternating N-form on the N-dimensional space $\mathscr{V}$ and if there is a basis $x]_1^n$ such that*

$$(22.20) \qquad \varphi(x_1, x_2, \ldots, x_N) = 0,$$

then φ is the identically zero N-form.

We give two proofs.   The first is a complicated induction.   The second requires you to visualize an enormous sum.   Take your choice.

FIRST PROOF.   Let ψ_1 be the 1-form defined by

$$\psi_1(z_1) = \varphi(z_1, x_2, x_3, \ldots, x_N) \quad \text{for all } z_1 \in \mathscr{V}.$$

Let ψ_2 be the 2-form defined by

$$\psi_2(z_1, z_2) = \varphi(z_1, z_2, x_3, \ldots, x_N) \quad \text{for all } z_1, z_2 \in \mathscr{V}$$

and, in general, for arbitrary $z_1, z_2, \ldots, z_k$, let

$$\psi_k(z_1, \ldots, z_k) = \varphi(z_1, \ldots, z_k, x_{k+1}, \ldots, x_N).$$

We will give an inductive proof that $\psi_1, \psi_2, \ldots, \psi_N$, are all identically zero.   Since $\psi_N = \varphi$ this will establish the theorem.

Consider an arbitrary $z_1 \in \mathscr{V}$.   Since $x]_1^N$ is a basis, $z_1 = \sum_i \zeta^i x_i$ where $\zeta^1, \zeta^2, \ldots, \zeta^N$ are the coordinates of z_1.   Hence

$$\begin{aligned}
\psi(z_1) &= \varphi(z_1, x_2, \ldots, x_N) \\
&= \varphi\left(\sum_i \zeta^i x_i, x_2, \ldots, x_N \right) \\
&= \sum_i \zeta^i \varphi(x_i, x_2, \ldots, x_N) \\
&= \zeta^1 \varphi(x_1, x_2, \ldots, x_N) \\
&\quad + \zeta^2 \varphi(x_2, x_2, \ldots, x_N) \\
&\quad + \cdots \\
&\quad + \zeta^N \varphi(x_N, x_2, \ldots, x_N).
\end{aligned}$$

The first term is zero by (22.20) while all the others are zero because each has one argument of φ repeated.   Thus $\psi(z_1) = 0$.

Now adopt the inductive hypothesis: ψ_{k-1} is identically zero.   To prove that ψ_k is identically zero assume, to the contrary, that there are vectors $y_1, y_2, \ldots, y_k$ such that

(22.21) $$\psi_k(y_1, y_2, \ldots, y_k) \neq 0.$$

From this assumption we will derive the contradiction that x_k is a linear combination of $x_{k+1}, \ldots, x_N$.

From (22.21) we infer

(22.22) $$\varphi(y_1, \ldots, y_k, x_{k+1}, \ldots, x_N) = \psi_k(y_1, \ldots, y_k) \neq 0.$$

It follows (Corollary 22.15) that the N vectors $y_1, \ldots, y_k, x_{k+1}, \ldots, x_N$ are linearly independent and hence form a basis. Let $\alpha^1, \ldots, \alpha^k$, $\beta^{k+1}, \ldots, \beta^N$ be the coordinates of x_k with respect to this basis. Thus

$$x_k = \sum_{i=1}^{k} \alpha^i y_i + \sum_{i=k+1}^{N} \beta^i x_i.$$

Our object is to show that $\alpha^1 = \cdots = \alpha^k = 0$.

For $j = 1, 2, \ldots, k-1$, we have

$$\text{j-th place}$$
$$\downarrow$$

$$
\begin{aligned}
(22.23) \quad 0 &= \psi_{k-1}(y_1, \ldots, y_k, \ldots, y_{k-1}) \\
&= \varphi(y_1, \ldots, y_k, \ldots, y_{k-1}, x_k, x_{k+1}, \ldots, x_N) \\
&= -\varphi(y_1, \ldots, x_k, \ldots, y_{k-1}, y_k, x_{k+1}, \ldots, x_N) \\
&= -\sum_{i=1}^{k} \alpha^i \varphi(y_1, \ldots, y_i, \ldots, y_{k-1}, y_k, x_{k+1}, \ldots, x_N) \\
&\quad - \sum_{i=k+1}^{N} \beta^i \varphi(y_1, \ldots, x_i, \ldots, y_{k-1}, y_k, x_{k+1}, \ldots, x_N).
\end{aligned}
$$

Except for the j-th term in the first sum, every term includes a repeated argument and hence vanishes. Thus (22.23) reduces to

$$
\begin{aligned}
0 &= -\alpha^j \varphi(y_1, \ldots, y_j, \ldots, y_{k-1}, y_k, x_{k+1}, \ldots, x_N) \\
&= +\alpha^j \psi_k(y_1, \ldots, y_k).
\end{aligned}
$$

By (22.21), $\psi_k(y_1, \ldots, y_k) \neq 0$; so we must have $\alpha^j = 0$.

Finally, for α^k, we have

$$
\begin{aligned}
0 &= \psi_{k-1}(y_1, \ldots, y_{k-1}) \\
&= \varphi(y_1, \ldots, y_{k-1}, x_k, x_{k+1}, \ldots, x_N) \\
&= \sum_{i=1}^{k} \alpha^i \varphi(y_1, \ldots, y_{k-1}, y_i, x_{k+1}, \ldots, x_N) \\
&\quad + \sum_{i=k+1}^{N} \beta^i \varphi(y_1, \ldots, y_{k-1}, x_i, x_{k+1}, \ldots, x_N)
\end{aligned}
$$

$$= \alpha^k \varphi(y_1, \ldots, y_{k-1}, y_k, x_{k+1}, \ldots, x_N)$$
$$= \alpha^k \psi_k(y_1, \ldots, y_k).$$

Hence $\alpha^k = 0$.

Q.E.D.

SECOND PROOF.   Let $y_1, y_2, \ldots, y_N$ be any given vectors.   We want to show that $\varphi(y_1, y_2, \ldots, y_N) = 0$.

Let η_i^j be the j-th coordinate of y_i relative to the basis $x]_1^N$.   Then

$$y_i = \sum_{j=1}^N \eta_i^j x_j.$$

Since we have to look at all these sums simultaneously, we need to distinguish the different variables of summation.   Accordingly we replace the dummy variable j in the i-th sum by the dummy variable j_i and write

$$y_i = \sum_{j_i=1}^n \eta_i^{j_i} x_{j_i}.$$

Now use the fact that φ is linear in each argument.   Thus:

(22.24) $\varphi(y_1, y_2, \ldots, y_N)$

$$= \varphi\left(\sum_{j_1=1}^N \eta_1^{j_1} x_{j_1}, \sum_{j_2=1}^N \eta_2^{j_2} x_{j_2}, \ldots, \sum_{j_N=1}^N \eta_N^{j_N} x_{j_N} \right)$$

$$= \sum_{j_1=1}^N \sum_{j_2=1}^N \cdots \sum_{j_N=1}^N \eta_1^{j_1} \eta_2^{j_2} \cdots \eta_N^{j_N} \varphi(x_{j_1}, x_{j_2}, \ldots, x_{j_N}).$$

This enormous sum contains N^N terms, but fortunately each one is very simple indeed.   Consider a particular choice of the integers $j_1, j_2, \ldots, j_N$.   There are two possibilities, either all of them are different, or at least two of them, say j_k and j_l are equal.   In the latter case x_{j_k} and x_{j_l} are one and the same and, since φ is an alternating form,

$$\varphi(x_{j_1}, x_{j_2}, \ldots, x_{j_N}) = \varphi(x_{j_1}, \ldots, x_{j_k}, \ldots, x_{j_l}, \ldots, x_{j_N}) = 0.$$

The case where the j's are all different requires a little more thought. The j's are integers between 1 and N, inclusive.   If they are different, each integer between 1 and N occurs exactly once in the list: $j_1, j_2, \ldots, j_N$.

If N happens to be j_N we have

$$\varphi(x_{j_1}, x_{j_2}, \ldots, x_{j_N}) = \varphi(x_{j_1}, x_{j_2}, \ldots, x_{j_{N-1}}, x_N).$$

On the other hand if $N = j_k$, for $k \neq N$ we have

$$\varphi(x_{j_1}, \ldots, x_{j_{k-1}}, x_{j_k}, x_{j_{k+1}}, \ldots, x_{j_N})$$
$$= -\varphi(x_{j_1}, \ldots, x_{j_{k-1}}, x_{j_N}, x_{j_{k-1}}, \ldots, x_{j_k}).$$

In either case

$$\varphi(x_{j_1}, x_{j_2}, \ldots, x_{j_N}) = \pm \varphi(x_{\sim}, x_{\sim}, \ldots, x_{\sim}, x_N)$$

where the indices indicated by "$\sim$" are just $1, 2, \ldots, N-1$ arranged in some unknown order. Luckily the sign is of no interest. We can repeat this process, interchanging the x whose subscript is $N-1$ with the x which appears just before x_N. Continuing this procedure until the x's appear in their natural order we get

$$\varphi(x_{j_1}, x_{j_2}, \ldots, x_{j_N}) = \pm \varphi(x_1, x_2, \ldots, x_N).$$

By hypothesis, this is zero. Thus every term on the right-hand side of (22.24) is zero and the whole equation says just

$$\varphi(y_1, y_2, \ldots, y_N) = 0$$

Q.E.D.

COROLLARY 22.18. *If φ is a non-zero alternating N-form*

$$\varphi(x_1, x_2, \ldots, x_N) = 0$$

if and only if $x_1, x_2, \ldots, x_N$ are linearly dependent.
Note that linear dependence among the x's *always* implies

$$\varphi(x_1, x_2, \ldots, x_n) = 0;$$

but the converse is valid only if φ is of maximal degree, i.e., if $n = \dim \mathscr{V}$.
After all the hard work we have put in on alternating forms, the really crucial theorem comes easily.

THEOREM 22.19. *The space of alternating N-forms is one-dimensional.*

PROOF. We know that there is at least one non-trivial alternating N-form. Pick one such form and call it φ. We will show that this single form is a basis for the space of all alternating N-forms.
Let $x_1, x_2, \ldots, x_N$ be any fixed vectors chosen so $\varphi(x_1, x_2, \ldots, x_N) \neq 0$. (By Corollary 22.15, the x's form a basis and, by Theorem 22.17, any basis will do.) Now consider an arbitrary alternating N-form, ψ. Our object is to show that there is some scalar α such that $\psi = \alpha \varphi$.
Let

$$\alpha = \psi(x_1, x_2, \ldots, x_N)/\varphi(x_1, x_2, \ldots, x_N).$$

Consider the alternating N-form θ, defined by $\theta = \psi - \alpha\varphi$. In other words, for $y_1, y_2, \ldots, y_N \in \mathcal{V}$.

$$\theta(y_1, y_2, \ldots, y_N) = \psi(y_1, y_2, \ldots, y_N) - \alpha\varphi(y_1, y_2, \ldots, y_N).$$

We chose α so that

$$\begin{aligned}
\theta(x_1, x_2, &\ldots, x_N)\\
&= \psi(x_1, x_2, \ldots, x_N) - \alpha\varphi(x_1, x_2, \ldots, x_N)\\
&= \psi(x_1, x_2, \ldots, x_N)\\
&\quad - [\psi(x_1, x_2, \ldots, x_N)/\varphi(x_1, x_2, \ldots, x_N)] \cdot \varphi(x_1, x_2, \ldots, x_N)\\
&= 0.
\end{aligned}$$

It follows from Theorem 22.17 that θ is the zero N-form. Thus $0 = \psi - \alpha\varphi$ or $\psi = \alpha\varphi$.

$$\text{Q.E.D.}$$

COROLLARY 22.20.   *If* $x]_1^N$ *is a basis for* $\mathcal{V}$*, then there is one and only one alternating N-form φ such that*

$$\varphi(x_1, x_2, \ldots, x_N) = 1.$$

Section 23.   Determinants of Linear Transformations

Determinants are intimately related to alternating N-forms and we will base our study of them upon Theorem 22.19. Traditionally, however, determinants were regarded as numbers associated with square arrays of numbers. For example

$$\begin{vmatrix} \alpha & \beta \\ \gamma & \delta \end{vmatrix}$$

was defined to be $\alpha\delta - \beta\gamma$. Thus the determinant was a function which associated with each square matrix $[\alpha]$ a number denoted by $\det [\alpha]$ or, more commonly, by $|\alpha_i^j|$.

When determinants were studied from this point of view it was necessary to show that the matrices which different bases associate with a single transformation all have the same determinant. We will turn the problem around. First we will define a function which associates with each transformation A a number $\det A$. Next we will derive a few simple properties of this function, det. Then we turn to matrices and show that if a particular matrix $[\alpha]$ is associated with two different transformations, A and B, then $\det A = \det B$. In symbols, if

$$[\alpha] = [A; x], x]] = [B; y], y]]$$

then $\det A = \det B$. This fact permits us to define the determinant of a matrix as the determinant of any one of the transformations associated with the matrix. Finally we turn to computation and show that the standard formulas concerning the determinants of matrices follow easily from what we know of transformations.

We need to know a little of the relationship between forms and linear transformations. The problems are wholly terminological and the main result just extends Theorems 21.8 and 21.9 from 1-forms to n-forms. We put both the proof and a definition before the theorem.

Suppose θ is an n-form and A is a linear transformation on $\mathscr{V}$ to $\mathscr{V}$. We can define a function φ of n vector-valued variables by the formula

$$(23.1) \quad \varphi(x_1, x_2, \ldots, x_n) = \theta(Ax_1, Ax_2, \ldots, Ax_n)$$
$$\text{for } x_1, x_2, \ldots, x_n \in \mathscr{V}.$$

It is probably obvious, and it is certainly easy to prove, that φ is also an n-form. Thus A determines a new function—a rule for associating with each n-form θ a corresponding n-form φ. Let us denote this function on forms to forms by $\overline{A}$. (For 1-forms we previously denoted it by $\tilde{A}$, a notation which we will continue to use when convenient.) From (23.1) we see that $\overline{A}\theta$ can be defined as the n-form such that

$$(23.2) \quad (\overline{A}\theta)(x_1, x_2, \ldots, x_n) = \theta(Ax_1, Ax_2, \ldots, Ax_n)$$
$$\text{for all } x_1, x_2, \ldots, x_n \in \mathscr{V}.$$

Since the n-forms themselves form a vector space it is natural to hope that $\overline{A}$ is a linear transformation on that space. A one-line computation based on Definition 22.8 will confirm this hope. Equally easy is the observation that if θ is an alternating n-form then so is $\overline{A}\theta$.

DEFINITION 23.1. If A is a linear transformation on $\mathscr{V}$ to $\mathscr{V}$, then the *transformation* on n-forms *induced by* A is the function $\overline{A}$ defined by

$$(23.3) \quad (\overline{A}\theta)(x_1, x_2, \ldots, x_n) = \theta(Ax_1, Ax_2, \ldots, Ax_n),$$
$$\text{for all } x_1, x_2, \ldots, x_n \in \mathscr{V}.$$

THEOREM 23.2. *If A is a linear transformation, then the function $\overline{A}$ is a linear transformation on the space of all n-forms to the same space. Moreover if θ is an alternating n-form, then so is $\overline{A}\theta$.*

It is essential to keep in mind what we have done. We start with a vector space $\mathscr{V}$. For each integer n we construct a new space. For $n = 1$ we have the space $\tilde{\mathscr{V}}$ of all 1-forms (or linear functionals) on $\mathscr{V}$ and give it a special name, the dual space. For $n > 1$ there is no such standard name and we use the longer but more descriptive phrase "the space of all n-forms on $\mathscr{V}$." For $n > 1$ we must consider not only the space of all n-forms, but also the subspace consisting of the alternating n-forms on $\mathscr{V}$. Each transformation A on $\mathscr{V}$ to $\mathscr{V}$ induces a corresponding transformation on each of the new spaces. We use the single symbol "$\bar{A}$" to denote any one of these induced transformations.

If we have two transformations A and B, we would like to know how the induced transformations $\overline{A+B}$ and $\overline{A\cdot B}$ are related to a $\bar{A}$ and $\bar{B}$. Unfortunately there is nothing useful to be said about $\overline{A+B}$ except in very special cases, but the analogues of Theorems 21.13 and 21.14 are true. We need the latter.

THEOREM 23.3.   *If A and B are linear transformations on $\mathscr{V}$, then*

$$(23.4) \qquad \overline{A\cdot B} = \bar{B}\cdot\bar{A}.$$

PROOF.   As might be expected, the proof consists in just looking to see what the equation means. We want a name for the space of all n-forms on $\mathscr{V}$. Let us call it $\mathscr{V}_n$. Now $\bar{A}$ and $\bar{B}$ are linear transformations on $\mathscr{V}_n$ so their product is defined to be the transformation, $\bar{B}\cdot\bar{A}$, which assigns to each $\theta \in \mathscr{V}_n$ the value

$$(23.5) \qquad (\bar{B}\cdot\bar{A})(\theta) = \bar{B}(\bar{A}(\theta)).$$

What we must show is that this n-form, $\bar{B}(\bar{A}(\theta))$, is the same as $\overline{A\cdot B}(\theta)$. That is to say, these forms assign the same value to each set of arguments $x_1, x_2, \ldots, x_n$. Thus our object is to prove that, for all $\theta \in \mathscr{V}_n$ and all $x_1, x_2, \ldots, x_n \in \mathscr{V}$,

$$(\overline{A\cdot B}(\theta))(x_1, x_2, \ldots, x_n) = (\bar{B}(\bar{A}(\theta)))(x_1, x_2, \ldots, x_n).$$

Using (23.3) three times we have

$$
\begin{aligned}
(\overline{A\cdot B}(\theta))(x_1, x_2, \ldots, x_n) &= \theta(ABx_1, ABx_2, \ldots, ABx_n) \\
&= (\bar{A}\theta)(Bx_1, Bx_2, \ldots, Bx_n) \\
&= (\bar{B}(\bar{A}\theta))(x_1, x_2, \ldots, x_n).
\end{aligned}
$$

$$\text{Q.E.D.}$$

We are now ready for determinants. Let A be a linear transformation on $\mathscr{V}$ to $\mathscr{V}$ and consider the induced transformation $\bar{A}$ acting on the space of alternating N-forms. From now on let us call this space $\mathscr{A}_N$. Since $N = \dim \mathscr{V}$, Theorem 22.19 tells us that $\dim \mathscr{A}_N = 1$, and any non-zero alternating N-form is a basis for $\mathscr{A}_N$. Thus if $\theta \in \mathscr{A}_N$ and $\theta \neq 0$ each form in $\mathscr{A}_N$ is simply a scalar multiple of θ. In particular $\bar{A}\theta$ is some multiple of θ: i.e., we can find a scalar α so

$$\bar{A}\theta = \alpha\cdot\theta.$$

The important fact is that α does not depend on θ.

THEOREM 23.4. *If $\mathscr{A}_N$ is the space of alternating N-forms on $\mathscr{V}$ and A is a linear transformation on $\mathscr{V}$ to $\mathscr{V}$, then there is one and only one scalar α such that*

$$\bar{A}\varphi = \alpha\varphi$$

for all $\varphi \in \mathscr{A}_N$.

PROOF. Choose any $\theta \in \mathscr{A}_N$, $\theta \neq 0$. Then θ is a basis for $\mathscr{A}_N$. There is one and only one number α (namely the coordinate of $\bar{A}\theta$ relative to the basis θ) such that

$$\bar{A}\theta = \alpha\theta.$$

We want to show that $\bar{A}\varphi = \alpha\varphi$ for all $\varphi \in \mathscr{A}_N$. Consider such a φ and let β be its coordinate relative to the basis θ. Then $\varphi = \beta\theta$ and, since $\bar{A}$ is linear,

$$\bar{A}\varphi = \bar{A}(\beta\theta) = \beta(\bar{A}\theta) = \beta(\alpha\theta) = \alpha(\beta\theta) = \alpha\varphi.$$

$$\text{Q.E.D.}$$

DEFINITION 23.5. If A is a linear transformation on $\mathscr{V}$ to $\mathscr{V}$, then its *determinant*, det A, is the scalar such that

(23.6) $A\varphi = (\det A)\varphi$

for all $\varphi \in \mathscr{A}_N$.

For future reference we state as a theorem a slightly varied form of equation (23.6).

THEOREM 23.6. *If A is a linear transformation on $\mathscr{V}$ to $\mathscr{V}$, φ is an alternating N-form, and $x_1, x_2, \ldots, x_N$ are vectors in $\mathscr{V}$, then*

(23.7) $(\det A)\varphi(x_1, x_2, \ldots, x_N) = \varphi(Ax_1, Ax_2, \ldots, Ax_N).$

COROLLARY 23.7. *If φ is an alternating N-form and $\varphi(x_1, x_2, \ldots, x_N) = 1$, then $\det A = \varphi(Ax_1, Ax_2, \ldots, Ax_N)$.*

THEOREM 23.8. *If A and B are linear transformations on $\mathscr{V}$ to $\mathscr{V}$, then*

$$\det (AB) = (\det A) \cdot (\det B).$$

PROOF. By definition, det (AB) is the only scalar, α, which satisfies the equation $\overline{AB}\varphi = \alpha\varphi$ for all $\varphi \in \mathscr{A}_N$. However, for each $\varphi \in \mathscr{A}_N$ we have

$$\begin{array}{lll}
\overline{AB}\varphi & = (\bar{B} \cdot \bar{A})\varphi & \text{[by Th. 23.3]} \\
 & = \bar{B}(\bar{A}\varphi) & \text{[by Def. 16.3]} \\
 & = \bar{B}((\det A)\varphi) & \text{[by Def. 23.5]} \\
 & = (\det A)\bar{B}(\varphi) & \text{[since } \bar{B} \text{ is linear]} \\
 & = (\det A)(\det B)\varphi. & \text{[by Def. 23.5]}
\end{array}$$

$$\text{Q.E.D.}$$

COROLLARY 23.9. *If C is an invertible linear transformation on $\mathscr{V}$ to $\mathscr{V}$, then $\det C \neq 0$ and*

$$\det (C^{-1}) = (\det C)^{-1}.$$

THEOREM 23.10. *If A is a linear transformation on $\mathscr{V}$ to $\mathscr{V}$ and $\det A \neq 0$, then A has an inverse.*

PROOF. Let $x]_1^N$ be a basis for $\mathscr{V}$ and use Corollary 22.20 to choose $\theta \in \mathscr{A}_N$ so $\theta(x_1, x_2, \ldots, x_N) = 1$. Let $y_i = Ax_i$. By Corollary 23.7,

$$\theta(y_1, y_2, \ldots, y_N) = \theta(Ax_1, Ax_2, \ldots, Ax_N)$$
$$= \det A \neq 0.$$

Corollary 22.15 tells us that the y's are linearly independent and hence form a basis.

Now define B by giving the values it assigns to the basis $y]_1^N$. Let

$$By_i = x_i.$$

Then, obviously, $ABy_i = Ax_i = y_i = Iy_i$. Since AB and I agree on a basis, they are the same transformation. Similarly $BA = I$, since $BAx_i = x_i$.

Q.E.D.

Combining this with Corollary 23.9 we have

COROLLARY 23.11. *A linear transformation on a vector space and to the same space is invertible if and only if its determinant is different from zero.*

COROLLARY 23.12. *If $x]_1^N$ is a basis for $\mathscr{V}$ and A is a linear transformation on $\mathscr{V}$ to $\mathscr{V}$ with $\det A \neq 0$, then $Ax_1, Ax_2, \ldots, Ax_N$ is a basis for $\mathscr{V}$.*

COROLLARY 23.13. *Assume that A is a linear transformation on a finite-dimensional space $\mathscr{V}$. The following conditions are equivalent:*

   (i) $\det A = 0$;

   (ii) *for some $x \neq 0$, $Ax = 0$;*

   (iii) $\mathscr{N}(A) \neq \{0\}$;

   (iv) $\operatorname{rng} A \neq \mathscr{V}$.

So are the following:

   (v) $\det A \neq 0$;

   (vi) *A has an inverse;*

   (vii) $\mathscr{N}(A) = \{0\}$;

   (viii) $\operatorname{rng} A = \mathscr{V}$.

PROOF.   See Corollary 17.7.

One important theorem about determinants is harder to prove.   It says that the determinant of the dual of a transformation is equal to the determinant of the original transformation.   The idea behind the proof is that the duality between $\mathscr{V}$ and $\tilde{\mathscr{V}}$ extends to a duality between the forms on $\mathscr{V}$ and those on $\tilde{\mathscr{V}}$.   Once this duality is thoroughly understood, the theorem is almost self-evident, but to avoid the long theoretical development of duality theory we prove only the particular result we need.   It is a strange-looking lemma.

LEMMA 23.14.   *Let $\tilde{\varphi}$ be a non-zero alternating N-form on $\tilde{\mathscr{V}}$ and let φ be the function defined by the formulas*

$$(23.8) \qquad \varphi(x_1, x_2, \ldots, x_N) = 0$$

if $x_1, x_2, \ldots, x_N$ are linearly dependent,

$$(23.9) \quad \varphi(x_1, x_2, \ldots, x_N) = \frac{1}{\tilde{\varphi}(\tilde{x}^1, \tilde{x}^2, \ldots, \tilde{x}^N)} \text{ if } x_1, x_2, \ldots, x_N \text{ are linearly}$$

independent and $\tilde{x}]_1^N$ is the basis dual to $x]_1^N$.

Then φ is an alternating N-form.

PROOF.   According to (23.8) φ vanishes whenever two of its arguments are equal, so once we prove that φ is linear we will know, without further effort, that it is an alternating N-form.   We will show only that φ is a linear function of its first argument, but it should be clear that the same reasoning—with slightly more complicated notations— can be used to show that φ is linear in each of its arguments.

Assume then that we are given $x_2, x_3, \ldots, x_N$.   First we seek a simple formula for

$$\psi(y) = \varphi(y, x_2, \ldots, x_N).$$

If $x_2, \ldots, x_N$ happen to be linearly dependent then, as a function of y, ψ is identically zero and hence linear in its first argument.   On the other hand, if $x_2, \ldots, x_N$ are linearly independent we can choose x_1 so $x_1, x_2, \ldots, x_N$ is a basis for $\mathscr{V}$.

For an arbitrary y let

$$(23.10) \qquad \begin{cases} y_1 = y, \\ y_i = x_i & \text{for } i = 2, 3, \ldots, N. \end{cases}$$

If y is in the span of $x_2, x_3, \ldots, x_N$, then $y, x_2, \ldots, x_N$ are linearly dependent and $\psi(y) = 0$.   Otherwise $y]_1^N$ is a basis and we can let $\tilde{y}]_1^N$ be its dual.

Abbreviate by letting $\tilde{y}^i(x_1) = \alpha^i$, then

$$(23.11) \qquad \tilde{y}^i = \sum_{j=1}^{N} \tilde{y}^i(x_j)\tilde{x}^j \qquad\qquad \text{[by (21.7)]}$$

$$= \tilde{y}^i(x_1)\tilde{x}^1 + \sum_{j=2}^{N} \tilde{y}^i(x_j)\tilde{x}^j$$

$$= \alpha^i\tilde{x}^1 + \sum_{j=2}^{N} \tilde{y}^i(y_j)\tilde{x}^j \qquad\qquad \text{[by (23.10)]}$$

$$= \alpha^i\tilde{x}^1 + \sum_{j=2}^{N} \delta^i_j\tilde{x}^j \qquad\qquad \text{[Since } \tilde{y} \text{] is dual to } y]$$

$$= \begin{cases} \alpha^1\tilde{x}^1 & \text{if } i = 1, \\ \alpha^i\tilde{x}^1 + \tilde{x}^i & \text{if } i = 2, 3, \ldots, N. \end{cases}$$

Next let

$$(23.12) \qquad \gamma_i = \tilde{\varphi}(\tilde{y}^1, \ldots, \tilde{y}^i, \tilde{x}^{i+1}, \ldots, \tilde{x}^N)$$

and observe:

$$\gamma_0 = \tilde{\varphi}(\tilde{x}^1, \tilde{x}^2, \ldots, \tilde{x}^N),$$

$$\gamma_1 = \tilde{\varphi}(\tilde{y}^1, \tilde{x}^2, \ldots, \tilde{x}^N) = \tilde{\varphi}(\alpha^1\tilde{x}^1, \tilde{x}^2, \ldots, \tilde{x}^N)$$

$$= \alpha^1\tilde{\varphi}(\tilde{x}^1, \tilde{x}^2, \ldots, \tilde{x}^N) = \alpha^1\gamma_0,$$

and, for $i = 2, 3, \ldots, N$

$$\gamma_i = \tilde{\varphi}(\tilde{y}^1, \ldots, \tilde{y}^{i-1}, \tilde{y}^i, \tilde{x}^{i+1}, \ldots, \tilde{x}^N) \qquad \text{[by (23.12)]}$$

$$= \tilde{\varphi}(\tilde{y}^1, \ldots, \tilde{y}^{i-1}, \alpha^i\tilde{x}^1 + \tilde{x}^i, \tilde{x}^{i+1}, \ldots, \tilde{x}^N) \qquad \text{[by (23.11)]}$$

$$= \alpha^i\tilde{\varphi}(\tilde{y}^1, \ldots, \tilde{y}^{i-1}, \tilde{x}^1, \tilde{x}^{i+1}, \ldots, \tilde{x}^N)$$
$$\quad + \tilde{\varphi}(\tilde{y}^1, \ldots, \tilde{y}^{i-1}, \tilde{x}^i, \tilde{x}^{i+1}, \ldots, \tilde{x}^N)$$

$$= \alpha^i\tilde{\varphi}(\alpha^1\tilde{x}^1, \ldots, \tilde{y}^{i-1}, \tilde{x}^1, \tilde{x}^{i+1}, \ldots, \tilde{x}^N) + \gamma_{i-1} \quad \text{[by (23.11) \& (23.12)]}$$

$$= \alpha^i\alpha^1\tilde{\varphi}(\tilde{x}^1, \ldots, \tilde{y}^{i-1}, \tilde{x}^1, \tilde{x}^{i+1}, \ldots, \tilde{x}^N) + \gamma_{i-1}$$

$$= 0 + \gamma_{i-1} = \gamma_{i-1} \qquad\qquad \text{[since } \varphi \text{ is alternating]}$$

Thus $\qquad \tilde{\varphi}(\tilde{y}^1, \tilde{y}^2, \ldots, \tilde{y}^N) = \gamma_N = \gamma_{N-1} = \cdots = \gamma_1 = \alpha^1\gamma_0$

$$= \alpha^1\tilde{\varphi}(\tilde{x}^1, \tilde{x}^2, \ldots, \tilde{x}^N).$$

By (23.10) and (23.11), $1 = \tilde{y}^1(y_1) = \alpha^1\tilde{x}^1(y)$; so $1/\alpha^1 = \tilde{x}^1(y)$, and hence

$$(23.13) \qquad \psi(y) = \frac{1}{\tilde{\varphi}(\tilde{y}^1, \tilde{y}^2, \ldots, \tilde{y}^N)} = \frac{1}{\alpha^1\tilde{\varphi}(\tilde{x}^1, \tilde{x}^2, \ldots, \tilde{x}^N)}$$

$$= \frac{\tilde{x}^1(y)}{\tilde{\varphi}(\tilde{x}^1, \tilde{x}^2, \ldots, \tilde{x}^N)}.$$

Equation (23.13) was derived under the assumption

$$y \notin \mathrm{Sp}\{x_2, x_3, \ldots, x_N\},$$

but it is still valid if $y = \sum_{j=2}^N \beta^j x_j$. In that case both $\psi(y) = 0$ and $\tilde{x}^1(y) = \sum_{j=2}^N \beta^j \tilde{x}^1(x_j) = 0$.

Since the numerator in (23.13) is a linear function of y and the denominator does not change as y varies, (23.13) says that ψ is linear.

Q.E.D.

THEOREM 23.15. *If A is a linear transformation on $\mathscr{V}$ to $\mathscr{V}$ and $\tilde{A}$ is its dual, then*

$$\det \tilde{A} = \det A.$$

PROOF. We consider first the case $\det A = 0$. In this case Corollary 23.13 tells us that $\mathrm{rng}\, A \neq \mathscr{V}$. Since $\mathrm{rng}\, A$ is a proper subspace of $\mathscr{V}$, there is a non-zero linear functional $\tilde{y}$ such that $\tilde{y}(z) = 0$ whenever $z \in \mathrm{rng}\, A$ (Corollary 21.4). Thus $\tilde{A}\tilde{y}(x) = \tilde{y}(Ax) = 0$ for all $x \in \mathscr{V}$, i.e., $\tilde{A}\tilde{y} = 0$. By Corollary 23.13, $\det \tilde{A} = 0$.

Now assume $\det A \neq 0$. Choose a basis $x]_1^N$ for $\mathscr{V}$ and let

(23.14) $$y_i = Ax_i.$$

Since $\det A \neq 0$, $y]_1^N$ is a basis (Corollary 23.12). Let $\tilde{x}]_1^N$ and $\tilde{y}]_1^N$ be the bases dual to $x]$ and to $y]$ respectively. We find

(23.15) $$\tilde{A}\tilde{y}^i = \sum_j [\tilde{A}\tilde{y}^i(x_j)]\tilde{x}^j \qquad \text{[by (21.7)]}$$

$$= \sum_j [\tilde{y}^i(Ax_j)]\tilde{x}^j \qquad \text{[by Def. 21.10]}$$

$$= \sum_j \tilde{y}^i(y_j)\tilde{x}^j \qquad \text{[by (23.14)]}$$

$$= \sum_j \delta_i^j \tilde{x}^j = \tilde{x}^i.$$

Let $\tilde{\varphi}$ be any non-zero alternating N-form on $\tilde{\mathscr{V}}$ and let φ be the alternating N-form on $\mathscr{V}$ defined in Lemma 23.14. Then

$$\det A = \varphi(Ax_1, Ax_2, \ldots, Ax_N)/\varphi(x_1, x_2, \ldots, x_N) \qquad \text{[by Th. 23.6]}$$

$$= \varphi(y_1, y_2, \ldots, y_N)/\varphi(x_1, x_2, \ldots, x_N) \qquad \text{[by (23.14)]}$$

$$= \frac{1}{\tilde{\varphi}(\tilde{y}^1, \tilde{y}^2, \ldots, \tilde{y}^N)} \Big/ \frac{1}{\tilde{\varphi}(\tilde{x}^1, \tilde{x}^2, \ldots, \tilde{x}^N)} \qquad \text{[by (23.9)]}$$

$$= \tilde{\varphi}(\tilde{x}^1, \tilde{x}^2, \ldots, \tilde{x}^N)/\tilde{\varphi}(\tilde{y}^1, \tilde{y}^2, \ldots, \tilde{y}^N)$$

$$= \tilde{\varphi}(\tilde{A}\tilde{y}^1, \tilde{A}\tilde{y}^2, \ldots, \tilde{A}\tilde{y}^N)/\varphi(\tilde{y}^1, \tilde{y}^2, \ldots, \tilde{y}^N) \qquad \text{[by (23.15)]}$$

$$= \det \tilde{A}. \qquad \text{[by Th. 23.6]}$$

Q.E.D.

Section 24.   Determinants of Matrices

Traditionally a determinant was thought of as a number associated with a square array of numbers—that is, as a scalar-valued function of square matrices.   For many purposes this approach is still the best, so we must introduce the determinant of a matrix.

For our computations we need a linear transformation associated with the matrix.   One such transformation would suffice, but it is comforting to know that it makes no difference which transformation we use; i.e., the determinant is a number which depends only on the matrix itself and not on an arbitrary choice of a transformation.

THEOREM 24.1.   *If A and B are linear transformations such that, for some bases $x]$ and $y]$, $[A; x], x]] = [B; y], y]]$, then $\det A = \det B$.*

PROOF.   Note that we do not even require that A and B be transformations on the same space!   However, the size of the matrix is equal to the dimension of the space, so the two spaces will have the same dimension.   Assume then that A is a linear transformation on the N-dimensional space $\mathscr{V}$, that B is a linear transformation on the N-dimensional space $\mathscr{W}$, that $x]_1^N$ and $y]_1^N$ are bases for $\mathscr{V}$ and for $\mathscr{W}$ respectively, and that $[A; x], x]] = [B; y], y]]$.

The key to the proof is to choose a transformation C on $\mathscr{V}$ to $\mathscr{W}$ which somehow carries A into B.   The choice is natural enough.   Let C be the transformation such that

$$Cx_i = y_i \quad \text{for } i = 1, 2, \ldots, N.$$

Now remember the definition of the matrix $[A; x], x]]$.   If $[A; x], x]] = [\alpha]$, then α_i^j is the j-th coordinate of Ax_i so

$$Ax_i = \sum_j \alpha_i^j x_j.$$

But, with respect to the basis $y]$, B has the same matrix $[\alpha]$.   Hence

$$By_i = \sum_j \alpha_i^j y_j.$$

Thus, for each $i = 1, 2, \ldots, N$,

$$CAx_i = C\left(\sum_j \alpha_i^j x_j\right) = \sum_j \alpha_i^j Cx_j$$
$$= \sum_j \alpha_i^j y_j = By_i = BCx_i,$$

and hence $CA = BC$.

Let θ be the alternating N-form on $\mathscr{W}$ such that $\theta(y_1, y_2, \ldots, y_N) = 1$. Define an alternating N-form φ on $\mathscr{V}$ by setting

$$\varphi(z_1, z_2, \ldots, z_N) = \theta(Cz_1, Cz_2, \ldots, Cz_N)$$

for all $z_1, z_2, \ldots, z_N$ in $\mathscr{V}$.

A quick mental computation should assure you that φ is an alternating N-form. (If not, write down the details. They only take a couple of lines.) Of course, $\varphi(x_1, x_2, \ldots, x_N) = \theta(Cx_1, Cx_2, \ldots, Cx_N) = \theta(y_1, y_2, \ldots, y_N) = 1$. Hence

$$\begin{aligned} \det A &= \varphi(Ax_1, Ax_2, \ldots, Ax_N) \\ &= \theta(CAx_1, CAx_2, \ldots, CAx_N) \\ &= \theta(BCx_1, BCx_2, \ldots, BCx_N) \\ &= \theta(By_1, By_2, \ldots, By_N) \\ &= \det B. \end{aligned}$$

Q.E.D.

If we are given a square matrix, $[\alpha]_N^N$, we can always find one transformation associated with it by taking $Ax_i = \sum_j \alpha_i^j x_j$ where x_i is the natural basis for $\mathscr{R}^N$ (or for $\mathscr{C}^N$ if the α_i^j are complex). Ordinarily we will do just that, but our very first theorem calls for the use of two spaces. To handle this case, we give a definition which exploits the fact that all transformations with the matrix $[\alpha]$ have the same determinant.

DEFINITION 24.2. If $[\alpha]$ is a square matrix, then *the determinant of* $[\alpha]$, det $[\alpha]$, *is the scalar* det A *where* A *is any linear transformation such that* $[\alpha] = [A; x], x]]$ *for some basis* x.

We will often use the standard symbol

$$\begin{vmatrix} \alpha_1^1 & \alpha_2^1 & \cdots & \alpha_N^1 \\ \alpha_1^2 & \alpha_2^2 & \cdots & \alpha_N^2 \\ \vdots & \vdots & & \vdots \\ \alpha_1^N & \alpha_2^N & \cdots & \alpha_N^N \end{vmatrix}$$

instead of

$$\det \begin{bmatrix} \alpha_1^1 & \alpha_2^1 & \cdots & \alpha_1^N \\ \alpha_1^2 & \alpha_2^2 & \cdots & \alpha_N^2 \\ \vdots & \vdots & & \vdots \\ \alpha_1^N & \alpha_2^N & \cdots & \alpha_N^N \end{bmatrix}.$$

DEFINITION 24.3. If

$$[\alpha] = \begin{bmatrix} \alpha_1^1 & \alpha_2^1 & \cdots & \alpha_N^1 \\ \alpha_1^2 & \alpha_2^2 & \cdots & \alpha_N^2 \\ \vdots & \vdots & & \vdots \\ \alpha_1^N & \alpha_2^n & \cdots & \alpha_N^N \end{bmatrix},$$

its *transpose* is the matrix

$$[\alpha]^T = \begin{bmatrix} \alpha_1^1 & \alpha_1^2 & \cdots & \alpha_1^N \\ \alpha_2^1 & \alpha_2^2 & \cdots & \alpha_N^2 \\ \vdots & \vdots & & \vdots \\ \alpha_N^1 & \alpha_N^2 & \cdots & \alpha_N^N \end{bmatrix}$$

obtained by interchanging rows for columns.

THEOREM 24.4.   *If $[\alpha]_N^N$ is any square matrix, then*

$$\det \lceil \alpha \rceil^T = \det [\alpha].$$

PROOF.   Remember Theorem 21.11.   It says that, referred to dual bases, dual transformations have matrices which are transposes of one another.   Moreover, Theorem 23.15 says that dual transformations have equal determinants.

Choose any N-dimensional space $\mathscr{V}$ and any basis $x]_1^N$ in $\mathscr{V}$ and let $\tilde{x}]_1^N$ be the dual basis for $\tilde{\mathscr{V}}$.   Let

$$A x_i = \sum_j \alpha_i^j x_j.$$

Then $[A\,;\,x],\,x]] = [\alpha]$ and $[\tilde{A}\,;\,\tilde{x}],\,\tilde{x}]] = [\alpha]^T$.   Hence

$$\det [\alpha]^T = \det \tilde{A} = \det A = \det [\alpha].$$
$$\text{Q.E.D.}$$

With the aid of this theorem every proof does double duty.   We work with rows or columns, whichever is easier, and then transpose to get the result for the other.

For the rest of this section we will deal exclusively with $\mathscr{R}^N$, but every argument works equally well for $\mathscr{C}^N$ and the results appear in a form independent of the scalar field.

It will help if we fix our notations once and for all.   Throughout, $x]_1^N$ will be the natural basis for $\mathscr{R}^N$.   If $[\alpha]_N^N$ is any square matrix, A will be the transformation defined by $A x_i = y_i$ where

$$y_i = \begin{bmatrix} \alpha_i^1 \\ \alpha_i^2 \\ \vdots \\ \alpha_i^N \end{bmatrix}.$$

Further, φ will be the alternating N-form such that $\varphi(x_1, x_2, \ldots, x_N) = 1$. Obviously,

$$
y_i = \begin{bmatrix} \alpha_i^1 \\ \alpha_i^2 \\ \vdots \\ \alpha_i^N \end{bmatrix} = \alpha_i^1 \begin{bmatrix} 1 \\ 0 \\ \vdots \\ 0 \end{bmatrix} + \alpha_i^2 \begin{bmatrix} 0 \\ 1 \\ \vdots \\ 0 \end{bmatrix} + \cdots + \alpha_i^N \begin{bmatrix} 0 \\ 0 \\ \vdots \\ 1 \end{bmatrix}
$$

$$
= \sum_j \alpha_i^j x_j
$$

so α_i^j is the j-th coordinate of $y_i = A x_i$, referred to the natural basis x]. But from the definition of the matrix associated with a transformation (Definition 19.2), the j-th entry in the i-th column of $[A; x], x]]$ is precisely the j-th coordinate of $A x_i$, i.e., α_i^j. Thus $[A; x], x]]$ and $[\alpha]$ are one and the same and, from the definition of $\det [\alpha]$,

$$
\det [\alpha] = \det A.
$$

An immediate consequence of these notations gives the connection between matrices, forms, and determinants.

THEOREM 24.5.   If φ is the alternating N-form on $\mathscr{R}^N$ whose value at the natural basis is 1 (i.e., $\varphi(x_1, x_2, \ldots, x_N) = 1$) then

$$
(24.1) \quad \det [\alpha] = \begin{vmatrix} \alpha_1^1 & \alpha_2^1 & \cdots & \alpha_N^1 \\ \alpha_1^2 & \alpha_2^2 & \cdots & \alpha_N^2 \\ \vdots & \vdots & & \vdots \\ \alpha_1^N & \alpha_2^N & \cdots & \alpha_N^N \end{vmatrix} = \varphi(y_1, y_2, \ldots, y_N)
$$

where y_i is the i-th column of the matrix $[\alpha]$.

PROOF.   Just look at it!   The right-hand side of (24.1) is $\det A$.
                                        Q.E.D.

Paraphrased informally the theorem says:
          To evaluate a determinant, substitute its columns in the
          basic N-form φ.

THEOREM 24.6.   If two columns of $[\alpha]_N^N$ are equal, then $\det [\alpha] = 0$.

PROOF.   By Theorem 24.5

$$
\det [\alpha] = \varphi(y_1, y_2, \ldots, y_N).
$$

The hypothesis of the theorem is that two of the columns of $[\alpha]$, i.e., two of the y's, are equal.   But an alternating form vanishes whenever two of its arguments are equal, so $\det [\alpha] = 0$.
                                        Q.E.D.

COROLLARY 24.7. *If two rows of $[\alpha]_N^N$ are equal then $\det[\alpha]=0$.*

PROOF. If two of the rows of $[\alpha]$ are identical then two of the columns of $[\alpha]^T$ are identical. Hence

$$\det[\alpha] = \det[\alpha]^T = 0.$$

Q.E.D.

In the future we will not write out similar trivial proofs by transposition.

More generally we have:

THEOREM 24.8. *If the columns of $[\alpha]$, regarded as elements of $\mathcal{R}^N$, are linearly dependent, then $\det[\alpha]=0$ and conversely.*

PROOF. Problem 25.30.

COROLLARY 24.9. *The determinant of $[\alpha]$ is zero if and only if the rows of $[\alpha]$ are linearly dependent.*

When we come to evaluate determinants we perform elementary row operations on the matrices. Accordingly, we must see how these row operations affect the determinant. It is often easier to prove things about columns and then transpose to obtain results about rows, so we next introduce elementary column operations.

We will say that a matrix $[\beta]_N^N$ is obtained from $[\alpha]_N^N$ by an elementary column operation of type $\mathrm{I}_{i,j}$ if

$$\beta_k^l = \begin{cases} \alpha_k^l & \text{for } k \neq i,\ k \neq j, \\ \alpha_j^l & \text{for } k = i, \\ \alpha_i^l & \text{for } k = j. \end{cases}$$

This is just a formal way of saying that $[\alpha]$ is exactly like $[\beta]$ except that the i-th and j-th columns have been interchanged. If B is the corresponding transformation (referred of course to the natural basis) then $Bx_k=y_k$ for $k \neq i$, $k \neq j$, $Bx_i=y_j$, and $Bx_j=y_i$.

THEOREM 24.10. *If $[\beta]$ is obtained from $[\alpha]$ by an elementary column operation of type $\mathrm{I}_{i,j}$, then $\det[\beta]=-\det[\alpha]$.*

PROOF. Using the B defined above we have

$\det[\beta] = \det B$
$\quad = \varphi(Bx_1, \ldots, Bx_{i-1}, Bx_i, Bx_{i+1}, \ldots,$
$\qquad\qquad Bx_{j-1}, Bx_j, Bx_{j+1}, \ldots, Bx_N)$
$\quad = \varphi(y_1, \ldots, y_{i-1}, y_j, y_{i+1}, \ldots, y_{j-1}, y_i, y_{j+1}, \ldots, y_N)$
$\quad = -\varphi(y_1, \ldots, y_{i-1}, y_i, y_{i+1}, \ldots, y_{j-1}, y_j, y_{j+1}, \ldots, y_N)$
$\quad = -\varphi(Ax_1, \ldots, Ax_{i-1}, Ax_i, Ax_{i+1}, \ldots,$
$\qquad\qquad Ax_{j-1}, Ax_j, Ax_{j+1}, \ldots, Ax_N)$
$\quad = -\det A = -\det[\alpha].$

Q.E.D.

COROLLARY 24.11. *Interchanging two rows of a matrix changes the sign of its determinant.*

The difference in phrasing between Theorem 24.10 and Corollary 24.11 is not significant. The Theorem is stated in more exact terms, but may be easier to remember if you paraphrase it, informally, as:

Interchanging two columns of a determinant changes its sign.

Going on to other column transformations, we will say that $[\beta]$ is obtained from $[\alpha]$ by an elementary column transformation of type $II_{i;\,\rho}$ if $\rho \neq 0$ and

$$\beta_k^l = \begin{cases} \alpha_k^l & \text{for } k \neq i, \\ \rho\alpha_k^l & \text{for } k = i. \end{cases}$$

Thus the columns of $[\beta]$ are just like those of $[\alpha]$ except that the i-th column of $[\beta]$ is obtained from that of $[\alpha]$ by multiplying it by ρ.

You will see that in the proof of the next theorem the condition $\rho \neq 0$ plays no role. We will state the theorem for column operations (i.e., assuming $\rho \neq 0$) but it may also be applied in the case of $\rho = 0$.

THEOREM 24.12. *If $[\beta]_N^N$ is obtained from $[\alpha]_N^N$ by an elementary column operation of type $II_{i;\,\rho}$, then $\det [\beta] = \rho \det [\alpha]$.*

PROOF. Again let B be the transformation corresponding to $[\beta]$. Now, $Bx_k = Ax_k$ for $k \neq i$, $Bx_i = \rho Ax_i$, and

$$\begin{aligned} \det [\beta] &= \det B \\ &= \varphi(Bx_1, \ldots, Bx_{i-1}, Bx_i, Bx_{i+1}, \ldots, Bx_n) \\ &= \varphi(Ax_1, \ldots, Ax_{i-1}, \rho Ax_i, Ax_{i+1}, \ldots, Ax_N) \\ &= \rho\varphi(Ax_1, \ldots, Ax_{i-1}, Ax_i, Ax_{i+1}, \ldots, Ax_N) \\ &= \rho \det A = \rho \det [\alpha]. \end{aligned}$$

Q.E.D.

COROLLARY 24.13. *If one row of a determinant is multiplied by a scalar, the determinant is multiplied by that scalar.*

We say that $[\beta]$ is obtained from $[\alpha]$ by an elementary column operation of type $III_{i,\,j;\,\rho}$ if

$$\beta_k^l = \begin{cases} \alpha_k^l & \text{for } k \neq i \\ \alpha_i^l - \rho\alpha_j^l & \text{for } k = i. \end{cases}$$

Such an operation leaves all columns save the i-th fixed, and from that column subtracts a multiple of the j-th. Thus if B is the corresponding transformation $Bx_k = y_k$ for $k \neq i$, $Bx_i = y_i - \rho y_j$.

THEOREM 24.14. *If $[\beta]_N^N$ is obtained from $[\alpha]_N^N$ by an elementary column operation of type $III_{i,\,j;\,\rho}$ then $\det [\beta] = \det [\alpha]$.*

PROOF.   With the notation described above we have

$$\det [\beta] = \det B$$
$$= \varphi(Bx_1, \ldots, Bx_{i-1}, Bx_i, Bx_{i+1}, \ldots, Bx_N)$$
$$= \varphi(y_1, \ldots, y_{i-1}, y_i - \rho y_j, y_{i+1}, \ldots, y_N)$$
$$= \varphi(y_1, \ldots, y_{i-1}, y_i, y_{i+1}, \ldots, y_N)$$
$$\quad - \rho\varphi(y_1, \ldots, y_{i-1}, y_j, y_{i+1}, \ldots, y_N)$$
$$= \varphi(Ax_1, \ldots, Ax_{i-1}, Ax_i, Ax_{i+1}, \ldots, Ax_N)$$
$$\quad - \rho\varphi(y_1, \ldots, y_{i-1}, y_j, y_{i+1}, \ldots, y_{j-1}, y_j, y_{j+1}, \ldots, y_N)$$
$$= \det A - \rho \cdot 0 = \det [\alpha].$$

COROLLARY 24.15.   *Subtracting a multiple of one row of a matrix from another does not change the value of its determinant.*

We now have enough machinery to evaluate any determinant.   By a suitable sequence of elementary row operations any matrix can be transformed to the standard echelon form described in Section 18. In this echelon form, each row starts with a sequence of 0's followed by a 1 and then other entries.   Each row starts with at least one more 0 than the row above.   (The first row may contain no 0's.) All entries above the first 1 in any row are 0's.   Such a matrix is either an identity matrix, whose determinant is 1, or a matrix with at least one row consisting of 0's alone.   It is easy to see that the determinant of the latter is zero.

By keeping track of how the elementary transformations affect the determinant, one finds the value of the original determinant.   It can be shown (see Problem 25.34) that the full reduction is unnecessary. Moreover, complete systematization is not very efficient unless the actual arithmetic is to be done by a high-speed computing device.

For human computation the work is facilitated by the introduction of certain subdeterminants, whose significance goes far beyond their computational advantages.

DEFINITION 24.16.   If one strikes out from a matrix (or determinant) certain rows and columns in such a way as to leave a square array of p rows and p columns, the determinant of the matrix so obtained is called a p-th order *minor* of the original matrix (or determinant).

The main theorem of this section is a famous result relating the value of a determinant to those of its minors.

THEOREM 24.17.   *If μ_j^i is the minor of $[\alpha]_N^N$ obtained by striking out its i-th column and j-th row, then*

$$(24.2) \qquad \det [\alpha] = \sum_{i=1}^{N} (-1)^{i+j} \alpha_i^j \mu_j^i$$

PROOF. Throughout, j stands for a fixed integer.

The idea of the proof is to translate equation (24.2) into the language of alternating forms. The essential tool is the fact that a determinant can be calculated by evaluating the basic form at the vectors which are the columns of the determinant (Theorem 24.5). Because the μ_j^i are $N-1$ by $N-1$ determinants we must use $\mathscr{R}^{N-1}$ as well as $\mathscr{R}^N$.

As usual let $x]_1^N$ be the natural basis for $\mathscr{R}^N$, $\tilde{x}]_1^N$ its dual, φ the alternating N-form such that $\varphi(x_1, x_2, \ldots, x_N) = 1$ and

$$
y_i = \begin{bmatrix} \alpha_i^1 \\ \vdots \\ \alpha_i^{j-1} \\ \alpha_i^j \\ \alpha_i^{j+1} \\ \vdots \\ \alpha_i^N \end{bmatrix}.
$$

Further let $u]_1^{N-1}$ be the natural basis for $\mathscr{R}^{N-1}$, let ψ be the alternating $N-1$ form on $\mathscr{R}^{N-1}$ such that $\psi(u_1, u_2, \ldots, u_{N-1}) = 1$, and let

$$
v_i = \begin{bmatrix} \alpha_i^1 \\ \vdots \\ \alpha_i^{j-1} \\ \alpha_i^{j+1} \\ \vdots \\ \alpha_1^N \end{bmatrix} \quad \text{for } i = 1, 2, \ldots, N.
$$

Finally, to be able to go from one space to the other, let P be the linear transformation on $\mathscr{R}^N$ to $\mathscr{R}^{N-1}$ which simply strikes out the entry in the j-th place in the column. Formally, for any $\zeta^1, \zeta^2, \ldots, \zeta^N$,

$$
P\left(\begin{bmatrix} \zeta^1 \\ \vdots \\ \zeta^{j-1} \\ \zeta^j \\ \zeta^{j+1} \\ \vdots \\ \zeta^N \end{bmatrix} \right) = \begin{bmatrix} \zeta^1 \\ \vdots \\ \zeta^{j-1} \\ \zeta^{j+1} \\ \vdots \\ \zeta^N \end{bmatrix}.
$$

In particular,

$$
P(y_i) = v_i \quad \text{and}
$$

$$
P(x_i) = \begin{cases} u_i & \text{if } i < j, \\ 0 & \text{if } i = j, \\ u_{i-1} & \text{if } i > j. \end{cases}
$$

For each i,

$$\mu_j^i = \begin{vmatrix} \alpha_1^1 & \cdots & \alpha_{i-1}^1 & \alpha_{i-1}^1 & \cdots & \alpha_N^1 \\ \vdots & & \vdots & \vdots & & \vdots \\ \alpha_1^{j-1} & \cdots & \alpha_{i-1}^{j-1} & \alpha_{i+1}^{j-1} & \cdots & \alpha_N^{j-1} \\ \alpha_1^{j+1} & \cdots & \alpha_{i-1}^{j+1} & \alpha_{i+1}^{j+1} & \cdots & \alpha_N^{j+1} \\ \vdots & & \vdots & \vdots & & \vdots \\ \alpha_1^N & \cdots & \alpha_{i-1}^N & \alpha_{i+1}^N & \cdots & \alpha_N^N \end{vmatrix}$$

so Theorem 24.5 says

$$\mu_j^i = \psi(v_1, \ldots, v_{i-1}, v_{i+1}, \ldots, v_N).$$

Similarly

$$\det \lceil \alpha \rceil = \varphi(y_1, y_2, \ldots, y_N).$$

As for α_i^j, it is the j-th coordinate of y_i or, by Corollary 21.6,

$$\alpha_i^j = \tilde{x}^j(y_i).$$

With these notations, the equation to be established, (24.2), becomes

$$(24.3) \quad \varphi(y_1, y_2, \ldots, y_N)$$

$$= \sum_{i=1}^N (-1)^{i+j} \tilde{x}^j(y_i) \psi(v_1, \ldots, v_{i-1}, v_{i+1}, \ldots, v_N)$$

$$= \sum_{i=1}^N (-1)^{i+j} \tilde{x}^j(y_i) \psi(Py_1, \ldots, Py_{i-1}, Py_{i+1}, \ldots, Py_N).$$

Now (24.3) exhibits a striking resemblance to the equation, (22.15), defining the exterior product; but to introduce an appropriate exterior product we need forms on $\mathscr{R}^N$. For arbitrary $z_1, z_2, \ldots, z_{N-1} \in \mathscr{R}^N$, let

$$\theta(z_1, z_2, \ldots, z_{N-1}) = \psi(Pz_1, Pz_2, \ldots, Pz_{N-1}).$$

It should be completely obvious that θ is an alternating $N-1$-form on $\mathscr{R}^N$ and, of course, $\tilde{x}^j$ is a 1-form on $\mathscr{R}^N$. Thus $\tilde{x}^j \wedge \theta$ is a well-defined alternating N-form on $\mathscr{R}^N$.

Using Definition 22.11,

$$(\tilde{x}^j \wedge \theta)(x_1, x_2, \ldots, x_N)$$

$$= \sum_{i=1}^N (-1)^{i-1} \tilde{x}^j(x_i) \theta(x_1, \ldots, x_{i-1}, x_{i+1}, \ldots, x_N) \quad [\text{by } (22.15)]$$

$$= \sum_{i=1}^N (-1)^{i-1} \delta_i^j \theta(x_1, \ldots, x_{i-1}, x_{i+1}, \ldots, x_N)$$

$$= (-1)^{j-1} \theta(x_1, \ldots, x_{j-1}, x_{j+1}, \ldots, x_N)$$

$$= (-1)^{j-1}\psi(Px_1, \ldots, Px_{j-1}, Px_{j+1}, \ldots, Px_N)$$

$$= (-1)^{j-1}\psi(u_1, \ldots, u_{j-1}, u_j, \ldots, u_{N-1})$$

$$= (-1)^{j-1} \cdot 1 = (-1)^{j-1}\varphi(x_1, x_2, \ldots, x_N).$$

Since the space of alternating N-forms is 1 dimensional, this implies that $\tilde{x}^j \wedge \theta = (-1)^{j-1}\varphi$ or, more conveniently, $\varphi = (-1)^{j+1} \cdot (\tilde{x}^j \wedge \theta)$.

Hence

$$\varphi(y_1, y_2, \ldots, y_N)$$

$$= (-1)^{j+1}[(\tilde{x}^j \wedge \theta)(y_1, y_2, \ldots, y_N)]$$

$$= (-1)^{j+1} \sum_{i=1}^{N} (-1)^{i-1}\tilde{x}^j(y_i)\theta(y_1, \ldots, y_{i-1}, y_{i+1}, \ldots, y_N)$$

$$= \sum_{i=1}^{N} (-1)^{j+i}\tilde{x}^j(y_i)\psi(Py_1, \ldots, Py_{i-1}, Py_{i+1}, \ldots, Py_N).$$

$$\text{Q.E.D.}$$

In words this important theorem says that if we multiply each element of a row by the *corresponding* minor, attach an appropriate sign, and add the results, we obtain the value of the determinant. For example, using the second row, we have

$$\begin{vmatrix} 1 & 3 & 1 \\ -2 & -2 & 5 \\ -1 & 2 & -3 \end{vmatrix}$$

$$= -(-2)\begin{vmatrix} 3 & 1 \\ 2 & -3 \end{vmatrix} + (-2)\begin{vmatrix} 1 & 1 \\ -1 & -3 \end{vmatrix} - 5\begin{vmatrix} 1 & 3 \\ -1 & 2 \end{vmatrix}.$$

Of course the value of a 1-by-1 determinant is just the scalar which appears in the determinant. Using this expansion by minors we have for a 2-by-2 determinant

$$\begin{vmatrix} \alpha & \beta \\ \gamma & \delta \end{vmatrix} = \alpha|\delta| - \beta|\gamma| = \alpha\delta - \beta\gamma.$$

The following extended version of Theorem 24.17 is sometimes useful.

THEOREM 24.18. *If μ_j^i is the minor of $[\alpha_N^N]$ obtained by striking out the i-th column and j-th row, then*

$$\sum_{i=1}^{N} (-1)^{i+j}\alpha_i^k\mu_j^i = \delta_j^k \det [\alpha],$$

where δ_j^k is the Kronecker δ.

PROOF.   For $k=j$ this is just Theorem 24.17.

For the case of $k \neq j$ we let

$$\beta_i^l = \begin{cases} \alpha_i^l & \text{if } l \neq j \\ \alpha_i^k & \text{if } l = j, \end{cases}$$

so $[\beta]$ is just like $[\alpha]$ except that β has

$$[\alpha_1^k, \alpha_2^k, \ldots, \alpha_N^k]$$

in the j-th row as well as in the k-th row.   Hence det $[\beta] = 0$.

Moreover, the minors corresponding to elements in the j-th row d
not involve elements in that row so the minor which goes with β_i^j
just the μ_j^i from the original determinant.   Thus, expanding det $[\beta]$ i
terms of the j-th row, we have

$$0 = \det [\beta] = \sum_{i=1}^{N} (-1)^{i+j} \beta_i^j \mu_j^i$$

$$= \sum_{i=1}^{N} (-1)^{i+j} \alpha_i^k \mu_j^i,$$

if $k \neq j$.

Q.E.D.

COROLLARY 24.19.   *With the same notations as in Theorems* 24.1
and 24.18,

$$\sum_{j=1}^{N} (-1)^{j+k} \alpha_k^j \mu_j^i = \delta_k^i \det [\alpha].$$

COROLLARY 24.20.   *If* det $[\alpha] \neq 0$, *then—still with the same notations—*
the inverse of $[\alpha]$ *is,*

$$\frac{1}{\det [\alpha]} [\gamma],$$

where $\gamma_j^i = (-1)^{i+j} \mu_j^i$.

In computing a determinant it is usually best to make first som
reductions by row and column operations—aimed at getting man
zeros—and then to expand by the minors of a row or column which i
made up largely of zeros.

We conclude with a very easy theorem.

THEOREM 24.21.   *If* $[\alpha]$ *and* $[\beta]$ *are N-by-N matrices, then*

$$\det ([\alpha][\beta]) = \det [\alpha] \cdot \det [\beta].$$

PROOF. If A and B are transformations corresponding to $[\alpha]$ and $[\beta]$, then by Theorem 19.6 and Definition 19.7, $[AB]=[A][B]=[\alpha][\beta]$, while by Theorem 23.8,

$$\det([\alpha]\cdot[\beta]) = \det[AB] = \det AB$$
$$= \det A \cdot \det B = \det[\alpha]\cdot\det[\beta].$$

$$\text{Q.E.D.}$$

Section 25.   Problems

[Other problems on determinants appear in Section 30]

1. Copy equation (21.5). At the end of each line except the fifth, sixth, and seventh give a parenthetical reference to the theorem, corollary, definition, or previous equation which justifies it—when possible do not look up the number of the theorem, etc., but put down a few words suggesting the result you are using. What justifies the fifth equality sign? The seventh?

2. Consider the set of all ordered pairs of scalars. Each such pair, (α,β), determines a corresponding element of $\widetilde{\mathscr{R}^2}$, which we will denote by $\tilde{y}_{\alpha,\beta}$. We define $\tilde{y}_{\alpha,\beta}$ by the formula

$$\tilde{y}_{\alpha,\beta}\left(\begin{bmatrix}\xi\\\eta\end{bmatrix}\right) = \alpha\xi+\beta\eta.$$

To save writing it is customary to use the symbol "(α,β)" for "$\tilde{y}_{\alpha,\beta}$." For example:

$$(\alpha,\beta)\left(\begin{bmatrix}1\\2\end{bmatrix}\right) = \alpha+2\beta, \quad (1,-3)\left(\begin{bmatrix}4\\2\end{bmatrix}\right) = 1\cdot4-3\cdot2 = -2.$$

With this notation, find the bases in $\widetilde{\mathscr{R}^2}$ dual to the following bases in $\mathscr{R}^2$:

(a) $x_1 = \begin{bmatrix}1\\0\end{bmatrix}, \quad x_2 = \begin{bmatrix}0\\1\end{bmatrix};$

(b) $y_1 = \begin{bmatrix}1\\2\end{bmatrix}, \quad y_2 = \begin{bmatrix}2\\1\end{bmatrix};$

(c) $z_1 = \begin{bmatrix}3\\4\end{bmatrix}, \quad z_2 = \begin{bmatrix}-4\\3\end{bmatrix}.$

3. Assume that $\mathscr{X}$ is a proper subspace of the N-dimensional space $\mathscr{V}$ and that x_1 is not an element of $\mathscr{X}$.

(a) Show that if $x_2, \ldots, x_n$ is a basis for $\mathscr{X}$, then $x_1, x_2, \ldots, x_n$ are linearly independent.

(b) What corollary says that $x_{n+1}, x_{n+2}, \ldots, x_N$, can be chosen so that $x]_1^N$ is a basis for $\mathscr{V}$?

(c) Let $\tilde{y}]_1^N$ be the basis dual to $x]_1^N$. Show that if $x \in \mathscr{X}$ then

$$\tilde{y}^1(x) = 0.$$

NOTE: This proves: if $\mathscr{X}$ is a subspace of $\mathscr{V}$ and $x_1 \notin \mathscr{X}$ then there is a $\tilde{y}^1 \in \tilde{\mathscr{V}}$ such that $\tilde{y}^1(x)=0$ if $x \in \mathscr{X}$, $\tilde{y}^1(x_1)=1$. This is precisely Corollary 21.4.

4. Show that if $x_1, x_2, \ldots, x_N$, are elements of an N-dimensional vector space $\mathscr{V}, \tilde{y}^1, \tilde{y}^2, \ldots, \tilde{y}^N$, are elements of $\tilde{\mathscr{V}}$ and if

(25.1) $$\tilde{y}^i(x_j) = \delta^i_j, \quad \text{for } i, j = 1, 2, \ldots, N$$

then $x]_1^N$ is a basis for $\mathscr{V}$ and $\tilde{y}]_1^N$ is a basis for $\tilde{\mathscr{V}}$. (Of course $\tilde{y}]$ is dual to $x]$.)

5. Show that if $x]_1^N$, and $\tilde{y}]_1^N$ are dual bases for $\mathscr{V}$ and $\tilde{\mathscr{V}}$, then, for all $z \in \mathscr{V}$

$$z = \sum_{i=1}^N \tilde{y}^i(z)x_i.$$

6. Prove Theorem 21.8.

7. Prove Theorem 21.9.

8. Let $x]_1^N$ and $\tilde{x}]_1^N$ be dual bases for $\mathscr{V}$ and $\tilde{\mathscr{V}}$. Show that, for any $y \in \mathscr{V}, \tilde{z} \in \tilde{\mathscr{V}}$,

$$\tilde{z}(y) = \sum_{i=1}^N \tilde{z}(x_i)\tilde{x}^i(y).$$

9. Each $x \in \mathscr{P}_1$ is of the form $x(\tau)=\alpha+\beta\tau$. Note, but do not bother to prove, that $\mathscr{P}_1$ is two-dimensional. Let

$$\tilde{y}^1(x) = x(0),$$
and $$\tilde{y}^2(x) = x(1),$$

(i.e., if $x(\tau)=\alpha+\beta\tau$, $\tilde{y}^1(x)=x(0)=\alpha$, $\tilde{y}^2(x)=x(1)=\alpha+\beta$).

(a) Show that $\tilde{y}^1$ and $\tilde{y}^2$ are linear functionals on $\mathscr{P}_1$.

(b) Find x_1 and x_2 in $\mathscr{P}_1$ so that $x]_1^2$ and $\tilde{y}]_1^2$ are dual bases. (Problem 25.4 tells you that it is unnecessary to check that x_1, x_2 and $\tilde{y}^1, \tilde{y}^2$ are bases. If they satisfy (25.1), they must be bases.)

(c) Let x be an arbitrary element of $\mathscr{P}_1$. Use equation (21.6) to express x as a linear combination of x_1 and x_2.

(d) The answer to part (c) is an equation with x on the left-hand side and a linear combination of x_1 and x_2 on the right. Each of these is an element of $\mathscr{P}_1$ and hence a function of τ. Evaluate each of them at τ and hence show

(25.2) $$x(\tau) = x(0)\cdot(1-\tau)+x(1)\cdot\tau.$$

NOTE: Equation (25.2) is an interpolation formula. It gives the value of x at τ in terms of its values at 0 and at 1. Of course, it is far easier to derive (25.2) directly, without using linear functionals.

10. Let α and δ be fixed real numbers.   For $x \in \mathscr{P}_2$ let

$$\tilde{y}^1(x) = x(\alpha - \delta),$$

$$\tilde{y}^2(x) = x(\alpha),$$

$$\tilde{y}^3(x) = x(\alpha + \delta), \quad \text{and}$$

$$\tilde{z}(x) = \int_{\alpha - \delta}^{\alpha + \delta} x(\tau)\, d\tau$$

(a) Show that $\tilde{z}$ is a linear functional on $\mathscr{V}$.   (So are $\tilde{y}^1$, $\tilde{y}^2$, and $\tilde{y}^3$, but you may take this for granted.)

(b) Let

$$x_1(\tau) = [(\tau - \alpha)^2 - \delta(\tau - \alpha)]/2\delta^2,$$

$$x_2(\tau) = 1 - (\tau - \alpha)^2/\delta^2, \quad \text{and}$$

$$x_3(\tau) = [(\tau - \alpha)^2 + \delta(\tau - \alpha)]/2\delta^2.$$

Use Problem 25.4 to show $x]_1^3$ and $\tilde{y}]_1^3$ are dual bases for $\mathscr{V}$ and $\tilde{\mathscr{V}}$.

(c) Evaluate $\tilde{z}(x_1)$, $\tilde{z}(x_2)$, and $\tilde{z}(x_3)$.

(d) Use equation (21.7) to express $\tilde{z}$ in terms of $\tilde{y}^1$, $\tilde{y}^2$, and $\tilde{y}^3$.   From this expression obtain Simpson's rule: if x is a quadratic function, then

$$\int_{\alpha - \delta}^{\alpha + \delta} x(\tau)\, d\tau = \frac{\delta}{3}[x(\alpha - \delta) + 4x(\alpha) + x(\alpha + \delta)].$$

11. Let $\alpha_1, \alpha_2, \ldots, \alpha_N$ be distinct real numbers and let

$$\tilde{y}^i(x) = x(\alpha_i) \quad \text{for } x \in \mathscr{P}_{N-1},\ i = 1, 2, \ldots, N.$$

Let

$$x_i(\tau) = \frac{(\tau - \alpha_1) \cdot \ \cdots \ \cdot (\tau - \alpha_{i-1}) \cdot (\tau - \alpha_{i+1}) \cdot \ \cdots \ \cdot (\tau - \alpha_N)}{(\alpha_i - \alpha_1) \cdot \ \cdots \ \cdot (\alpha_i - \alpha_{i-1}) \cdot (\alpha_i - \alpha_{i+1}) \cdot \ \cdots \ \cdot (\alpha_i - \alpha_N)}$$

$$= \prod_{j \neq i} \frac{\tau - \alpha_j}{\alpha_i - \alpha_j}.$$

(a) Show that $x]_1^N$ and $\tilde{y}]_1^N$ are dual bases for $\mathscr{P}_{N-1}$ and $\tilde{\mathscr{P}}_{N-1}$.

(b) Use equation (21.6) to give a formula for the value at τ of an arbitrary polynomial of degree less than N in terms of its values at $\alpha_1, \alpha_2, \ldots, \alpha_N$.

NOTE: The polynomials x_i are called the Lagrangian interpolation coefficients, and the answer to part (b) is called the Lagrange interpolation formula.

12. Prove:

THEOREM 25.1.   *If $\mathscr{V}$ is an N-dimensional vector space and $\mathscr{X}$ is an m-dimensional subspace of $\mathscr{V}$, then*

$$\mathscr{X}^\perp = \{\tilde{y} \mid \text{for all } x \in \mathscr{X},\ \tilde{y}(x) = 0\}$$

is an $(N - m)$-dimensional subspace of $\tilde{\mathscr{V}}$.

13. Assume that $\mathscr{X}$ and $\mathscr{Y}$ are complementary subspaces of a finite dimensional vector space $\mathscr{V}$ and let

$$\mathscr{X}^{\perp} = \{\tilde{x} \mid \text{for all } x \in \mathscr{X},\ \tilde{x}(x) = 0\},$$

$$\mathscr{Y}^{\perp} = \{\tilde{y} \mid \text{for all } y \in \mathscr{Y},\ \tilde{y}(y) = 0\},$$

Show that $\mathscr{X}^{\perp}$ and $\mathscr{Y}^{\perp}$ are complementary subspaces of $\mathscr{V}$.

14. Assume that $\mathscr{V}$ is a finite-dimensional vector space and that $\tilde{x}]_1^N$ is basis for its dual $\tilde{\mathscr{V}}$. Let $y]$ be some basis for $\mathscr{V}$ and let $\tilde{y}]$ be its dual There are scalars γ_j^i such that $\tilde{y}^i = \sum_j \gamma_j^i \tilde{x}^j$. For $j = 1, 2, \ldots, N$, let $x_j = \sum_i \gamma_j^i y_i$.

(a) Show that for all $z \in \mathscr{V}$, $z = \sum_j \tilde{x}^j(z) x_j$.

(b) Why does part (a) guarantee that $x_1, x_2, \ldots, x_N$ is a basis for $\mathscr{V}$?

(c) Show that the basis $\tilde{x}]$ is dual to $x]$.   HINT: Exploit parts (a) and (b)

15. Show that if a basis $\tilde{z}]$ for $\tilde{\mathscr{V}}$ is dual both to $x]$ and to $y]$, then $x]$ and are identical.

NOTE: Problems 14 and 15 together prove:

THEOREM 25.2. *If $\mathscr{V}$ is a finite-dimensional vector space, then every bas for $\tilde{\mathscr{V}}$ is the dual of one and only one basis for $\mathscr{V}$.*

16. Prove Theorem 21.12.

17. Prove:

THEOREM 25.3. *Assume that A is a linear transformation on a vect space $\mathscr{V}$. If*

$$\mathscr{X} = \{\tilde{x} \mid \text{for all } y \in \text{rng } A,\ \tilde{x}(y) = 0\}$$

then $$\mathscr{X} = \mathscr{N}(\tilde{A}).$$

18. Prove:

THEOREM 25.4. *If A is a linear transformation on $\mathscr{V}$ and if*

$$\mathscr{Y} = \{\tilde{y} \mid \text{for all } z \in \mathscr{N}(A),\ \tilde{y}(z) = 0\},$$

then $$\mathscr{Y} = \text{rng } \tilde{A}.$$

HINT: Prove rng $\tilde{A} \subseteq \mathscr{Y}$; then use Theorems 25.3, 17.4, and 25.1.

19. (a) Let $\mathscr{V}$ and $\mathscr{W}$ be finite-dimensional vector spaces, and let $w]$ $\tilde{w}]_1^N$, be dual bases for $\mathscr{W}$ and $\tilde{\mathscr{W}}$. Suppose B is an arbitrary linear tran formation on $\tilde{\mathscr{W}}$ to $\tilde{\mathscr{V}}$ and set

$$Ax = \sum_{i=1}^{N} [(B\tilde{w}^i)(x)]w_i.$$

Prove that $B = \tilde{A}$.

(b) Show that every transformation on $\tilde{\mathscr{W}}$ to $\tilde{\mathscr{V}}$ is the dual of at mo one transformation on $\mathscr{V}$ to $\mathscr{W}$.

20. Assume that $Ax_1, Ax_2, \ldots, Ax_N$ is a basis for $\mathscr{V}$. Show that $x_1, x_2, \ldots, x_N$ is a basis for $\mathscr{V}$. If $y]_1^N$ is the dual to $Ax]_1^N$, what is the dual of $x]_1^N$?

21. List all the formulas which must be established to prove Theorem 22.9. If any of them are not obvious to you, prove them.

22. (a) Let $\tilde{x}$ and $\tilde{y}$ be linearly independent elements of $\mathscr{V}$ and let

$$\varphi(z_1, z_2) = \tilde{x}(z_1)\tilde{y}(z_2) - \tilde{x}(z_2)\tilde{y}(z_1) \quad \text{for } z_1, z_2 \in \mathscr{V}.$$

Show that φ is a non-zero, alternating 2-form on $\mathscr{V}$.

(b) Let $\tilde{y}^1, \tilde{y}^2, \ldots, \tilde{y}^N$ be a basis for $\mathscr{V}$, and let

$$\varphi_{ij}(x_1, x_2) = \tilde{y}^i(x_1)\tilde{y}^j(x_2) - \tilde{y}^i(x_2)\tilde{y}^j(x_1) \quad \text{for } x_1, x_2 \in \mathscr{V}.$$

Show that

$$\varphi_{ij} = -\varphi_{ji}.$$

What is φ_{ii}?

(c) Show that the forms

$$\varphi_{12}, \varphi_{13}, \varphi_{23}, \ldots, \varphi_{1i}, \varphi_{2i}, \ldots, \varphi_{i-1, i}, \ldots, \varphi_{1N}, \varphi_{2N}, \ldots, \varphi_{N-1, N}$$

are linearly independent. HINT: consider an arbitrary linear combination and evaluate it at y_k, y_l where $\tilde{y}]_1^N$ is dual to $y]_1^N$. Theorem 25.2 guarantees the existence of such a $y]_1^N$.

(d) Show that the $N \cdot (N-1)/2$ different 2-forms listed in part (c) form a basis for the space of alternating 2-forms.

23. Let φ be a 2-form on an N-dimensional space $\mathscr{V}$ and let $\tilde{\varphi}$ be a 2-form on $\mathscr{V}$. (They need not be alternating forms.) Let $x]_1^N$, $y]_1^N$ be two bases for $\mathscr{V}$ and let $\tilde{x}]_1^N$, $\tilde{y}]_1^N$ be their duals.

Use the formulas

$$x_i = \sum_k \tilde{y}^k(x_i)y_k \quad \text{and} \quad \tilde{y}^k = \sum_i \tilde{y}^k(x_i)\tilde{x}^i,$$

to show that

$$\sum_{i,j} \varphi(x_i, x_j)\tilde{\varphi}(\tilde{x}^i, \tilde{x}^j) = \sum_{k,j} \varphi(y_k, x_j)\tilde{\varphi}(\tilde{y}^k, \tilde{x}^j)$$

$$= \sum_{k,l} \varphi(y_k, y_l)\tilde{\varphi}(\tilde{y}^k, \tilde{y}^l).$$

24. Let x_1, x_2 be the natural basis for $\mathscr{R}^2$ and let $\tilde{x}^1, \tilde{x}^2$ be the dual basis for $\widetilde{\mathscr{R}^2}$. Let $y = \begin{bmatrix} \eta^1 \\ \eta^2 \end{bmatrix}$, $z = \begin{bmatrix} \zeta^1 \\ \zeta^2 \end{bmatrix}$. What is $(\tilde{x}^1 \wedge \tilde{x}^2)(y, z)$?

25. Let $x]_1^3$ be the natural basis for $\mathscr{R}^3$ and let $\tilde{x}]_1^3$ be its dual. Let $\theta = \tilde{x}^1$, $\varphi = \tilde{x}^2 \wedge \theta$, $\psi = \tilde{x}^3 \wedge \varphi$. What are

$$\varphi\left(\begin{bmatrix} \xi^1 \\ \xi^2 \\ \xi^3 \end{bmatrix}, \begin{bmatrix} \eta^1 \\ \eta^2 \\ \eta^3 \end{bmatrix}\right) \quad \text{and} \quad \psi\left(\begin{bmatrix} \xi^1 \\ \xi^2 \\ \xi^3 \end{bmatrix}, \begin{bmatrix} \eta^1 \\ \eta^2 \\ \eta^3 \end{bmatrix}, \begin{bmatrix} \zeta^1 \\ \zeta^2 \\ \zeta^3 \end{bmatrix}\right)?$$

26. Let φ be an alternating n-form and let θ be a 1-form. Let $\psi = \theta \wedge \varphi$. Show that $\theta \wedge \psi$ is the identically zero $n+2$ form (i.e., $\theta \wedge (\theta \wedge \varphi) = 0$, no matter what φ may be).

27. Let A be a linear transformation on an N-dimensional space $\mathscr{V}$ and let φ be any alternating N-form on $\mathscr{V}$. Let

$$\psi(x_1, x_2, \ldots, x_N) = \sum_{i=1}^{N} \varphi(x_1, \ldots, x_{i-1}, Ax_i, x_{i+1}, \ldots, x_N).$$

(a) Show that ψ is an alternating N-form.

(b) It follows from part (a) and the fact that the space of alternating N-forms is one-dimensional, that there is a constant α such that $\psi = \alpha\varphi$. Show that α does not depend on the choice of the form φ. HINT: modify the proof of Theorem 23.4.

NOTE: You have just proved

THEOREM 25.5. *If A is a linear transformation on an N-dimensional space $\mathscr{V}$ then there is a uniquely determined scalar, called the trace of A and denoted by $\mathrm{Tr}\, A$, such that for all alternating N-forms, φ, on $\mathscr{V}$ and all $x_1, x_2, \ldots, x_N$*

$$\sum_{i=1}^{N} \varphi(x_1, \ldots, x_{i-1}, Ax_i, x_{i+1}, \ldots, x_N) = \mathrm{Tr}\, A \cdot \varphi(x_1, x_2, \ldots, x_N).$$

(c) Show that if $x]_1^N$ is a basis for $\mathscr{V}$ and $[A; x], x]] = [\alpha]$, then $\mathrm{Tr}\, A = \sum_{i=1}^{N} \alpha_i^i$.

28. Let $x]_1^N$ be a basis for $\mathscr{V}$ and let θ be an alternating N-form on $\mathscr{V}$ such that $\theta(x_1, x_2, \ldots, x_N) = 1$. Use equation (23.7) to calculate $(\det A) \cdot (\det B)$ and $\det (AB)$, and show that these are equal.

29. (a) Show that $\det I = 1$.

(b) Prove Corollary 23.9.

30. Prove Theorem 24.8.

31. Evaluate the following determinants:

(a) $\begin{vmatrix} a & b & c \\ d & e & f \\ g & h & i \end{vmatrix}$,

(b) $\begin{vmatrix} 2 & -1 & 4 \\ 3 & 2 & -2 \\ 2 & -1 & 5 \end{vmatrix}$,

(c) $\begin{vmatrix} 1 & 2 & 3 & 4 \\ 5 & 6 & 7 & 8 \\ 9 & 10 & 11 & 12 \\ 13 & 14 & 15 & 16 \end{vmatrix}$,

(d) $\begin{vmatrix} 1 & 1 & 1 & 1 \\ 1 & 2 & 3 & 4 \\ 1 & 4 & 9 & 16 \\ 1 & 8 & 27 & 64 \end{vmatrix}$,

(e) $\begin{vmatrix} 1 & 5 & 0 & -3 \\ -1 & 2 & 3 & 2 \\ 3 & 5 & -3 & 4 \\ 2 & 0 & 4 & 1 \end{vmatrix}$,

(f) $\begin{vmatrix} 2 & 4 & -1 & 0 & 2 \\ 1 & -3 & 2 & 2 & 1 \\ 4 & 2 & 0 & 0 & 5 \\ -3 & 1 & 2 & 0 & 3 \\ 2 & -5 & 3 & 4 & 2 \end{vmatrix}$.

32. Let A be the transformation on $\mathscr{R}^2$ defined by

$$A\left(\begin{bmatrix} \xi^1 \\ \xi^2 \end{bmatrix}\right) = \begin{bmatrix} 4\xi^1 + 2\xi^2 \\ -3\xi^1 - 3\xi^2 \end{bmatrix},$$

let I be the identity transformation, and let

$$x_1 = \begin{bmatrix} 1 \\ 0 \end{bmatrix}, \qquad x_2 = \begin{bmatrix} 0 \\ 1 \end{bmatrix}.$$

(a) Find the matrix $[\alpha] = [A; x], x]$.

(b) Write down the matrices of $A - I$ and $A - 2I$, and calculate their determinants.

(c) Show that $\det(A - \lambda I)$ is a quadratic polynomial in λ and find its roots λ_1 and λ_2.

(d) Find a vector $y_1 \neq 0$ so $Ay_1 = \lambda_1 y_1$ and a vector $y_2 \neq 0$ so $Ay_2 = \lambda_2 y_2$.

(e) Show that y_1 and y_2 are linearly independent.

(f) Find the matrices $[\beta] = [I; x], y]]$ and $[\gamma] = [I; y], x]]$.

(g) Calculate $[\beta][\gamma]$ and $[\beta][\alpha][\gamma]$.

(h) What is $[A; y], y]]$?

33. Consider the transformation A on $\mathscr{R}^3$ whose matrix relative to the natural basis $x]_1^3$ is

$$\begin{bmatrix} 4 & -8 & 5 \\ 1 & 1 & 3 \\ -2 & 4 & -3 \end{bmatrix}.$$

(a) Show that $\det(A - \lambda I) = -6 + 5\lambda + 2\lambda^2 - \lambda^3$.

(b) Show that $-6I + 5A + 2A^2 - A^3 = 0$.

(c) Find the roots of $\det(A - \lambda I) = 0$.

(d) For each root λ_i, $i = 1, 2, 3$ of $\det(A - \lambda I) = 0$, find a non-zero vector y_i such that $Ay_i = \lambda_i y_i$.

34. An N-by-N matrix $[\alpha]$ is called a *lower triangular matrix* if $\alpha_j^i = 0$ for $j < i$, i.e., if $[\alpha]$ is of the form

$$\begin{bmatrix} \alpha_1^1 & 0 & 0 & \cdots & 0 & 0 \\ \alpha_1^2 & \alpha_2^2 & 0 & \cdots & 0 & 0 \\ \alpha_1^3 & \alpha_2^3 & \alpha_3^3 & \cdots & 0 & 0 \\ \vdots & \vdots & \vdots & & \vdots & \vdots \\ \alpha_1^{N-1} & \alpha_2^{N-1} & \alpha_3^{N-1} & \cdots & \alpha_N^{N-1} & 0 \\ \alpha_1^N & \alpha_2^N & \alpha_3^N & \cdots & \alpha_{N-1}^N & \alpha_N^N \end{bmatrix}.$$

(Similarly, $[\alpha]$ is said to be in *upper triangular form* if $\alpha_j^i = 0$ for $j > i$.) Assume that $[\alpha]_N^N = [A; x], x]]$ is in upper triangular form, so

$$Ax_i = \sum_{j=1}^{N} \alpha_i^j x_j = \sum_{j=1}^{i} \alpha_i^j x_j.$$

Let φ be alternating N-form such that $\varphi(x_1, x_2, \ldots, x_N)=1$, let $\beta_0=\det A$, and for $n=1, 2, \ldots, N$ let

$$\beta_n = \alpha_1^1 \cdot \alpha_2^2 \cdots \cdot \alpha_n^n \varphi(x_1, \ldots, x_n, Ax_{n+1}, \ldots, Ax_N).$$

Show that, for $n=1, 2, \ldots, N$,

$$\beta_n = \beta_{n-1}.$$

NOTE: This proves:

THEOREM 25.6.   *The determinant of an upper triangular matrix is the product of its diagonal elements.*

By transposing, one gets a similar result for lower triangular matrices.

35. Let $x=\begin{bmatrix}\xi_1\\\xi_2\end{bmatrix}$, and $y=\begin{bmatrix}\eta_1\\\eta_2\end{bmatrix}$, and let $\langle\ ,\ \rangle$ be the inner product defined

in Section 6.   Show that

$$\begin{vmatrix}\langle x, x\rangle & \langle x, y\rangle \\ \langle y, x\rangle & \langle y, y\rangle\end{vmatrix} = \begin{vmatrix}\xi_1 & \eta_1 \\ \xi_2 & \eta_2\end{vmatrix}^2.$$

36. (a) Use Theorem 24.5 to show that

$$\begin{vmatrix} \alpha_1^1 & \cdots & \alpha_{i-1}^1 & \beta^1+\gamma^1 & \alpha_{i+1}^1 & \cdots & \alpha_N^1 \\ \alpha_1^2 & \cdots & \alpha_{i-1}^2 & \beta^2+\gamma^2 & \alpha_{i+1}^2 & \cdots & \alpha_N^2 \\ \vdots & & \vdots & \vdots & \vdots & & \vdots \\ \alpha_1^N & \cdots & \alpha_{i-1}^N & \beta^N+\gamma^N & \alpha_{i+1}^N & \cdots & \alpha_N^N \end{vmatrix}$$

$$= \begin{vmatrix} \alpha_1^1 & \cdots & \alpha_{i-1}^1 & \beta^1 & \alpha_{i+1}^1 & \cdots & \alpha_N^1 \\ \alpha_1^2 & \cdots & \alpha_{i-1}^2 & \beta^2 & \alpha_{i+1}^2 & \cdots & \alpha_N^2 \\ \vdots & & \vdots & \vdots & \vdots & & \vdots \\ \alpha_1^N & \cdots & \alpha_{i-1}^N & \beta^N & \alpha_{i+1}^N & \cdots & \alpha_N^N \end{vmatrix}$$

$$+ \begin{vmatrix} \alpha_1^1 & \cdots & \alpha_{i-1}^1 & \gamma^1 & \alpha_{i+1}^1 & \cdots & \alpha_N^1 \\ \alpha_1^2 & \cdots & \alpha_{i-1}^2 & \gamma^2 & \alpha_{i+1}^2 & \cdots & \alpha_N^2 \\ \vdots & & \vdots & \vdots & \vdots & & \vdots \\ \alpha_1^N & \cdots & \alpha_{i-1}^N & \gamma^N & \alpha_{i+1}^N & \cdots & \alpha_N^N \end{vmatrix}.$$

(b) Prove:

THEOREM 25.7.   *If the i-th column of $[\alpha]_N^N$ is a linear combination, $\sum_{j=1}^n \rho_j z_j$, of vectors $z_1, z_2, \ldots z_n$, in $\mathscr{R}^N$, and if $[\beta_j]$ is just like $[\alpha]$ except that its i-th*

column is z_j instead of $\begin{bmatrix}\alpha_i^1\\\alpha_i^2\\\vdots\\\alpha_i^N\end{bmatrix}$, then

$$\det [\alpha] = \sum_{j=i}^n \rho_j \det [\beta_j].$$

37. Prove that

$$
\begin{vmatrix}
\alpha_1^1 & \cdots & \alpha_m^1 & 0 & \cdots & 0 \\
\vdots & & \vdots & \vdots & & \vdots \\
\alpha_1^m & \cdots & \alpha_m^m & 0 & \cdots & 0 \\
0 & \cdots & 0 & \beta_1^1 & \cdots & \beta_n^1 \\
\vdots & & \vdots & \vdots & & \vdots \\
0 & \cdots & 0 & \beta_1^n & \cdots & \beta_n^n
\end{vmatrix}
=
\begin{vmatrix}
\alpha_1^1 & \cdots & \alpha_m^1 \\
\vdots & & \vdots \\
\alpha_1^m & \cdots & \alpha_m^m
\end{vmatrix}
\cdot
\begin{vmatrix}
\beta_1^1 & \cdots & \beta_n^1 \\
\vdots & & \vdots \\
\beta_1^n & \cdots & \beta_n^n
\end{vmatrix}.
$$

38. In the text we use alternating forms to construct determinants, but one can equally well go in the opposite direction. For definiteness work in $\mathscr{R}^3$.

Let

$$
(25.3) \qquad \varphi\left(\begin{bmatrix} \xi^1 \\ \xi^2 \\ \xi^3 \end{bmatrix}, \begin{bmatrix} \eta^1 \\ \eta^2 \\ \eta^3 \end{bmatrix}, \begin{bmatrix} \zeta^1 \\ \zeta^2 \\ \zeta^3 \end{bmatrix} \right) = \begin{vmatrix} \xi^1 & \eta^1 & \zeta^1 \\ \xi^2 & \eta^2 & \zeta^2 \\ \xi^3 & \eta^3 & \zeta^3 \end{vmatrix}.
$$

(a) Apply either Problem 31(a) or Theorem 24.17 to write out the explicit formula for φ.

(b) Show, directly from the formula in part (a), that φ is linear in its first argument.

(c) Which theorem says that φ is an alternating form?

39. Alternating N-forms (or determinants) can be used to construct the dual basis. Let φ be defined by (25.3) and let $(\alpha_1, \alpha_2, \alpha_3)$ stand for the element of $\widetilde{\mathscr{R}}^3$ such that

$$
(25.4) \qquad (\alpha_1, \alpha_2, \alpha_3)\left(\begin{bmatrix} \xi^1 \\ \xi^2 \\ \xi^3 \end{bmatrix} \right) = \alpha_1 \xi^1 + \alpha_2 \xi^2 + \alpha_3 \xi^3.
$$

Assume that x_1, x_2, x_3 form a basis for $\mathscr{R}^3$, and let

$$
\tilde{x}^1(y) = \varphi(y, x_2, x_3)/\varphi(x_1, x_2, x_3),
$$
$$
\tilde{x}^2(y) = \varphi(x_1, y, x_3)/\varphi(x_1, x_2, x_3), \quad \text{and}
$$
$$
\tilde{x}^3(y) = \varphi(x_1, x_2, y)/\varphi(x_1, x_2, x_3).
$$

It should be obvious that $\tilde{x}^1, \tilde{x}^2, \tilde{x}^3$ are elements of $\widetilde{\widetilde{\mathscr{R}}}^3$ and form, in fact, the basis dual to x_1, x_2, x_3. Let

$$
x_i = \begin{bmatrix} \xi_i^1 \\ \xi_i^2 \\ \xi_i^3 \end{bmatrix} \quad \text{for } i = 1, 2, 3,
$$

and let $\Delta = \varphi(x_1, x_2, x_3)$.

(a) Show that

$$
\tilde{x}^1 = \left(\frac{\begin{vmatrix} \xi_2^2 & \xi_3^2 \\ \xi_2^3 & \xi_3^3 \end{vmatrix}}{\Delta}, \ -\frac{\begin{vmatrix} \xi_2^1 & \xi_3^1 \\ \xi_2^3 & \xi_3^3 \end{vmatrix}}{\Delta}, \ \frac{\begin{vmatrix} \xi_2^1 & \xi_3^1 \\ \xi_2^2 & \xi_3^2 \end{vmatrix}}{\Delta} \right).
$$

(b) Find the analogous formulas for $\tilde{x}^2$, and $\tilde{x}^3$.

(c) Use these formulas to find the basis dual to

$$
x_1 = \begin{bmatrix} 1 \\ -2 \\ 1 \end{bmatrix}, \qquad x_2 = \begin{bmatrix} -2 \\ 0 \\ 1 \end{bmatrix}, \qquad x_3 = \begin{bmatrix} -3 \\ 4 \\ -1 \end{bmatrix}.
$$

(d) Use the methods of Chapter IV to solve

$$
\begin{aligned}
\eta^1 - 2\eta^2 - 3\eta^3 - &\zeta^1, \\
-2\eta^1 \qquad\quad +4\eta^3 = &\zeta^2, \\
\eta^1 + \eta^2 - \eta^3 = &\zeta^3.
\end{aligned}
$$

(e) What is the inverse of

$$
\begin{bmatrix} 1 & -2 & -3 \\ -2 & 0 & 4 \\ 1 & 1 & -1 \end{bmatrix} ?
$$

Summary

Linear functionals are easy. They are simply those scalar-valued functions on the vector space which have the linearity property:

$$
\tilde{y}(\textstyle\sum \alpha^i x_i) = \sum \alpha^i \tilde{y}(x_i).
$$

They form a vector space in an obvious way. The really new feature which the dual space brings is the convenience of dual bases. You must be familiar with the Kronecker δ and with formulas (21.6) and (21.7).

The idea of the dual of a transformation occurs frequently in contemporary mathematics, but we exploit it only to get results about transposed determinants. For this purpose, the key result is Theorem 21.11: Referred to dual bases, the matrix of the dual is the transpose of the original.

In spite of their general importance, we use alternating forms solely as a means to a specific end: determinants. The crucial Theorem 22.19 says that there is a non-zero alternating form of maximal degree and that every other alternating form of maximal degree is a multiple of it. Formula (22.15), which defines the exterior product, is of a type common in advanced mathematics. We need it because it gives the clue to the expansion of determinants in terms of their minors.

Applying to functions of several variables exactly the same procedure that led from a transformation to its dual, we obtain the *induced transformation* on the space of forms. The induced transformation on alternating forms of maximal degree gives the determinant. Since $\bar{A}$ is a transformation and $\det A$ is a scalar, they are not quite the same thing; nevertheless, if φ is any alternating N-form, we have

$$\bar{A}\varphi = (\det A)\cdot\varphi.$$

You must also know:

$\quad$ $(\det A)\varphi(x_1, x_2, \ldots, x_N) = \varphi(Ax_1, Ax_2, \ldots, Ax_N)$;

$\quad$ $\det(AB) = (\det A)\cdot(\det B)$;

$\quad$ A is invertible if and only if $\det A \neq 0$;

$\quad$ if $\det A = 0$ then there is an $x \neq 0$ such that $Ax = 0$; and

$\quad$ $\det \tilde{A} = \det A$.

Given a square matrix $[\alpha]$, introduce any transformation A with $[\alpha]$ as its matrix. All such transformations have the same determinant and $\det[\alpha]$ is just $\det A$. The determinant of the transpose of a matrix is equal to the determinant of the original matrix. If two rows or columns are equal, the determinant is zero. Interchanging two rows or columns changes the sign of the determinant. Multiplying one row or column by a scalar multiplies the determinant by the same factor. Adding a multiple of one row or column to another does not change the value of the determinant. Most important, both for computation and for further development of the theory, is the expansion by minors—Theorems 24.17 and 24.18, and Corollary 24.19.

CHAPTER VI

DETERMINANTS:
A TRADITIONAL TREATMENT

Consider the system of simultaneous linear equations

$$\begin{cases} \alpha_1^1 \xi^1 + \alpha_2^1 \xi^2 = \eta^1, \\ \alpha_1^2 \xi^1 + \alpha_2^2 \xi^2 = \eta^2. \end{cases}$$

Instead of solving by the methods of Section 18 we may multiply the first by α_2^2, the second by α_2^1, and subtract. We obtain

$$(\alpha_1^1 \alpha_2^2 - \alpha_2^1 \alpha_1^2) \xi^1 = \eta^1 \alpha_2^2 - \eta^2 \alpha_2^1.$$

Eliminating ξ^1 instead of ξ^2, we get

$$(\alpha_1^1 \alpha_2^2 - \alpha_2^1 \alpha_1^2) \xi^2 = \alpha_1^1 \eta^2 - \alpha_1^2 \eta^1.$$

A similar, but more tedious, elimination process applied to

$$\begin{cases} \alpha_1^1 \xi^1 + \alpha_2^1 \xi^2 + \alpha_3^1 \xi^3 = \eta^1, \\ \alpha_1^2 \xi^1 + \alpha_2^2 \xi^2 + \alpha_3^2 \xi^3 = \eta^2, \\ \alpha_1^3 \xi^1 + \alpha_2^3 \xi^2 + \alpha_3^3 \xi^3 = \eta^3, \end{cases}$$

would yield

$$(\alpha_1^1 \alpha_2^2 \alpha_3^3 - \alpha_1^1 \alpha_3^2 \alpha_2^3 + \alpha_2^1 \alpha_3^2 \alpha_1^3 - \alpha_2^1 \alpha_1^2 \alpha_3^3 + \alpha_3^1 \alpha_1^2 \alpha_2^3 - \alpha_3^1 \alpha_2^2 \alpha_1^3) \xi^1$$
$$= \text{an equally elaborate expression in the } \alpha\text{'s and } \eta\text{'s.}$$

This elimination process is not a good way to compute the solutions of linear equations, but the beautifully symmetric expressions

$$\alpha_1^1 \alpha_2^2 - \alpha_2^1 \alpha_1^2$$

and $\qquad \alpha_1^1 \alpha_2^2 \alpha_3^3 - \alpha_1^1 \alpha_3^2 \alpha_2^3 + \alpha_2^1 \alpha_3^2 \alpha_1^3 - \alpha_2^1 \alpha_1^2 \alpha_3^3 + \alpha_3^1 \alpha_1^2 \alpha_2^3 - \alpha_3^1 \alpha_2^2 \alpha_1^3$

have many other uses. Each is a sum and difference of products. In each term each superscript appears exactly once and each subscript also appears just once. Moreover, there is one term for each possible arrangement of the subscripts. There are two possible ways of

166

arranging the subscripts 1 and 2—namely (1, 2) and (2, 1)—and each of these arrangements appears in $\alpha_1^1 \alpha_2^2 - \alpha_2^1 \alpha_1^2$. Similarly in the more complicated expression we find the six possible arrangements: (1, 2, 3), (1, 3, 2), (2, 3, 1), (2, 1, 3), (3, 1, 2), and (3, 2, 1).

The difficulty lies in deciding which sign to attach to each product. Our first task is to study the properties of arrangements in general and to unravel the mystery of the signs.

Section 26. Permutations

Above, we considered the possible ways of listing the integers 1, 2, and 3.   In general we will need to consider all possible orders in which we might list the integers $1, 2, \ldots, N$.   Such a list is often called a permutation of $1, 2, \ldots, N$, but we will always refer to it as a list and reserve the word "permutation" for another aspect of the listing process.

If $(k_1, k_2, \ldots, k_N)$ is a list of the integers $1, 2, \ldots, N$, the symbol "k" is really the name of a function—a function which assigns the value k_1 to the first place in the list, k_2 to the second place, and so on.   This functional aspect of listing lies at the heart of our work.   From now on, let us use ordinary functional notation.

Each list $(k_1, k_2, \ldots, k_N)$ of $1, 2, \ldots, N$, determines a function f defined by

APP.
F.9
FNS.

$$f(i) = k_i \quad \text{for } i = 1, 2, \ldots, N.$$

The domain of f is the set of integers from 1 to N inclusive and, since $(k_1, k_2, \ldots, k_N)$ is an arrangement of these same integers, the range of f also consists precisely of the integers $1, 2, \ldots, N$.   We will call such a function a permutation.

Since a permutation f on the integers $1, 2, \ldots, N$, has exactly N values, $f(1), f(2), \ldots, f(N)$, and each of the N integers, $1, 2, \ldots, N$, must occur somewhere in the list, none of them can be repeated.   In other words, if f is a permutation of $1, 2, \ldots, N$, and $f(i) = f(j)$, then $i = j$.

The collection of permutations on the integers $1, 2, \ldots, N$, has a natural algebraic structure.   There is an obvious way of putting two permutations together to get a third permutation—take a "function of a function."   If f and g are permutations, let h be the function defined by

$$h(i) = f(g(i)).$$

As i ranges over the integers from 1 to N so does $g(i)$ and hence so does $f(g(i))$.   Thus h, too, is a permutation.   Let "$\circ$" denote the operation of combining two permutations in this way. Thus $f \circ g$ is the function such that

$$(f \circ g)(i) = f(g(i)) \quad \text{for } i = 1, 2, \ldots, N.$$

The operation $\circ$ is a binary operation; i.e., it is used to combine just two things. If f, g, and h are three permutations we may use $\circ$ to combine them in different ways. We may form either $f \circ (g \circ h)$ or $(f \circ g) \circ h$. However, a quick look at the meaning of $\circ$ will suffice to show that both of these new functions assign to i the same value: $f(g(h(i)))$. Thus $\circ$ has the associative property:

$$f \circ (g \circ h) = (f \circ g) \circ h,$$

and there is no ambiguity if we write $f \circ g \circ h$ instead of $f \circ (g \circ h)$ or $(f \circ g) \circ h$.

It is essential to remember that $\circ$ is not commutative: usually

$$f \circ g \neq g \circ f.$$

There is one particularly simple permutation. Hereafter, e will always denote the permutation defined by

$$e(i) = i, \quad \text{for } i = 1, 2, \ldots, N.$$

Obviously $e \circ f = f \circ e = f$ for all permutations f.

One further algebraic fact is important. Let f be a permutation and consider the list

$$(f(1), f(2), \ldots, f(N)).$$

Each of the integers $1, 2, \ldots, N$ occurs once and only once in the list. That is to say, for each $i = 1, 2, \ldots, N$ there is exactly one integer j such that $f(j) = i$. We have just described a function—a rule for assigning to i a corresponding value, namely the j such that $f(j) = i$. It is customary to denote this function by f^{-1}. Note that $f \circ f^{-1} = f^{-1} \circ f = e$.

The standard name for the set of all permutations on $1, 2, \ldots, N$ thought of as an algebraic system with the operation $\circ$ is *the symmetric group S_N*.

Let us summarize this discussion as a formal definition and theorem.

DEFINITION 26.1. The *symmetric group S_N* is the set of all functions f whose domain and range are $1, 2, \ldots, N$, thought of as an algebraic system with the operation $\circ$ defined by

$$(f \circ g)(i) = f(g(i)).$$

THEOREM 26.2.   *The symmetric group* S_N has the following properties:*

(i) *if $f, g \in S_N$ then $f \circ g \in S_N$;*

(ii) *if $f, g, h \in S_N$ then*
$$f \circ (g \circ h) = (f \circ g) \circ h;$$

(iii) *there is an element $e \in S_N$ such that for all $f \in S_N$,*
$$f \circ e = e \circ f = f;$$

(iv) *for each $f \in S_N$ there is an $f^{-1} \in S_N$ such that*
$$f \circ f^{-1} = f^{-1} \circ f = e.$$

There are many ways to attack the problem of the signs, but all involve some method of measuring the degree to which a list $f(1)$, $f(2), \dots, f(N)$, distorts the natural order $1, 2, \dots, N$.   Unfortunately, S_3 is just too small to illustrate the general principles.

If you were to go through the elimination procedure for a system of four equations in four unknowns, you would find that the list $(2,4,3,1)$ goes with a "$+$," while $(3,2,1,4)$ is associated with a "$-$". Let us call the corresponding permutations f and g respectively.   Then

$$f(1) = 2, \qquad g(1) = 3,$$

$$f(2) = 4, \qquad g(2) = 2,$$

$$f(3) = 3, \qquad g(3) = 1,$$

$$f(4) = 1, \quad \text{and} \quad g(4) = 4.$$

The idea is to look at each pair of integers i and j and see if the permutation upsets their order.   There are six ways to choose a pair of integers from the set $1,2,3,4$.   Let us make a table showing the pairs and, for each pair, the corresponding values of f.   In the last column we state whether the order of $f(i), f(j)$ is the same as that of i, j or opposite to it. Consider, for example, the pair $\{2,4\}$.   Observe that $f(2) = 4$ and $f(4) = 1$.

---

* It is quite possible to make a general abstract study of arbitrary systems possessing the four properties (i), (ii), (iii) and (iv).   Any such system is called a group.   The properties themselves are extremely simple.   To say that a system consisting of a set with a binary operation is a group would seem to say very little indeed about the system. Nevertheless, the startling fact is that the theory of groups is a rich and varied branch of mathematics, full of sweeping general results, striking examples, and challenging unsolved problems. It has innumerable applications in mathematics and physics.

Since $2 < 4$ but $f(2) > f(4)$, "opp" is entered in the row which starts with $\{2,4\}$.

PAIR $\{i,j\}$	$f(i)$	$f(j)$	ORDER
$\{1,2\}$	2	4	same
$\{1,3\}$	2	3	same
$\{1,4\}$	2	1	opp
$\{2,3\}$	4	3	opp
$\{2,4\}$	4	1	opp
$\{3,4\}$	3	1	opp

The corresponding table for g is:

PAIR $\{i,j\}$	$g(i)$	$g(j)$	ORDER
$\{1,2\}$	3	2	opp
$\{1,3\}$	3	1	opp
$\{1,4\}$	3	4	same
$\{2,3\}$	2	1	opp
$\{2,4\}$	2	4	same
$\{3,4\}$	1	4	same

For f, the last column contains 4 entries *opp*; for g it contains 3 *opp*'s. Were you to construct the tables for all the twenty-four permutations in S_4 the pattern would emerge clearly. If f goes with a " $+$ " the number of *opp*'s is even; if the sign is " $-$ " the number of *opp*'s is odd.

What we want is a formula that will yield $+1$ if the number of *opp*'s is even and -1 if their number is odd. Such a formula is not hard to come by. A non-zero product is positive if and only if the number of negative factors is even. Obviously then, we want a product with one factor for each pair $\{i,j\}$; this factor is to be positive if $f(i)$ and $f(j)$ have the same order as i and j and negative otherwise. One easy choice for the factor is

$$\frac{f(j) - f(i)}{j - i}.$$

This factor is chosen just to make the sign come out correctly, but it does more than that.

Once again, look at a table.

$\{i,j\}$	$f(i)$	$f(j)$	$\dfrac{f(j)-f(i)}{j-i}$
$\{1,2\}$	2	4	$2/1$
$\{1,3\}$	2	3	$1/2$
$\{1,4\}$	2	1	$(-1)/3$
$\{2,3\}$	4	3	$(-1)/1$
$\{2,4\}$	4	1	$(-3)/2$
$\{3,4\}$	3	1	$(-2)/1$

As $\{i,j\}$ ranges over all possible pairs of distinct integers from 1 to N so does $\{f(i),f(j)\}$. Except for the signs the numerators in the last column are the same as the denominators; they simply appear in a different order!

One point calls for special comment: $\{i,j\}$ is not an ordered pair. We consider all ways of choosing two *distinct* integers i and j, but if our list of pairs contains i and j in that order it must not contain them in the order j,i. On the other hand, it does not matter whether our list contains $\{i,j\}$ or $\{j,i\}$. What is important is that one of them, but not both, shall appear. The reason why it is immaterial whether we use $\{i,j\}$ or $\{j,i\}$ is that the corresponding factors

$$\frac{f(j)-f(i)}{j-i} \quad \text{and} \quad \frac{f(i)-f(j)}{i-j}$$

are equal.

For the rest of this section let P_N stand for the set of all unordered pairs of distinct integers chosen from among $1, 2, \ldots, N$.

DEFINITION 26.3.   If $f \in S_N$, then the *signum* (or sign) of f is

(26.1)
$$\operatorname{sgn} f = \prod_{\{i,\,j\}\,\in\,P_N} \frac{f(j)-f(i)}{j-i}.$$

APP.
E.10
IND.

We say that f is an *even permutation* if sgn $f = +1$ and that it is *odd* if sgn $f = -1$.

THEOREM 26.4.   *If $f \in S_N$ then either* sgn $f = +1$ *or* sgn $f = -1$ *(i.e., every permutation is either even or odd).*

PROOF.   We have already outlined the proof. For each $\{i,j\} \in P_N$, $f(i), f(j) \in P_N$ and, conversely, for each $\{k,l\} \in P_N$ there is exactly one $\{i,j\} \in P_N$ such that $\{f(i),f(j)\} = \{k,l\}$. This means that as the pairs $\{i,j\}$ range over P_N, so do the pairs $\{f(i),f(j)\}$.

Thus, except for the signs, the totality of numerators in (26.1) is the same as the totality of denominators.   Hence the product must be either $+1$ or -1.

Q.E.D.

THEOREM 26.5.   *If $f,g \in S$, then*

$$\text{sgn } (f \circ g) = (\text{sgn } f)(\text{sgn } g).$$

PROOF.   We have

$$\text{sgn } (f \circ g) = \prod_{\{i,j\} \in P_N} \frac{f(g(j)) - f(g(i))}{j - i}$$

$$= \prod_{\{i,j\} \in P_N} \frac{f(g(j)) - f(g(i))}{g(j) - g(i)} \cdot \frac{g(j) - g(i)}{j - i}.$$

As $\{i,j\}$ ranges over P_N, so does $\{g(i), g(j)\}$.   Hence, if we collect together all the factors $[f(g(j)) - f(g(i))]/[g(j) - g(i)]$ as $\{i,j\}$ ranges over P_N we get precisely the product defining sgn f.   The product of the other factors, $[g(j) - g(i)]/[j - i]$, is exactly sgn g; so the right-hand side is $(\text{sgn } f)(\text{sgn } g)$.

Q.E.D.

COROLLARY 26.6.   *The sign of e is $+1$.*

PROOF.   We have

$$\text{sgn } e = \text{sgn } (e \circ e) = (\text{sgn } e)(\text{sgn } e) = (\pm 1)^2 = +1.$$
Q.E.D.

COROLLARY 26.7.   *If $f \in S_N$ then*

$$\text{sgn } f^{-1} = \text{sgn } f.$$

We will need to know explicitly the value of sgn f for one special type of permutation.

THEOREM 26.8.   *Let f be the permutation on $1, 2, \ldots, N$ which interchanges k and l leaving the other integers fixed, i.e.,*

$$f(i) = \begin{cases} i & \text{if } i \neq k \text{ and } i \neq l, \\ l & \text{if } i = k, \\ k & \text{if } i = l. \end{cases}$$

Then

$$\text{sgn } f = -1.$$

PROOF.   Divide the set P_N into four parts $Q, R, S,$ and T.   Into Q put all the pairs $\{i,j\}$ containing neither k nor l.   Let R consist of all pairs which contain k but not l. For convenience let us agree that we will always write a pair in R in the form $\{k,j\}$ never as $\{j,k\}$. Similarly let S consist of the pairs $\{l,j\}$ with $j \neq k$. Finally let T consist of the single pair $\{k,l\}$.

Since P_N is made up precisely of the four subsets Q, R, S, and T, any product over all of P_N can be regrouped so that we multiply first the terms corresponding to Q, then those corresponding to R, and so on. This regrouping yields

$$
\operatorname{sgn} f = \prod_{\{i,j\} \in P_N} \frac{f(j)-f(i)}{j-i}
$$

$$
= \prod_{\{i,j\} \in Q} \frac{f(j)-f(i)}{j-i} \cdot \prod_{\{k,j\} \in R} \frac{f(j)-f(k)}{j-k} \cdot \prod_{\{l,j\} \in S} \frac{f(j)-f(l)}{j-l} \cdot \frac{f(l)-f(k)}{l-k}
$$

$$
= \prod_{\{i,j\} \in Q} \frac{j-i}{j-i} \cdot \prod_{\{k,j\} \in R} \frac{j-l}{j-k} \cdot \prod_{\{l,j\} \in S} \frac{j-k}{j-l} \cdot \frac{k-l}{l-k}.
$$

The first product is 1, while the numerators of the second cancel the denominators of the third and vice versa. Thus

$$
\operatorname{sgn} f = \frac{k-l}{l-k} = -1.
$$

Q.E.D.

To get the important results in Section 28 we will want to calculate $\operatorname{sgn} f$ in a slightly different way. Look at the list $f(1), f(2), \ldots, f(N)$. An inversion in the list is a pair of entries such that the larger precedes the smaller. For example the three inversions in $(3,2,1,4)$ are the pairs $3,2$; $3,1$; and $2,1$. If we list the elements $\{i,j\}$ of the set of pairs P_N in such a way that i is always less than j, then the denominators in

$$
\prod_{\{i,j\} \in P_N} \frac{f(j)-f(i)}{j-i}
$$

are all positive. The numerator $f(j)-f(i)$ is negative if and only if the pair $f(i), f(j)$ corresponds to an inversion in the list $f(1), f(2)$, $\ldots, f(N)$. It follows that $\operatorname{sgn} f$ is $+1$ if the number of inversions is even and -1 if their number is odd. Another way of putting it is: if n is the number of inversions in $f(1), f(2), \ldots, f(N)$, then $\operatorname{sgn} f = (-1)^n$.

Section 27.   Determinants

Consider a square matrix $[\alpha]_N^N$. At the beginning of the chapter we tried to suggest that it might be worthwhile to look at sums of terms of the form

$$
(\pm 1)\alpha_{f(1)}^1 \alpha_{f(2)}^2 \ldots \alpha_{f(N)}^N
$$

where $f \in S_N$. In Section 26 we devised a rule for determining the appropriate sign. The stage is set for the entrance of the definition.

DEFINITION 27.1.   If $[\alpha]_N^N$ is a square matrix, then the *determinant* of $[\alpha]$ is the scalar

(27.1) $$\det [\alpha] = \sum_{f \in S_N} \operatorname{sgn} f \cdot \alpha_{f(1)}^1 \alpha_{f(2)}^2 \ldots \alpha_{f(N)}^N.$$

Note that *det* is a function which assigns to each square matrix $[\alpha]$ a corresponding scalar $\det [\alpha]$.

Following the traditional notation, we will usually write

(27.2)
$$
\begin{vmatrix}
\alpha_1^1 & \alpha_2^1 & \cdots & \alpha_N^1 \\
\alpha_1^2 & \alpha_2^2 & \cdots & \alpha_N^2 \\
\vdots & \vdots & & \vdots \\
\alpha_1^N & \alpha_2^N & \cdots & \alpha_N^N
\end{vmatrix}
$$

instead of

$$
\det
\begin{bmatrix}
\alpha_1^1 & \alpha_2^1 & \cdots & \alpha_N^1 \\
\alpha_1^2 & \alpha_2^2 & \cdots & \alpha_N^2 \\
\vdots & \vdots & & \vdots \\
\alpha_1^N & \alpha_2^N & \cdots & \alpha_N^N
\end{bmatrix}.
$$

Clearly the symbol (27.2) is simply an elaborate name for a certain number—the number which may be calculated by means of the formula (27.1). It is customary to speak of (27.2) as a determinant, but, logically, there is no such animal as *a* determinant; there is only the function, det. Nevertheless the symbol (27.2), which not only names the number $\det [\alpha]$ but also displays the matrix $[\alpha]$, is often convenient. Furthermore, the logically indefensible language which speaks of (27.2) as if it were more than a mere number occasionally avoids cumbersome circumlocutions. We will not hesitate to use such language.

The superscripts on the α's correspond to the rows in the matrix $[\alpha]$. Definition 27.1 appears to give precedence to the rows, because superscripts appear in their natural order while the subscripts appear in the order $f(1), f(2), \ldots, f(n)$. The following theorem shows that the appearance is deceptive.

THEOREM 27.2.   *If* $[\alpha]_N^N$ *is a square matrix, then*

(27.3) $$\det [\alpha] = \sum_{g \in S_N} \operatorname{sgn} g \cdot \alpha_1^{g(1)} \alpha_2^{g(2)} \ldots \alpha_N^{g(N)}.$$

PROOF.   Consider one particular $g \in S_N$ and examine the corresponding term in (27.3). In Section 26 we introduced the inverse function g^{-1}. This was defined so that $g^{-1}(j)$ would be the integer i such that $g(i)=j$. Thus if the superscript on $\alpha_i^{g(i)}$ happens to be j, the subscript will be $g^{-1}(j)$. Now the superscripts $g(1), g(2), \ldots, g(N)$ consist precisely of the integers $1, 2, \ldots, N$ arranged in some order. As we have just seen, the subscript on the term with j as superscript is $g^{-1}(j)$. If we rearrange the factors in the order of their superscripts the term will be

$$\text{sgn } g \cdot \alpha^1_{g^{-1}(1)} \alpha^2_{g^{-1}(2)} \cdots \alpha^N_{g^{-1}(N)}.$$

However, Corollary 26.7 says sgn $g = $ sgn g^{-1} so this term is really

$$\text{sgn } g^{-1} \cdot \alpha^1_{g^{-1}(1)} \alpha^2_{g^{-1}(2)} \cdots \alpha^N_{g^{-1}(N)},$$

and the sum is

$$\sum_{g \in S_N} \text{sgn } g^{-1} \cdot \alpha^1_{g^{-1}(1)} \alpha^2_{g^{-1}(2)} \cdots \alpha^N_{g^{-1}(N)}.$$

Only one question remains. As g ranges over S_N, does g^{-1} also range over S_N? The answer is obvious, but the argument is not quite trivial.

The symmetric group S_N is a finite set. (In fact it has $N! = 1 \times 2 \times \cdots \times N$ elements.) For each $g \in S_N$ there is a uniquely determined g^{-1}. If g^{-1} did not take on each value in S_N once and only once when g ranges over S_N, there would have to be two different values of g, call them g_1 and g_2, such that

$$g_1^{-1} = g_2^{-1}.$$

Now we invoke the group properties of Theorem 26.2 to provide the contradiction:

$$g_1 = g_1 \circ e = g_1 \circ (g_2^{-1} \circ g_2) = (g_1 \circ g_2^{-1}) \circ g_2$$
$$= (g_1 \circ g_1^{-1}) \circ g_2 = e \circ g_2 = g_2.$$
$$\text{Q.E.D.}$$

DEFINITION 27.3.   If $[\alpha]_M^N$ is an N-by-M matrix then its *transpose*, $[\alpha]^T$, is the M-by-N matrix $[\beta]_N^M$ defined by

$$\beta_j^i = \alpha_i^j \quad \text{for } i = 1, 2, \ldots, M; j = 1, 2, \ldots, N.$$

Informally this definition says that $[\alpha]^T$ is obtained from $[\alpha]$ by interchanging rows for columns.

THEOREM 27.4.   *If $[\alpha]$ is a square matrix, then*

$$\det [\alpha]^T = \det [\alpha].$$

PROOF. If $[\beta] = [\alpha]^T$, then $\beta_j^i = \alpha_i^j$ and

$$\det [\beta] = \sum_{f \in S_N} \operatorname{sgn} f \cdot \beta_{f(1)}^1 \beta_{f(2)}^2 \cdots \beta_{f(N)}^N$$

$$= \sum_{f \in S_N} \operatorname{sgn} f \cdot \alpha_1^{f(i)} \alpha_2^{f(2)} \cdots \alpha_N^{f(N)},$$

so Theorem 27.4 is just another way of putting Theorem 27.2.

Q.E.D.

Theorem 27.4 is a great convenience. If we know how a change in the rows of a matrix affects its determinant, we may infer, with no further argument, that the corresponding change in the columns has the same effect.

The changes we have in mind correspond to the elementary row operations introduced in Section 18.

What happens to the determinant of a matrix when we interchange two of its rows? If $[\beta]$ is obtained from $[\alpha]$ by interchanging its k-th and l-th rows then the j-th column of $[\beta]$ is

$$\begin{bmatrix} \beta_j^1 \\ \vdots \\ \beta_j^{k-1} \\ \beta_j^k \\ \beta_j^{k+1} \\ \vdots \\ \beta_j^{l-1} \\ \beta_j^l \\ \beta_j^{l+1} \\ \vdots \\ \beta_j^N \end{bmatrix} = \begin{bmatrix} \alpha_j^1 \\ \vdots \\ \alpha_j^{k-1} \\ \alpha_j^l \\ \alpha_j^{k+1} \\ \vdots \\ \alpha_j^{l-1} \\ \alpha_j^k \\ \alpha_j^{l+1} \\ \vdots \\ \alpha_j^N \end{bmatrix}$$

In a formula

(27.4)
$$\beta_j^i = \begin{cases} \alpha_j^i & \text{if } i \neq k \text{ and } i \neq l, \\ \alpha_j^l & \text{if } i = k, \\ \alpha_j^k & \text{if } i = l. \end{cases}$$

THEOREM 27.5. *If $[\alpha]$ is an N-by-N matrix and*

$$\beta_j^i = \begin{cases} \alpha_j^i & \text{if } i \neq k \text{ and } i \neq l, \\ \alpha_j^l & \text{if } i = k, \\ \alpha_j^k & \text{if } i = l, \end{cases}$$

then $\det [\beta] = - \det [\alpha]$.

PROOF. Let g be the permutation which interchanges k and l. As stated in Theorem 26.8,

$$(27.5) \qquad g(i) = \begin{cases} i & \text{if } i \neq k \text{ and } i \neq l, \\ l & \text{if } i = k, \\ k & \text{if } i = l, \end{cases}$$

and

$$\operatorname{sgn} g = -1.$$

The proof is very like that of Theorem 27.2. Consider the formula

$$\det [\beta] = \sum_{f \in S_N} \operatorname{sgn} f \cdot \beta^1_{f(1)} \cdots \beta^k_{f(k)} \cdots \beta^l_{f(l)} \cdots \beta^N_{f(N)}$$

and examine the term corresponding to one particular f. Let $h = f \circ g$ and note that

$$\operatorname{sgn} h = \operatorname{sgn} f \cdot \operatorname{sgn} g = -\operatorname{sgn} f.$$

The term we are examining is

$$
\begin{array}{cccccc}
 & & k\text{-th} & & l\text{-th} & \\
 & & \text{place} & & \text{place} & \\
\operatorname{sgn} f \cdot \beta^1_{f(1)} & \cdots & \beta^k_{f(k)} & \cdots & \beta^l_{f(l)} & \cdots & \beta^N_{f(N)} \\
= \quad \operatorname{sgn} f \cdot \alpha^1_{f(1)} & \cdots & \alpha^l_{f(k)} & \cdots & \alpha^k_{f(k)} & \cdots & \alpha^N_{f(N)} \\
= \quad \operatorname{sgn} f \cdot \alpha^1_{f(g(1))} & \cdots & \alpha^l_{f(g(l))} & \cdots & \alpha^k_{f(g(k))} & \cdots & \alpha^N_{f(g(N))} \\
= -\operatorname{sgn} h \cdot \alpha^1_{h(1)} & \cdots & \alpha^l_{h(l)} & \cdots & \alpha^k_{h(k)} & \cdots & \alpha^N_{h(N)} \\
= -\operatorname{sgn} h \cdot \alpha^1_{h(1)} & \cdots & \alpha^k_{h(k)} & \cdots & \alpha^l_{h(l)} & \cdots & \alpha^N_{h(N)}.
\end{array}
$$

Except for the change of sign this is clearly one of the terms in the expression for $\det [\alpha]$. There is only one thing more to prove. We must show that as f assumes all the various values in S_N, the corresponding h assumes each value in S_N once and only once. Consider an arbitrary $h_0 \in S_N$. The h corresponding to $f = h_0 \circ g^{-1}$ is

$$f \circ g = (h_0 \circ g^{-1}) \circ g = h_0 \circ (g^{-1} \circ g) = h_0 \circ e = h_0.$$

Thus h assumes every possible value. If there were two different values of f, say f_1 and f_2, which gave rise to the same value, say h', of h, we could derive the contradiction

$$
\begin{aligned}
f_1 &= f_1 \circ e = f_1 \circ (g \circ g^{-1}) = (f_1 \circ g) \circ g^{-1} \\
&= h' \circ g^{-1} = (f_2 \circ g) \circ g^{-1} = f_2 \circ (g \circ g^{-1}) = f_2 \circ e = f_2.
\end{aligned}
$$

$$\text{Q.E.D.}$$

An informal paraphrase of Theorem 27.5 is probably more comprehensible than the correct statement as given. Roughly speaking the theorem says:

Interchanging two rows of a determinant changes its sign.

Let us use similar language for the corollaries.

COROLLARY 27.6. *Interchanging two columns of a matrix changes the sign of its determinant.*

COROLLARY 27.7. *If two rows (or two columns) of a matrix are identical, then its determinant is zero.*

PROOF. If the k-th and l-th rows of $[\alpha]$ are identical, then interchanging these rows leaves $[\alpha]$ unchanged. On the other hand the same change yields a matrix whose determinant is $-\det[\alpha]$. Thus $\det[\alpha] = -\det[\alpha]$; whence $\det[\alpha] = 0$.

Q.E.D.

What happens when we multiply one row by a scalar?

THEOREM 27.8. *If $[\alpha]$ is an N-by-N matrix and*

$$\beta^i_j = \begin{cases} \alpha^i_j & \text{if } i \neq k, \\ \rho\alpha^k_j & \text{if } i = k, \end{cases}$$

then $\det[\beta] = \rho \det[\alpha].$

PROOF. Simply compute:

$$\det[\beta] = \sum_{f \in S_N} \text{sgn} f \cdot \beta^1_{f(1)} \cdots \beta^k_{f(k)} \cdots \beta^N_{f(N)}$$

$$= \sum_{f \in S_N} \text{sgn} f \cdot \alpha^1_{f(1)} \cdots \rho\alpha^k_{f(k)} \cdots \alpha^N_{f(N)}$$

$$= \rho \sum_{f \in S_N} \text{sgn} f \cdot \alpha^1_{f(1)} \cdots \alpha^k_{f(k)} \cdots \alpha^N_{f(N)}$$

$$= \rho \det[\alpha].$$

Q.E.D.

COROLLARY 27.9. *Multiplying all the elements of one column of a matrix by the same scalar multiplies its determinant by that scalar.*

COROLLARY 27.10. *If every element of one row or of one column of a matrix is 0, then its determinant is zero.*

What is the effect of a transformation of the third type: subtracting a multiple of one row from another? Instead of attacking this question directly we prove quite a different theorem and get our answer as a corollary.   What we wish to prove is that if all the rows except one are held fixed, then as a function of that one row alone, the determinant is a linear function.

More precisely, we will consider three matrices $[\alpha]$, $[\beta]$, and $[\gamma]$, which are identical save for their k-th rows.   That is to say,

$$\alpha_j^i = \beta_j^i = \gamma_j^i \quad \text{if } i \neq k.$$

On the other hand, if the k-th row of $[\gamma]$ is a linear combination of the k-th rows of $[\alpha]$ and $[\beta]$, then there are scalars λ and μ such that

$$\gamma_j^k = \lambda\alpha_j^k + \mu\beta_j^k.$$

Theorem 27.11.   *If $[\alpha]$, $[\beta]$, and $[\gamma]$ are N-by-N matrices,*

$$\alpha_j^i = \beta_j^i = \gamma_j^i \quad \text{for } i \neq k,$$

and
$$\gamma_j^k = \lambda\alpha_j^k + \mu\beta_j^k,$$

then
$$\det [\gamma] = \lambda \det [\alpha] + \mu \det [\beta].$$

PROOF.   Again we simply compute

$$\det [\gamma] = \sum_{f \in S_N} \operatorname{sgn} f \cdot \gamma_{f(1)}^1 \cdot \cdots \cdot \gamma_{f(k)}^k \cdot \cdots \cdot \gamma_{f(N)}^N$$

$$= \sum_{f \in S_N} \operatorname{sgn} f \cdot \gamma_{f(1)}^1 \cdot \cdots \cdot (\lambda\alpha_{f(k)}^k + \mu\beta_{f(k)}^k) \cdot \cdots \cdot \gamma_{f(N)}^N$$

$$= \lambda \sum_{f \in S_N} \operatorname{sgn} f \cdot \gamma_{f(1)}^1 \cdot \cdots \cdot \alpha_{f(k)}^k \cdot \cdots \cdot \gamma_{f(N)}^N$$

$$+ \mu \sum_{f \in S_N} \operatorname{sgn} f \cdot \gamma_{f(1)}^1 \cdot \cdots \cdot \beta_{f(k)}^k \cdot \cdots \cdot \gamma_{f(N)}^N$$

$$= \lambda \sum_{f \in S_N} \operatorname{sgn} f \cdot \alpha_{f(1)}^1 \cdot \cdots \cdot \alpha_{f(k)}^k \cdot \cdots \cdot \alpha_{f(N)}^N$$

$$+ \mu \sum_{f \in S_N} \operatorname{sgn} f \cdot \beta_{f(1)}^1 \cdot \cdots \cdot \beta_{f(k)}^k \cdot \cdots \cdot \beta_{f(N)}^N$$

$$= \lambda \det [\alpha] + \mu \det [\beta].$$

Q.E.D.

We phrase the corresponding fact about columns most informally. The precise statement is easily obtained from the theorem—simply interchange subscripts and superscripts.

Corollary 27.12.   *Regarded as a function of one column alone,* det *is a linear function.*

Corollary 27.13.   *Subtracting a multiple of one row of a matrix from another leaves its determinant unchanged.*

PROOF. Consider a matrix $[\alpha]$. Subtract ρ times its l-th row from its k-th row and call the result $[\gamma]$. Then

$$\gamma_j^i = \alpha_j^i \quad \text{if } i \neq k,$$
$$\gamma_j^k = \alpha_j^k - \rho\alpha_j^l.$$

Now introduce a third matrix $[\beta]$ like $[\alpha]$ in every respect except that its k-th row repeats the l-th of $[\alpha]$. Explicitly

$$\beta_j^i = \begin{cases} \alpha_j^i & \text{if } i \neq k, \\ \alpha_j^l & \text{if } i = k. \end{cases}$$

Since its k-th and l-th rows are identical, $\det[\beta]=0$. Moreover, $\alpha_j^i=\beta_j^i=\gamma_j^i$ if $i\neq k$ and $\gamma_j^k=\alpha_j^k-\rho\beta_j^l=1\cdot\alpha_j^k+(-\rho)\beta_j^k$. Hence $\det[\gamma]=\det[\alpha]+(-\rho)\det[\beta]=\det[\alpha]$.

Q.E.D.

The final corollary is the corresponding result for columns.

COROLLARY 27.14. *If $[\alpha]$ is an N-by-N matrix and*

$$\beta_j^i = \begin{cases} \alpha_j^i & \text{if } j \neq k, \\ \alpha_k^i - \rho\alpha_i^i & \text{if } j = k, \end{cases}$$

then $\det[\beta]=\det[\alpha]$.

Section 28.   Expansion of Minors

For both computational and theoretical purposes we need a rather complicated formula for the determinant of a matrix in terms of certain subdeterminants.

Consider an arbitrary matrix, square or not. Say it has m rows and n columns. If you strike from the matrix p rows and q columns, you are left with a matrix of $m-p$ rows and $n-q$ columns. If this resulting matrix is square, i.e., if $m-p=n-q$, its determinant is called a minor of the original matrix. This procedure can be described more formally.

DEFINITION 28.1. If $[\alpha]_n^m$ is an m-by-n matrix, a k-th order *minor* of $[\alpha]$ is a determinant of the form

$$\begin{vmatrix} \alpha_{j_1}^{i_1} & \alpha_{j_2}^{i_1} & \cdots & \alpha_{j_k}^{i_1} \\ \alpha_{j_1}^{i_2} & \alpha_{j_2}^{i_2} & \cdots & \alpha_{j_k}^{i_2} \\ \vdots & \vdots & & \vdots \\ \alpha_{j_1}^{i_k} & \alpha_{j_2}^{i_k} & \cdots & \alpha_{j_k}^{i_k} \end{vmatrix}$$

where $1 \leqslant i_1 < i_2 < \cdots < i_k \leqslant m$
$1 \leqslant j_1 < j_2 < \cdots < j_k \leqslant n$.

Examine the 3-by-3 determinant

$$\begin{vmatrix} a & b & c \\ d & e & f \\ g & h & i \end{vmatrix} = aei + bfg + dhc - afh - dbi - gec.$$

Collecting the terms containing a, those containing b, and those containing c, you will observe that its value is

(28.1) $\qquad\qquad a(ei - fh) + b(fg - di) + c(dh - ge).$

Now

$$ei - fh = \begin{vmatrix} e & f \\ h & i \end{vmatrix}$$

is a minor of the original determinant. Specifically, it is the minor obtained by deleting the row and the column containing a. Similarly, the third term, $c(dh - ge)$, is c times the minor obtained after striking out the row and column containing c. On the other hand, the minor corresponding to b is

$$\begin{vmatrix} d & f \\ g & i \end{vmatrix} = di - fg$$

whereas in (28.1) b is multiplied by the negative of this minor.

These observations suggest a general question. Can one evaluate an arbitrary determinant by taking the elements of a given row, multiplying each by its corresponding minor, attaching an appropriate sign, and adding the results? We will derive the correct formula before stating the theorem.

Consider the matrix

$$\begin{bmatrix} \alpha_1^1 & \cdots & \alpha_{j-1}^1 & \alpha_j^1 & \alpha_{j+1}^1 & \cdots & \alpha_N^1 \\ \vdots & & \vdots & \vdots & \vdots & & \vdots \\ \alpha_1^{i-1} & \cdots & \alpha_{j-1}^{i-1} & \alpha_j^{i-1} & \alpha_{j+1}^{i-1} & \cdots & \alpha_N^{i-1} \\ \alpha_1^i & \cdots & \alpha_{j-1}^i & \alpha_j^i & \alpha_{j+1}^i & \cdots & \alpha_N^i \\ \alpha_1^{i+1} & \cdots & \alpha_{j-1}^{i+1} & \alpha_j^{i+1} & \alpha_{j+1}^{i+1} & \cdots & \alpha_N^{i+1} \\ \vdots & & \vdots & \vdots & \vdots & & \vdots \\ \alpha_1^N & \cdots & \alpha_{j-1}^N & \alpha_j^N & \alpha_{j+1}^N & \cdots & \alpha_N^N \end{bmatrix}$$

Its determinant is

(28.2) $\qquad \det[\alpha] = \sum_{f \in S_N} \operatorname{sgn} f \cdot \alpha_{f(1)}^1 \cdots \alpha_{f(i-1)}^{i-1} \alpha_{f(i)}^i \alpha_{f(i+1)}^{i+1} \cdots \alpha_{f(N)}^N.$

Our object is to collect together all the terms which appear in the minor corresponding to α_j^i. The element α_j^i is somewhere in the i-th row.   Here and throughout the argument, i denotes an integer fixed once and for all, but at first j will be a dummy index.

As f ranges over the set of permutations S_N, $f(i)$ takes on various values.   For each j, we want to collect together those terms in (28.2) which contain α_j^i.   Thus we need a symbol for the set of those $f \in S_N$ such that $f(i)=j$.   Let $T_{i,j}$ denote this set.   Hence, when $f \in T_{i,j}$, $\alpha_{f(i)}^i = \alpha_j^i$.

Of course, each $f \in S_N$ belongs to one and only one of the $T_{i,j}$, $j = 1, 2, \ldots, N$.   If we sum, first as f ranges over the elements of $T_{i,j}$, and then add together these sums as j ranges from 1 to N we have a sum over the elements of S_N.   This means that (28.2) can be re-written as

$$\det [\alpha] = \sum_{j=1}^{N} \sum_{f \in T_{i,j}} \operatorname{sgn} f \cdot \alpha_{f(1)}^1 \ldots \alpha_{f(i-1)}^{i-1} \alpha_j^i \alpha_{f(i+1)}^{i+1} \ldots \alpha_{f(N)}^N.$$

As far as the inner summation is concerned, j is not varying, and α_j^i is a constant factor appearing in every term.   Taking out this common factor we obtain

$$(28.3) \quad \det [\alpha] = \sum_{j=1}^{N} \alpha_j^i \sum_{f \in T_{i,j}} \operatorname{sgn} f \cdot \alpha_{f(1)}^1 \ldots \alpha_{f(i-1)}^{i-1} \alpha_{f(i+1)}^{i+1} \ldots \alpha_{f(N)}^N.$$

We can now concentrate on the inner sum.   Let

$$(28.4) \qquad \gamma_{ij} = \sum_{f \in T_{i,j}} \operatorname{sgn} f \cdot \alpha_{f(1)}^1 \ldots \alpha_{f(i-1)}^{i-1} \alpha_{f(i+1)}^{i+1} \ldots \alpha_{f(N)}^N,$$

and, for the moment, think of a particular value of j.   For $f \in T_{i,j}$, $f(i)=j$.   Hence the subscripts $f(1), \ldots, f(i-1), f(i+1), \ldots, f(N)$, give a listing of the remaining integers, $1, \ldots, j-1, j+1, \ldots, N$.   As f ranges over $T_{i,j}$ each such list occurs once and only once.

It is time to examine the minor corresponding to α_j^i.   Denote it by M_i^j, so

$$M_i^j = \begin{vmatrix} \alpha_1^1 & \cdots & \alpha_{j-1}^1 & \alpha_{j+1}^1 & \cdots & \alpha_N^1 \\ \vdots & & \vdots & \vdots & & \vdots \\ \alpha_1^{i-1} & \cdots & \alpha_{j-1}^{i-1} & \alpha_{j+1}^{i-1} & \cdots & \alpha_N^{i-1} \\ \alpha_1^{i+1} & \cdots & \alpha_{j-1}^{i+1} & \alpha_{j+1}^{i+1} & \cdots & \alpha_N^{i+1} \\ \vdots & & \vdots & \vdots & & \vdots \\ \alpha_1^N & \cdots & \alpha_{j-1}^N & \alpha_{j+1}^N & \cdots & \alpha_N^N \end{vmatrix}.$$

Each term in the expression for M_i^j is a product of α's one from each row and one from each column.   As for the sign, what matters is the number of inversions in the list of subscripts, not what symbols are used as indices. In the minor the superscripts, $1, \ldots, i-1, i+1,$ $\ldots, N$, and subscripts, $1, \ldots, j-1, j+1, \ldots, N$, appear in their natural order. Thus the sign to attach to the term

$$\alpha^1_{k_1} \cdots \alpha^{i-1}_{k_{i-1}} \alpha^{i+1}_{k_{i+1}} \cdots \alpha^N_{k_N}$$

is $(-1)^n$, where n is the number of inversions in the list $k_1, \ldots, k_{i-1}, k_{i+1}, \ldots, k_N$.

The value of the minor is the sum of all such terms—one for each list, $k_1, \ldots, k_{i-1}, k_{i+1}, \ldots, k_N$. Comparing this with (28.4) you will see that γ_{ij} and M^j_i are expressed by sums of exactly the same type. The terms can be matched one for one and the only problem is the relation of their signs. What sign is to be attached to

$$\alpha^1_{f(1)} \cdots \alpha^{i-1}_{f(i-1)} \alpha^{i+1}_{f(i+1)} \cdots \alpha^N_{f(N)}$$

when this product is regarded as a term in M^j_i?

Compare the lists

(28.5) $f(1), \ldots, f(i-1), f(i), f(i+1), \ldots, f(N)$

and

(28.6) $f(1), \ldots, f(i-1), f(i+1), \ldots, f(N)$.

Every inversion in the latter occurs in the former, but the list (28.5) has additional inversions associated with the entry $f(i)$. Let m and n be the numbers of inversions in the lists (28.5) and (28.6), respectively. Since $f(i)=j$, the number of *additional* inversions in (28.5) is the number of integers in $f(1), \ldots, f(i-1)$ which are greater than j plus the number of integers in $f(i+1), \ldots, f(N)$ which are less than j. If p of the integers $f(1), \ldots, f(i-1)$, are greater than j then $(i-1)-p$ of them must be less than j. The whole list (28.5) contains $j-1$ integers less than j. If $(i-1)-p$ of them appear among $f(1), \ldots, f(i-1)$ then the remaining $(j-1)-[(i-1)-p]$ of them must appear among $f(i+1), \ldots, f(N)$. Hence the number of additional inversions is

$$p + \{(j-1)-[(i-1)-p]\} = j-i+2p$$
$$= j+i-2(i-p)$$

so

$$m = n+j+i-2(i-p).$$

The sign assigned to the product

$$\alpha^1_{f(1)} \cdots \alpha^{i-1}_{f(i-1)} \alpha^{i+1}_{f(i+1)} \cdots \alpha^N_{f(N)}$$

when regarded as a term in M^i_j is $(-1)^n$. When regarded as a term in γ_{ij}

its sign is sgn $f = (-1)^m = (-1)^n(-1)^{i+j}(-1)^{-2(i-p)} = (-1)^n(-1)^{i+j} \cdot 1$. If $i+j$ is odd *all* the signs are changed; if it is even, *none* are changed. Thus

$$\gamma_{ij} = (-1)^{i+j} M_i^j$$

and (28.3) becomes

$$\det [\alpha] = \sum_{j=1}^{N} (-1)^{i+j} \alpha_j^i M_i^j.$$

This completes the proof of the following theorem.

THEOREM 28.2. *If* $[\alpha]$ *is an N-by-N matrix and* M_i^j *is the minor of* $[\alpha]$ *obtained by deleting its i-th row and j-th column then*

$$\det [\alpha] = \sum_{j=1}^{N} (-1)^{i+j} \alpha_j^i M_i^j.$$

The next theorem is most conveniently stated with the aid of a notation useful in many other contexts as well.

NOTATION.   Hereafter δ will be used exclusively for the Kronecker delta symbol defined by

$$\delta_j^i = \begin{cases} 1 & \text{if } i = j, \\ 0 & \text{if } i \neq j. \end{cases}$$

In the next chapter we will use δ_{ij} instead of δ_j^i.   Elsewhere, you may also meet δ^{ij}.

THEOREM 28.3.   *With the same notations as in Theorem* 28.2

(28.7) $$\sum_{j=1}^{N} (-1)^{i+j} \alpha_j^k M_i^j = \delta_i^k \det [\alpha].$$

PROOF.   If $i = k$, equation (28.7) simply reiterates Theorem 28.2. To see what happens when $i \neq k$ consider the matrix $[\beta]$, where

(28.8) $$\beta_j^l = \begin{cases} \alpha_j^l & \text{if } l \neq i, \\ \alpha_j^k & \text{if } l = i. \end{cases}$$

Thus $[\beta]$ is just like $[\alpha]$ except for its i-th row.   In particular the minor of β obtained by striking out the i-th row and j-th column is identical with the corresponding minor in $[\alpha]$!   That is, the minor corresponding to β_j^i is M_i^j.   Thus Theorem 28.2 applied to $[\beta]$ gives, with the aid of (28.8),

(28.9) $$\det [\beta] = \sum_{j=1}^{N} (-1)^{i+j} \beta_j^i M_i^j$$

$$= \sum_{j=1}^{N} (-1)^{i+j} \alpha_j^k M_i^j.$$

On the other hand, both the i-th and the k-th rows of $[\beta]$ are the k-th row of $[\alpha]$. Since $[\beta]$ contains these two identical rows, its determinant is zero; also, since $k \neq i$, $\delta_i^k = 0$. It follows that we can write det $[\beta]$ in the form that we wish:

$$\det [\beta] = 0 = 0 \cdot \det [\alpha] = \delta_i^k \det [\alpha].$$

Combining this with equation (28.9) we obtain (28.7).

Q.E.D.

Of course, there is a corollary to be obtained by interchanging columns for rows.

COROLLARY 28.4.   *With the same notations as before,*

$$\sum_{j=1}^{N} (-1)^{i+j} \alpha_i^j M_j^k = \delta_i^k \det [\alpha].$$

To evaluate the determinant of a matrix, first apply Corollaries 27.13 and 27.14 in such a way as to express everything in terms of a determinant with many zeros in one row or column. Then apply Theorem 28.2 or Corollary 28.4 to evaluate the determinant by means of the minors of the chosen row or column.

Section 29.   The Determinant of a Product

A given linear transformation has, associated with it, many different matrices. There is no reason to expect that the determinants of these different matrices will be equal, and in general they are not. When one considers linear transformations on a space to itself, however, a startling fact emerges. If A is a linear transformation on $\mathscr{V}$ to $\mathscr{V}$ then the determinant, det $[A; x], x]$, depends solely on the transformation A and does not change when the basis x is changed.

To prove this result we need the following theorem, which is also of interest in its own right.

THEOREM 29.1.   *If $[\alpha]$ and $[\beta]$ are N-by-N matrices, then*

(29.1) $$\det ([\alpha] \cdot [\beta]) = \det [\alpha] \cdot \det [\beta].$$

The proof itself will not be hard. In outline it runs as follows. For a certain type of matrix the theorem is very easy indeed. Every matrix is a product of matrices of the special type. In equation (29.1) we will write $[\alpha]$ as a product of such special matrices and apply the special case of the theorem several times.

Unfortunately, we need a large number of preliminary results. The groundwork was laid in Section 18 when we introduced echelon-matrices and elementary row transformations. We need to formalize those ideas and see how they are related to determinants and to matrix multiplication.

DEFINITION 29.2. A matrix $[\alpha]_M^N$ is an *echelon matrix* if there are integers $1 \leqslant k_1 < k_2 < \cdots < k_l \leqslant N$ such that

$$\alpha_{k_i}^i = 1 \quad \text{for } i = 1, 2, \ldots, l;$$

$$\alpha_j^i = 0 \quad \text{if } i \leqslant l \text{ and } j < k_i$$

$$\alpha_{k_i}^j = 0 \quad \text{if } j \neq i;$$

$$\alpha_j^i = 0 \quad \text{if } i > l.$$

THEOREM 29.3. *If* $[\alpha]$ *is an N-by-N echelon matrix, then either*

$$[\alpha] = \begin{bmatrix} 1 & 0 & \ldots & 0 \\ 0 & 1 & \ldots & 0 \\ \vdots & \vdots & & \vdots \\ 0 & 0 & \ldots & 1 \end{bmatrix}$$

or at least one row of $[\alpha]$ *consists entirely of zeros.*

PROOF. Examine Definition 29.2.

If $l = N$, then the k's must be $1, 2, \ldots, N$, i.e., $k_i = i$. In this case the $\alpha_{k_i}^i = 1$ are the diagonal elements and $\alpha_j^i = \alpha_{k_i}^j = 0$ if $j \neq k_i = i$.

If $l < N$ then the rows below the l-th consist entirely of zeros.

Q.E.D.

DEFINITION 29.4. A matrix is an *elementary matrix* if it is of one of the following three forms:

I: $[\epsilon(m, n)]$ where

$$\epsilon_i^j(m, n) = \begin{cases} 1 & \text{if } i = j \neq m \text{ and } i = j \neq n, \\ 1 & \text{if } i = m \text{ and } j = n, \\ 1 & \text{if } i = n \text{ and } j = m, \\ 0 & \text{otherwise;} \end{cases}$$

II: $[\mu(m, \rho)]$ where $\rho \neq 0$ and

$$\mu_j^i(m, \rho) = \begin{cases} 1 & \text{if } i = j \neq m, \\ \rho & \text{if } i = j = m, \\ 0 & \text{otherwise;} \end{cases}$$

III: $[\sigma(m, n, \rho)]$ where

$$\sigma_j^i(m, n, \rho) = \begin{cases} 1 & \text{if } i = j, \\ -\rho & \text{if } i = m, j = n, \\ 0 & \text{otherwise.} \end{cases}$$

These matrices have the following appearance:

(29.2) $[\epsilon(m, n)] = \begin{bmatrix} 1 & 0 & \cdots & 0 & \cdots & 0 & \cdots & 0 \\ 0 & 1 & \cdots & 0 & \cdots & 0 & \cdots & 0 \\ \vdots & \vdots & & \vdots & & \vdots & & \vdots \\ 0 & 0 & \cdots & 0 & \cdots & 1 & \cdots & 0 \\ \vdots & \vdots & & \vdots & & \vdots & & \vdots \\ 0 & 0 & \cdots & 1 & \cdots & 0 & \cdots & 0 \\ \vdots & \vdots & & \vdots & & \vdots & & \vdots \\ 0 & 0 & \cdots & 0 & \cdots & 0 & \cdots & 1 \end{bmatrix}$ $\begin{matrix} \\ \\ \\ m\text{-th row} \\ \\ n\text{-th row} \\ \\ \end{matrix}$

where the m-th col and n-th col are indicated.

(29.3) $[\mu(m, \rho)] = \begin{bmatrix} 1 & 0 & \cdots & 0 & \cdots & 0 \\ 0 & 1 & \cdots & 0 & \cdots & 0 \\ \vdots & \vdots & & \vdots & & \vdots \\ 0 & 0 & \cdots & \rho & \cdots & 0 \\ \vdots & \vdots & & \vdots & & \vdots \\ 0 & 0 & \cdots & 0 & \cdots & 1 \end{bmatrix}$ $\begin{matrix} \\ \\ \\ m\text{-th row} \\ \\ \end{matrix}$

where the m-th col is indicated.

and

(29.4) $[\sigma(m, n, \rho)] = \begin{bmatrix} 1 & 0 & \cdots & 0 & \cdots & 0 & \cdots & 0 \\ 0 & 1 & \cdots & 0 & \cdots & 0 & \cdots & 0 \\ \vdots & \vdots & & \vdots & & \vdots & & \vdots \\ 0 & 0 & \cdots & 1 & \cdots & -\rho & \cdots & 0 \\ \vdots & \vdots & & \vdots & & \vdots & & \vdots \\ 0 & 0 & \cdots & 0 & \cdots & 1 & \cdots & 0 \\ \vdots & \vdots & & \vdots & & \vdots & & \vdots \\ 0 & 0 & \cdots & 0 & \cdots & 0 & \cdots & 1 \end{bmatrix}$ $\begin{matrix} \\ \\ \\ m\text{-th row} \\ \\ n\text{-th row} \\ \\ \end{matrix}$

where the m-th col and n-th col are indicated.

The elementary row operations of Section 18 are easily described in terms of elementary matrices.

THEOREM 29.5. *If a matrix $[\beta]$ is obtained from a matrix $[\alpha]$ by an elementary row operation, then there is an elementary matrix $[\gamma]$ such that $[\beta] = [\gamma][\alpha]$.*

PROOF. The elementary row operations are: type I, interchange two rows; type II, multiply one row by a non-zero constant; type III, subtract a multiple of one row from another.

Now consider an arbitrary matrix $[\alpha]$ and compute

$$[\epsilon(m,n)][\alpha], \qquad [\mu(m,\rho)][\alpha], \quad \text{and} \quad [\sigma(m,n,\rho)][\alpha].$$

Look at the computations below and observe how each of the multiplications effects the corresponding row operation.

We have

(29.5)

$$[\epsilon(m,n)]\cdot[\alpha] =
\begin{bmatrix}
1 & 0 & \cdots & 0 & \cdots & 0 & \cdots & 0 \\
0 & 1 & \cdots & 0 & \cdots & 0 & \cdots & 0 \\
\vdots & & & \vdots & & \vdots & & \vdots \\
0 & 0 & \cdots & 0 & \cdots & 1 & \cdots & 0 \\
\vdots & \vdots & & \vdots & & \vdots & & \vdots \\
0 & 0 & \cdots & 1 & \cdots & 0 & \cdots & 0 \\
\vdots & \vdots & & \vdots & & \vdots & & \vdots \\
0 & 0 & \cdots & 0 & \cdots & 0 & \cdots & 1
\end{bmatrix}
\times
\begin{bmatrix}
\alpha_1^1 & \alpha_2^1 & \cdots & \alpha_m^1 & \cdots & \alpha_n^1 & \cdots & \alpha_M^1 \\
\alpha_1^2 & \alpha_2^2 & \cdots & \alpha_m^2 & \cdots & \alpha_n^2 & \cdots & \alpha_M^2 \\
\vdots & \vdots & & \vdots & & \vdots & & \vdots \\
\alpha_1^m & \alpha_2^m & \cdots & \alpha_m^m & \cdots & \alpha_n^m & \cdots & \alpha_M^m \\
\vdots & \vdots & & \vdots & & \vdots & & \vdots \\
\alpha_1^n & \alpha_2^n & \cdots & \alpha_m^n & \cdots & \alpha_n^n & \cdots & \alpha_M^n \\
\vdots & \vdots & & \vdots & & \vdots & & \vdots \\
\alpha_1^N & \alpha_2^N & \cdots & \alpha_m^N & \cdots & \alpha_n^N & \cdots & \alpha_M^N
\end{bmatrix}$$

(the m-th row and n-th row marked; m-th col and n-th col marked)

$$=
\begin{bmatrix}
\alpha_1^1 & \alpha_2^1 & \cdots & \alpha_m^1 & \cdots & \alpha_n^1 & \cdots & \alpha_M^1 \\
\alpha_1^2 & \alpha_2^2 & \cdots & \alpha_m^2 & \cdots & \alpha_n^2 & \cdots & \alpha_M^2 \\
\vdots & \vdots & & \vdots & & \vdots & & \vdots \\
\alpha_1^n & \alpha_2^n & \cdots & \alpha_m^n & \cdots & \alpha_n^n & \cdots & \alpha_M^n \\
\vdots & \vdots & & \vdots & & \vdots & & \vdots \\
\alpha_1^m & \alpha_2^m & \cdots & \alpha_m^m & \cdots & \alpha_n^m & \cdots & \alpha_M^m \\
\vdots & \vdots & & \vdots & & \vdots & & \vdots \\
\alpha_1^N & \alpha_2^N & \cdots & \alpha_m^N & \cdots & \alpha_n^N & \cdots & \alpha_M^N
\end{bmatrix},$$

(m-th row and n-th row positions interchanged)

(29.6)

$$[\mu(m,\rho)]\cdot[\alpha] =
\begin{bmatrix}
1 & 0 & \cdots & 0 & \cdots & 0 \\
0 & 1 & \cdots & 0 & \cdots & 0 \\
\vdots & \vdots & & \vdots & & \vdots \\
0 & 0 & \cdots & \rho & \cdots & 0 \\
\vdots & \vdots & & \vdots & & \vdots \\
0 & 0 & \cdots & 0 & \cdots & 1
\end{bmatrix}
\times
\begin{bmatrix}
\alpha_1^1 & \alpha_2^1 & \cdots & \alpha_m^1 & \cdots & \alpha_M^1 \\
\alpha_1^2 & \alpha_2^2 & \cdots & \alpha_m^2 & \cdots & \alpha_M^2 \\
\vdots & \vdots & & \vdots & & \vdots \\
\alpha_1^m & \alpha_2^m & \cdots & \alpha_m^m & \cdots & \alpha_M^m \\
\vdots & \vdots & & \vdots & & \vdots \\
\alpha_1^N & \alpha_2^N & \cdots & \alpha_m^N & \cdots & \alpha_M^N
\end{bmatrix}$$

(m-th col marked; m-th row marked)

$$=
\begin{bmatrix}
\alpha_1^1 & \alpha_2^1 & \cdots & \alpha_m^1 & \cdots & \alpha_M^1 \\
\alpha_1^2 & \alpha_2^2 & \cdots & \alpha_m^2 & \cdots & \alpha_M^2 \\
\vdots & \vdots & & \vdots & & \vdots \\
\rho\alpha_1^m & \rho\alpha_2^m & \cdots & \rho\alpha_m^m & \cdots & \rho\alpha_M^m \\
\vdots & \vdots & & \vdots & & \vdots \\
\alpha_1^N & \alpha_2^N & \cdots & \alpha_m^N & \cdots & \alpha_M^N
\end{bmatrix},$$

(m-th col marked; m-th row marked)

and

(29.7)

$$[\sigma(m,n,\rho)]\cdot[\alpha] =
\begin{bmatrix}
1 & 0 \cdots 0 & \cdots & 0 \cdots 0 \\
0 & 1 \cdots 0 & \cdots & 0 \cdots 0 \\
\vdots & \vdots \quad \vdots & & \vdots \quad \vdots \\
0 & 0 \cdots 1 & \cdots & -\rho \cdots 0 \\
\vdots & \vdots \quad \vdots & & \vdots \quad \vdots \\
0 & 0 \cdots 0 & \cdots & 1 \cdots 0 \\
\vdots & \vdots \quad \vdots & & \vdots \quad \vdots \\
0 & 0 \cdots 0 & \cdots & 0 \cdots 1
\end{bmatrix}
\times
\begin{bmatrix}
\alpha_1^1 & \alpha_2^1 & \cdots & \alpha_m^1 & \cdots & \alpha_n^1 & \cdots & \alpha_M^1 \\
\alpha_1^2 & \alpha_2^2 & \cdots & \alpha_m^2 & \cdots & \alpha_n^2 & \cdots & \alpha_M^2 \\
\vdots & \vdots & & \vdots & & \vdots & & \vdots \\
\alpha_1^m & \alpha_2^m & \cdots & \alpha_m^m & \cdots & \alpha_n^m & \cdots & \alpha_M^m \\
\vdots & \vdots & & \vdots & & \vdots & & \vdots \\
\alpha_1^n & \alpha_2^n & \cdots & \alpha_m^n & \cdots & \alpha_n^n & \cdots & \alpha_M^n \\
\vdots & \vdots & & \vdots & & \vdots & & \vdots \\
\alpha_1^N & \alpha_2^N & \cdots & \alpha_m^N & \cdots & \alpha_n^N & \cdots & \alpha_M^N
\end{bmatrix}$$

$$=
\begin{bmatrix}
\alpha_1^1 & \alpha_2^1 & \cdots & \alpha_m^1 & \cdots & \alpha_n^1 & \cdots & \alpha_M^1 \\
\alpha_1^2 & \alpha_2^2 & \cdots & \alpha_m^2 & \cdots & \alpha_n^2 & \cdots & \alpha_M^2 \\
\vdots & \vdots & & \vdots & & \vdots & & \vdots \\
\alpha_1^m - \rho\alpha_1^n & \alpha_2^m - \rho\alpha_2^n & \cdots & \alpha_m^m - \rho\alpha_m^n & \cdots & \alpha_N^m - \rho\alpha_m^n & \cdots & \alpha_N^m - \rho\alpha_M^n \\
\vdots & \vdots & & \vdots & & \vdots & & \vdots \\
\alpha_1^n & \alpha_2^n & \cdots & \alpha_m^n & \cdots & \alpha_n^n & \cdots & \alpha_M^n \\
\vdots & \vdots & & \vdots & & \vdots & & \vdots \\
\alpha_1^N & \alpha_2^N & \cdots & \alpha_m^N & \cdots & \alpha_n^N & \cdots & \alpha_M^N
\end{bmatrix}.$$

Q.E.D.

For the time being let us call a matrix an E-matrix if it is either an echelon matrix or an elementary matrix. Most of Section 18 was devoted to showing that an arbitrary matrix $[\alpha]$ could be reduced to an echelon matrix by a sequence of row transformations. In view of the previous theorem this means that there is an echelon matrix $[\beta]$ and elementary matrices $[\gamma_1], [\gamma_2], \ldots, [\gamma_n]$ such that

$$[\beta] = [\gamma_n]\cdots[\gamma_2][\gamma_1][\alpha].$$

Our object is to turn this around and write $[\alpha]$ as a product of E-matrices. To this end, we need to know the inverses of elementary matrices.

THEOREM 29.6.   *If $[\gamma]$ is an elementary matrix, then it has an inverse, $[\gamma]^{-1}$, which is also an elementary matrix.*

PROOF.   As you can easily verify by writing down the matrices and computing the products,

$$[\epsilon(m, n)]^{-1} = [\epsilon(m, n)],$$

$$[\mu(m, \rho)]^{-1} = [\mu(m, 1/\rho)], \quad \text{and}$$

$$[\sigma(m, n, \rho)]^{-1} = [\sigma(m, n, -\rho)].$$

Q.E.D.

THEOREM 29.7.   *Every matrix is a product of* E-*matrices.*

PROOF.   Consider an arbitrary matrix $[\alpha]$.   As was pointed out above, there are elementary matrices $[\gamma_1], [\gamma_2], \ldots, [\gamma_n]$ and an echelon matrix $[\beta]$ such that

$$[\beta] = [\gamma_n]\cdots[\gamma_2][\gamma_1][\alpha].$$

Hence, $$[\alpha] = [\gamma_1]^{-1}[\gamma_2]^{-1}\cdots[\gamma_n]^{-1}[\beta].$$

(Why is the order of the factors reversed?)   By virtue of the choice of $[\beta]$ and Theorem 29.6, all the factors on the right-hand side are E-matrices.

Q.E.D.

Let us return to the question of determinants.

THEOREM 29.8.   *If* $[\alpha]$ *is an* N-*by-*N *echelon matrix and* $[\beta]$ *is an arbitrary* N-*by-*N *matrix, then*

$$\det([\alpha][\beta]) = \det[\alpha]\det[\beta].$$

PROOF.   According to Theorem 29.3, either $[\alpha]$ is the N-by-N identity matrix or the N-th row of $[\alpha]$ consists entirely of zeros.   In the former case $[\alpha][\beta] = [\beta]$ and $\det[\alpha] = 1$.   In the latter case you can easily check that the N-th row of $[\alpha][\beta]$ must also consist entirely of zeros.   Hence by Corollary 27.10, $\det([\alpha][\beta]) = 0$ and $\det[\alpha] = 0$.

Q.E.D.

THEOREM 29.9.   *The determinants of the elementary matrices are*

(29.8) $$\det[\epsilon(m, n)] = -1,$$

(29.9) $$\det[\mu(m, \rho)] = \rho, \quad \text{and}$$

(29.10) $$\det[\sigma(m, n, \rho)] = 1.$$

PROOF.   Look at equations (29.2), (29.3), and (29.4).   You will see that interchanging the m-th and n-th rows of $[\epsilon(m, n)]$ yields the identity matrix, $[I]$.   Hence, by Theorem 27.5,

$$\det[\epsilon(m, n)] = -\det[I] = -1.$$

Similarly, Theorem 27.8 implies

$$\det[\mu(m, \rho)] = \rho,$$

and Corollary 27.13 implies

$$\det[\sigma(m, n, \rho)] = 1.$$

Q.E.D.

THEOREM 29.10. *If $[\gamma]$ is an N-by-N elementary matrix and $[\alpha]$ is an arbitrary N-by-N matrix, then*

(29.11) $\det([\gamma][\alpha]) = \det[\gamma]\det[\alpha]$.

PROOF. Consider first the case $[\gamma]=[\epsilon(m, n)]$ and look at equation (29.5). According to Theorem 27.5, the determinant of the matrix on the right-hand side of (29.5) is

$$-\det[\alpha].$$

Hence, using equation (29.8),

$$\det([\epsilon(m, n)][\alpha]) = -\det[\alpha]$$
$$= \det[\epsilon(m, n)]\det[\alpha].$$

Similar applications of Theorem 27.8 and Corollary 27.13 establish (29.11) when $[\gamma]=[\mu(m, \rho)]$ and when $[\gamma]=[\sigma(m, n, \rho)]$, respectively.

Q.E.D.

This concludes the preliminaries.

PROOF OF THEOREM 29.1. Consider two arbitrary N-by-N matrices $[\alpha]$ and $[\beta]$. We know that $[\alpha]$ is a product of E-matrices; say

$$[\alpha] = [\gamma_1][\gamma_2]\cdots[\gamma_n].$$

Now

$$\det([\alpha][\beta]) = \det([\gamma_1]\{[\gamma_2]\cdots[\gamma_n][\beta]\})$$
$$= \det[\gamma_1]\cdot\det\{[\gamma_2]\cdots[\gamma_n][\beta]\}$$
$$= \det[\gamma_1]\cdot\det[\gamma_2]\cdot\det\{[\gamma_3]\cdots[\gamma_n][\beta]\}$$
$$= \cdots$$
$$= \det[\gamma_1]\cdot\det[\gamma_2]\cdot\,\cdots\,\cdot\det[\gamma_n]\det[\beta]$$
$$= \det[\gamma_1]\cdot\det[\gamma_2]\cdot\,\cdots\,\cdot\det\{[\gamma_{n-1}][\gamma_n]\}\cdot\det[\beta]$$
$$= \cdots$$
$$= \det[\gamma_1]\cdot\det\{[\gamma_2]\cdots[\gamma_{n-1}][\gamma_n]\}\cdot\det[\beta]$$
$$= \det\{[\gamma_1][\gamma_2]\cdots[\gamma_n]\}\cdot\det[\beta]$$
$$= \det[\alpha]\cdot\det[\beta].$$

Q.E.D.

Section 30. The Determinant of a Linear Transformation

We now seek to relate determinants to linear transformations.

Let $\mathscr{V}$ be an N-dimensional vector space and let A be a linear transformation on $\mathscr{V}$ to $\mathscr{V}$. In Section 19 when we discussed the connection between matrices and transformations, we dealt with transformations from one space to another. There we were forced to use different bases because we had different spaces. Now we have but a single space, but we have to look at the space from different points of view. Different bases describe the space in different ways.

Examine the schematic diagram of Fig. 30.1. To relate the matrix $[A; y], y]]$ for the lower half of the picture to the matrix $[A; x], x]]$ that goes with the upper half, we must have some way of going up and down. There is one beautifully simple transformation from a space to itself, namely, the identity transformation, I.

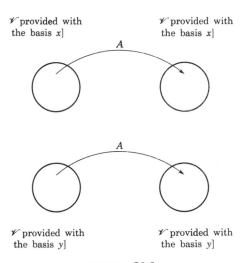

FIGURE 30.1

Before we employ I for the job of raising and lowering A, let us recapitulate the relation between matrix products and transformation products. If B is a transformation from $\mathscr{U}$ to $\mathscr{V}$ and C is a transformation from $\mathscr{V}$ to $\mathscr{W}$, then the product of the matrices, $[C] \cdot [B]$, is the matrix of the product $[CB]$, *provided we use just one basis for each space.* Taking explicit account of the bases we have:

> If $x]$ is a basis for $\mathscr{U}$, $y]$ a basis for $\mathscr{V}$, and $z]$ a basis for $\mathscr{W}$, then

(30.1) $[C; y], z]][B; x], y]] = [CB; x], z]].$

In deriving this formula we made no use of the fact that $\mathscr{U}$, $\mathscr{V}$, and $\mathscr{W}$ were different spaces. If they happen to be the same, we may still employ (30.1) even though it involves various bases. Since (30.1) is not easy to remember, you will be wise to remember the simple formula, $[C][B] = [CB]$, and to use the diagram of Fig. 30.2 to remind you which bases to use where.

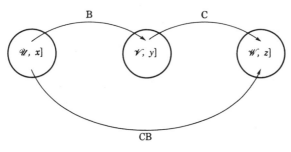

FIGURE 30.2

After all this talk the proof of the following theorem is almost trivial.

THEOREM 30.1.   *If A is a linear transformation on $\mathscr{V}$ to $\mathscr{V}$ and if $x]_1^N$ and $y]_1^N$ are bases for $\mathscr{V}$, then*

$$\det [A; x], x]] = \det [A; y], y]].$$

PROOF.   Consider the diagram, Fig. 30.3.

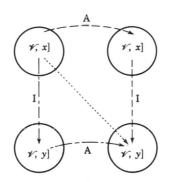

FIGURE 30.3

Since I is the identity transformation $AI = A = IA$.   In other words, it makes no difference whether, in the diagram, you use the route marked — · —, the route marked · · · · ·, or the one marked — — —. In a formula

$$[A; y], y]][I; x], y]] = [A; x], y]]$$
$$= [I; x], y]][A; x], x]].$$

According to Theorem 29.1, it follows that

$$(\det [A; y], y]]) \cdot (\det [I; x], y]]) = \det [A; x], y]]$$
$$= (\det [I; x], y]]) \cdot (\det [A; x], x]])$$

If we can show that

(30.2) $\det [I; x], y]] \neq 0,$

we can cancel this common factor and the proof will be complete.

Happily, (30.2) also comes easily from a diagram (Fig. 30.4). Since $I \cdot I = I$ we see that

$$[I; y], x]][I; x], y]] = [I; x], x]].$$

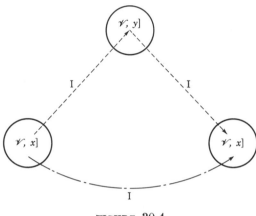

FIGURE 30.4

However, $[I; x], x]]$ is the ordinary identity matrix with 1's on its main diagonal and 0's elsewhere. Its determinant is 1 so we have

$$(\det [I; y], x]]) \cdot (\det [I; x], y]]) = 1.$$

If a product of scalars is not zero, neither factor is zero. Hence we infer

$$\det [I; x], y]] \neq 0.$$
                                                            Q.E.D.

Of course, we cannot hope for anything like Theorem 30.1 when A is a transformation from one space to another. However, there is a very limited, but very important, connection between the determinants of the different matrices associated with a given transformation.

THEOREM 30.2. *Assume that A is a linear transformation from one N-dimensional vector space $\mathscr{V}$ to another N-dimensional vector space $\mathscr{W}$. If there is one pair of bases, $x]$ for $\mathscr{V}$ and $y]$ for $\mathscr{W}$, such that*

$$\det [A; x], y]] = 0,$$

then for every pair of bases $u]$ in $\mathscr{V}$ and $v]$ in $\mathscr{W}$,

$$\det [A\,;\, u],\, v]] = 0.$$

PROOF. Again, everything is implicit in a diagram, Fig. 30.5.

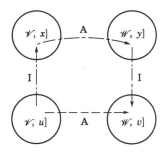

FIGURE 30.5

Comparing the route: up, over, down, with the straight path across and remembering that $A = I_{\mathscr{W}} A I_{\mathscr{V}}$, we have

$$[A\,;\, u],\, v]] = [I_{\mathscr{W}}\,;\, y],\, v]]\cdot[A\,;\, x],\, y]]\cdot[I_{\mathscr{V}}\,;\, u],\, x]].$$

According to Theorem 29.1, the determinant of the product of the determinants so

$$\det [A\,;\, u],\, v]] = (\det [I_{\mathscr{W}}\,;\, y],\, v]])(\det [A\,;\, x],\, y]])(\det [I_{\mathscr{V}}\,;\, u],\, x]]).$$

The hypothesis of our theorem is that the middle factor on the right-hand side of this equation is zero. Hence, the left-hand side is also zero.

$$\text{Q.E.D.}$$

In view of this theorem we may write, briefly,

$$\det [A] = 0 \text{ (or } \det [A] \neq 0)$$

instead of the complete phrase:

> For some, and hence for all, bases $x]$ and $y]$, $\det [A\,;\, x],\, y]] = 0$
> (or $\det [A\,;\, x],\, y]] \neq 0$).

Look back at Corollary 17.7. That corollary suffers from one great defect—it does not suggest any routine way to decide whether a transformation A satisfies the equivalent conditions (i), (ii), and (iii) or whether it satisfies (iv), (v), (vi), and (vii). We are now ready to supply the needed condition.

THEOREM 30.3. *Assume that A is a linear transformation from one N-dimensional space $\mathscr{V}$ to another space $\mathscr{W}$ with the same dimension. The following conditions are equivalent:*

 (i) $\det [A] = 0;$

 (ii) *for some $x \in \mathscr{V}$, $x \neq 0$ and $Ax = 0;$*

 (iii) $\mathscr{N}(A) \neq 0;$

 (iv) $\operatorname{rng} A \neq \mathscr{W}.$

So are the following:

 (v) $\det [A] \neq 0;$

 (vi) *A has an inverse;*

 (vii) $\mathscr{N}(A) = \{0\};$

 (viii) $\operatorname{rng} A = \mathscr{W}.$

PROOF. Corollary 17.7 says that (ii), (iii), and (iv) are equivalent and so are (vi), (vii), and (viii). Clearly either one set of conditions holds or else the others must. We will prove that when (vi) holds then so does (v) and that when (ii) holds so does (i).

There is no need to give any argument in the opposite direction. If (i) holds, we cannot have (vi), (vii), and (viii), for they would imply $\det [A] \neq 0$ and we know $\det [A] = 0$. Thus we must have the other alternative, namely: (ii), (iii), and (iv) are correct. Similarly when (v) is correct (ii), (iii), and (iv) cannot be, and so (vi), (vii), and (viii) must be.

Assume that A has an inverse, A^{-1}. Let $x]$ and $y]$ be bases for $\mathscr{V}$ and $\mathscr{W}$. Then

$$\det [A^{-1}; y], x]] \cdot \det [A; x], y]] = \det ([A^{-1}; y], x]] \cdot [A; x], y]])$$

$$= \det [I; x], x]]$$

$$= \begin{vmatrix} 1 & 0 & \ldots & 0 \\ 0 & 1 & \ldots & 0 \\ \vdots & \vdots & & \vdots \\ 0 & 0 & \ldots & 1 \end{vmatrix}$$

$$= 1.$$

It follows that $\det [A; x], y]] \neq 0$.

Now assume that (ii) holds. Choose an $x_1 \neq 0$ such that $Ax_1 = 0$. Since $x_1 \neq 0$, we may choose $x_2, x_3, \ldots, x_N$, in such a way that $x_1, x_2, \ldots, x_N$ is a basis for $\mathscr{V}$. Let $y]$ be any basis for $\mathscr{W}$. The coordinates of 0 relative to any basis are always zero. Hence the coordinates of Ax_1 relative to y] are all 0's. Thus the first column of $[A; x], y$]] consists entirely of 0's—Definition 19.2—and det $[A; x], y$]] $= 0$—Corollary 27.10.

$$Q.E.D.$$

A transformation which satisfies the conditions (v)–(viii) is often called a non-singular transformation.

Because det$[A; x], y$]] varies as x] and y] vary, we must not speak of *the* determinant of A if A is a transformation from one space to a different space. It is convenient, however, to introduce the determinant of the transformation when A is a transformation on a space and to the same space.

DEFINITION 30.4.   If A is a linear transformation on a finite dimensional space $\mathscr{V}$ then its *determinant*, det A, is any one of the equal numbers det $[A; x], x$]] where x is an arbitrary basis for $\mathscr{V}$.

Section 31.   Problems

[Other problems on determinants appear in Section 25]

1. Write down the lists corresponding to all elements of S_4.

2. Let f and g be the permutations on 1, 2, 3 defined by
$$f(1) = 2, \qquad f(2) = 3, \qquad f(3) = 1,$$
$$g(1) = 2, \qquad g(2) = 1, \qquad g(3) = 3.$$
   (a) What are $f{\circ}g$ and $g{\circ}f$?
   (b) What are f^{-1} and g^{-1}?

3. Prove: If $f, g \in S_N$ then there is one and only one $h \in S_N$ such that $f \circ h = g$.

4. Consider the list (3,2,4,5,1).
   (a) Write down the values $f(1), f(2), \ldots, f(5)$ of the corresponding permutation.
   (b) Make a table listing all pairs of distinct integers between 1 and 5 inclusive. For each pair $\{i,j\}$:
   (i) Give $f(i)$ and $f(j)$.
   (ii) State whether the order of $f(i)$ and $f(j)$ is the same as or opposite to that of i and j.
   (iii) Give $[f(j)-f(i)]/[j-i]$.
   (c) Determine sgn f.
   (d) How many inversions are there in the list (3,2,4,5,1)?

5. Write down the lists corresponding to the elements of S_3. For each list give the corresponding sign. Apply Definition 27.1 to calculate
$$\begin{vmatrix} \alpha_1^1 & \alpha_2^1 & \alpha_3^1 \\ \alpha_1^2 & \alpha_2^2 & \alpha_3^2 \\ \alpha_1^3 & \alpha_2^3 & \alpha_3^3 \end{vmatrix}.$$

6. Evaluate the following determinants.

(a) $\begin{vmatrix} 1 & 0 & 2 & 3 \\ 0 & 1 & 2 & 5 \\ 4 & -2 & 0 & 1 \\ 3 & 1 & 4 & -3 \end{vmatrix}$,

(c) $\begin{vmatrix} 1 & 0 & 0 & 2 & -1 \\ 3 & 1 & 0 & 2 & 4 \\ 0 & -3 & 4 & 2 & 1 \\ -1 & 0 & 1 & 3 & -2 \\ 4 & -1 & 2 & 0 & 0 \end{vmatrix}$,

(b) $\begin{vmatrix} 2 & -1 & 0 & 1 \\ 1 & -2 & 3 & 4 \\ -1 & 2 & -3 & 1 \\ 4 & 0 & 2 & 3 \end{vmatrix}$,

(d) $\begin{vmatrix} 1 & 2 & 3 & 4 & 5 & 6 \\ 7 & 8 & 9 & 10 & 11 & 12 \\ 13 & 14 & 15 & 16 & 17 & 18 \\ 19 & 20 & 21 & 22 & 23 & 24 \\ 25 & 26 & 27 & 28 & 29 & 30 \\ 31 & 32 & 33 & 34 & 35 & 36 \end{vmatrix}$.

7. Evaluate the following determinants and simplify your answers (the superscripts are exponents, not indices).

(a) $\begin{vmatrix} 1 \end{vmatrix}$,

(c) $\begin{vmatrix} \alpha^0 & \beta^0 & \gamma^0 \\ \alpha^1 & \beta^1 & \gamma^1 \\ \alpha^2 & \beta^2 & \gamma^2 \end{vmatrix}$,

(b) $\begin{vmatrix} 1 & 1 \\ \alpha & \beta \end{vmatrix}$,

(d) $\begin{vmatrix} \alpha^0 & \beta^0 & \gamma^0 & \delta^0 \\ \alpha^1 & \beta^1 & \gamma^1 & \delta^1 \\ \alpha^2 & \beta^2 & \gamma^2 & \delta^2 \\ \alpha^3 & \beta^3 & \gamma^3 & \delta^4 \end{vmatrix}$.

8. Prove: If $\alpha_1, \alpha_2, \ldots, \alpha_N$ are scalars and β^i_j is the $(i-1)$-th power of α_j, then

$$\det[\beta] = (\alpha_N - \alpha_1) \cdot (\alpha_N - \alpha_2) \cdot \cdots \cdot (\alpha_N - \alpha_{N-1})$$
$$\times (\alpha_{N-1} - \alpha_1) \cdot (\alpha_{N-1} - \alpha_2) \cdot \cdots \cdot (\alpha_{N-1} - \alpha_{N-2})$$
$$\times \cdots$$
$$\times (\alpha_3 - \alpha_1) \cdot (\alpha_3 - \alpha_2)$$
$$\times (\alpha_2 - \alpha_1).$$

9. (a) Show that if $Ax = \lambda x$, $Ay = \mu y$, $x \neq 0$, $y \neq 0$, and $\lambda \neq \mu$ then x and y are linearly independent.

(b) Show that if $\lambda_1, \lambda_2, \ldots, \lambda_n$ are distinct scalars and, for $i = 1, 2, \ldots, n$, $Ay_i = \lambda_i y_i$, where $y_i \neq 0$, then $y_1, y_2, \ldots, y_n$ are linearly independent.

(c) Prove: If $\mathscr{V}$ is N-dimensional and the equation $\det(\lambda I - A) = 0$ has N distinct roots $\lambda_1, \lambda_2, \ldots, \lambda_N$, then

$$(\lambda_1 I - A) \cdot (\lambda_2 I - A) \cdot \cdots \cdot (\lambda_N I - A) = 0.$$

10. Let A be a linear transformation on a finite-dimensional, real, vector space and suppose that

$$Ax = \lambda x + \mu y$$
$$Ay = -\mu x + \lambda y$$

where $x \neq 0$, $y \neq 0$. Show that $\det((\lambda^2 + \mu^2)I - 2\lambda A + A^2) = 0$. HINT: Calculate $(\lambda^2 + \mu^2)x - 2\lambda Ax + A^2x$.

11. Consider the system of simultaneous linear equations

$$(31.1) \qquad \sum_{j=1}^{N} \alpha_j^i \xi^j = \eta^i, \quad i = 1, 2, \ldots, N.$$

Let $\Delta = \det[\alpha]$, let

$$\Delta_j = \begin{vmatrix} \alpha_1^1 & \cdots & \alpha_{j-1}^1 & \eta^1 & \alpha_{j+1}^1 & \cdots & \alpha_N^1 \\ \alpha_1^2 & \cdots & \alpha_{j-1}^2 & \eta^2 & \alpha_{j+2}^2 & \cdots & \alpha_N^2 \\ \vdots & & \vdots & \vdots & \vdots & & \vdots \\ \alpha_1^N & \cdots & \alpha_{j-1}^N & \eta^N & \alpha_{j+1}^N & \cdots & \alpha_N^N \end{vmatrix},$$

and let M_i^j be the minor of $[\alpha]$ obtained by deleting the i-th row and j-th column.

(a) Use Corollary 28.4 to express Δ_j as a linear combination of M_1^j, $M_2^j, \ldots, M_N^j$.

(b) Use part (a) and Theorem 28.3 to give a simple formula for $\sum_{j=1}^{N} \alpha_j^i \Delta_j$.

(c) Prove CRAMER'S RULE: If $\Delta \neq 0$, then the system (31.1) has one and only one solution. It is $\xi^j = \Delta_j / \Delta$, $j = 1, 2, \ldots, N$.

NOTE: Cramer's rule is a most inefficient method for computing solutions. It is useful when you want to avoid calculation, but need a simple, explicit, formula for the solution.

12. Let $x]_1^3$ be the natural basis for $\mathcal{R}^3$ and let A be the transformation such that

$$[A; x], x]] = \begin{bmatrix} 5 & 2 & -2 \\ -16 & -7 & 14 \\ -6 & -3 & 8 \end{bmatrix}.$$

(a) For what values of λ is $\det(\lambda I - A) = 0$? Call these values λ_1, λ_2, and λ_3.

(b) For $i = 1, 2, 3$, find a $y_i \neq 0$ such that $Ay_i = \lambda_i y_i$.

(c) What are $[I; x], y]]$ and $[I; y], x]]$?

(d) What are

$$[I; x], y]] \cdot [I; y], x]] \quad \text{and}$$
$$[I; x], y]] \cdot [A; x], x]] \cdot [I; y], x]]?$$

13. Prove:

THEOREM 31.1. *Let*

$$x_i = \begin{bmatrix} \xi_i^1 \\ \xi_i^2 \\ \vdots \\ \xi_i^N \end{bmatrix} \quad for\ i = 1, 2, \dots, N.$$

Then $x_1, x_2, \dots, x_N$ *is a basis for* $\mathscr{R}^N$ *if and only if*

$$\begin{vmatrix} \xi_1^1 & \xi_2^1 & \cdots & \xi_N^1 \\ \xi_1^2 & \xi_2^2 & \cdots & \xi_N^2 \\ \vdots & \vdots & & \vdots \\ \xi_1^N & \xi_2^N & \cdots & \xi_N^N \end{vmatrix} \neq 0.$$

14. Let

$$\Delta_{i,j} = \begin{vmatrix} i! & (i+1)! & (i+2)! & \cdots & (i+j-1)! & (i+j)! \\ (i+1)! & (i+2)! & (i+3)! & \cdots & (i+j)! & (i+j+1)! \\ (i+2)! & (i+3)! & (i+4)! & \cdots & (i+j+1)! & (i+j+2)! \\ \vdots & \vdots & \vdots & & \vdots & \vdots \\ (i+j+1)! & (i+j)! & (i+j+1)! & \cdots & (i+2j-2)! & (i+2j-1)! \\ (i+j)! & (i+j+1)! & (i+j+2)! & \cdots & (i+2j-1)! & (i+2j)! \end{vmatrix}.$$

(a) Show that

$$\Delta_{i,j} = i!j!\Delta_{i+1,j-1}.$$

HINT: Subtract a suitable multiple of each column from the next column.

(b) What is

$$\begin{vmatrix} 0! & 1! & \cdots & n! \\ 1! & 2! & \cdots & (n+1)! \\ \vdots & \vdots & & \vdots \\ n! & (n+1)! & \cdots & (2n)! \end{vmatrix} ?$$

Summary

The following important theorems and corollaries are most easily remembered in verbal form.

The determinant of a matrix is equal to that of its transpose (Th. 27.4).

Interchanging two rows or columns of a determinant changes its sign (Th. 27.5 and Cor. 27.6).

Multiplying a row or column by a scalar multiplies the determinant by that scalar (Th. 27.8 and Cor. 27.9).

Subtracting a multiple of one row or column from another leaves the determinant unchanged (Cor. 27.13 and Cor. 27.14).

If any row or column is zero or if two rows or two columns are equal then the determinant is zero (Cor. 27.10 and Cor. 27.7).

The determinant of a product is the product of the determinants (Th. 29.1).

The expansion by minors is useful both as a method of computation and as a theoretical tool.

If A is a linear transformation on a space of finite dimension then $\det [A; x], x]]$ depends only on A not on the basis $x]$. The common value of all such determinants is $\det A$.

Theorem 30.3 is the most important of all. You should know it in its entirety. Most particularly remember that: $Ax = 0$ for some $x \neq 0$ if and only if $\det A = 0$, and that A is invertible if and only if $\det A \neq 0$.

CHAPTER VII

INNER PRODUCT SPACES

To introduce a concept such as *work* the physicist employs two closely related vector spaces. He considers the space of forces and the space of displacements. The work done by a force $\vec{F}$ acting through a displacement $\vec{\Delta r}$ is a scalar, commonly called the dot product (or scalar product) of $\vec{F}$ and $\vec{\Delta r}$ and denoted by $\vec{F} \cdot \vec{\Delta r}$. One of the fundamental facts of mechanics is that this dot product is a bilinear function, i.e.,

$$(\alpha_1 F_1 + \alpha_2 F_2) \cdot \Delta r = \alpha_1 (F_1 \cdot \Delta r) + \alpha_2 (F_2 \cdot \Delta r),$$

and

$$F \cdot (\alpha_1 \cdot \Delta r_1 + \alpha_2 \cdot \Delta r_2) = \alpha_1 (F \cdot \Delta r_1) + \alpha_2 (F \cdot \Delta r_2).$$

For further discussion, consult any book on mechanics, e.g., R. B. Lindsay, *Physical Mechanics*, § 4.1.

In studying dot products physicists usually gloss over the fact that they are dealing with two quite different spaces. They can afford to do so because the spaces are distinguished by the physical nature of their elements. It is quite possible to give a mathematical theory of such dot products between related spaces and it turns out to be very like the simpler theory of products both of whose factors belong to a single space. For most of mathematics and much of physics the latter theory is the more important.

Most mathematicians and many physicists prefer to denote this so called inner product by (x, y) or by $\langle x, y \rangle$ rather than by $x \cdot y$. We will use $\langle x, y \rangle$.

If we required merely that an inner product be linear in each factor we would be studying bilinear functions in general. The most useful results appear when additional conditions—equations (32.3), (32.4), and (32.5)—are imposed on the product.

In spaces of two and three dimensions the familiar Euclidean notions of distance and perpendicularity can be phrased in terms of an inner product. Section 33 is devoted to analogous concepts in spaces of arbitrary dimension. If perpendicularity is meaningful, it is natural to expect that rectangular coordinate systems will be useful. Accordingly, in Section 34, we introduce the kind of basis most appropriate to an inner-product space.

The remaining three sections of the chapter have a single aim: spectral theorems. In a space with an inner product a special class of linear transformations, the symmetric transformations, are particularly important. If A is any transformation, symmetric or not, one may ask about its eigenvectors—non-zero vectors x such that, for some scalar λ, $Ax = \lambda x$. The corresponding scalars, λ, are called the eigenvalues of A and the set of all its eigenvalues is called the spectrum* of A. A spectral theorem describes the relationship between a transformation, its spectrum, and its eigenvectors. Three different versions appear in the text and a fourth in the problems.

Section 32. Inner Products

In this chapter the properties of the scalar field become decisive. Throughout, $\mathscr{R}$ stands for the field of real numbers and $\mathscr{C}$ for the field of complex numbers.

DEFINITION 32.1. We say that $\langle\ ,\ \rangle$ is an *inner product* on a real vector space $\mathscr{V}$ if for all $x, y, z \in \mathscr{V}$ and all $\alpha, \beta \in \mathscr{R}$,

$$(32.1) \qquad \langle x, y \rangle \in \mathscr{R},$$

$$(32.2) \qquad \langle \alpha x + \beta y, z \rangle = \alpha\langle x, z \rangle + \beta\langle y, z \rangle,$$

$$(32.3) \qquad \langle x, y \rangle = \langle y, x \rangle,$$

$$(32.4) \qquad \langle x, x \rangle \geqslant 0, \quad \text{and}$$

$$(32.5) \qquad \langle x, x \rangle = 0 \quad \text{if and only if } x = 0.$$

It is clear that (32.2) and (32.3) imply

$$(32.6) \qquad \langle x, \alpha y + \beta z \rangle = \alpha\langle x, y \rangle + \beta\langle x, z \rangle,$$

so the inner product is linear in each of its arguments. Thus an inner product is any bilinear function which has the symmetry property described by (32.3) and the property described by the two equations (32.4) and (32.5).

For bilinear forms these last two equations may be replaced by the single condition:

$$(32.7) \qquad \text{If } x \neq 0 \quad \text{then} \quad \langle x, x \rangle > 0.$$

* For transformations on infinite-dimensional spaces this definition of the spectrum is inadequate. The spectrum of such an operator may include scalars which are not eigenvalues.

(It should be obvious that (32.2) implies $(0, 0) = 0$ and that the pair of statements: $(0, 0) = 0$ and (32.7), is equivalent to the pair: (32.4) and (32.5). If this is not obvious to you, the construction of a proof will be a useful exercise in elementary logic.)

We will often say simply "$\mathscr{V}$ is an inner product space" meaning "$\mathscr{V}$ is a vector space and $\langle\ ,\ \rangle$ is a bilinear form which is an inner product for $\mathscr{V}$." It is quite possible to consider more than one inner product on a single vector space. This is done in the problems, but never in the text.

A real inner-product space is sometimes called, perhaps inappropriately, a Euclidean space.

It might seem most natural to obtain the definition of a complex inner product space by the same process as is used to obtain the definition of a complex vector space: take the definition of a real space and replace the word "real" by the word "complex" throughout. Unfortunately, this is not quite enough. The most useful definition calls for one other small, but critically important, change. If $\langle x, y \rangle$ is a complex number then it has real and imaginary parts. Say $\langle x, y \rangle = \alpha + i\beta$ where $\alpha, \beta \in \mathscr{R}$. The useful form of symmetry turns out to be not

$$\langle y, x \rangle = \alpha + i\beta = \langle x, y \rangle,$$

but $$\langle y, x \rangle = \alpha - i\beta.$$

We must recall a few facts about the complex numbers. When one sees an expression like $\alpha + i\beta$ it is usually clear from the context whether α and β are themselves complex numbers or whether they stand for the real and imaginary parts of some complex number γ. For the moment we will be precise and write explicitly $\alpha, \beta \in \mathscr{R}$, or $\alpha, \beta \in \mathscr{C}$, as the case may be.

If $\gamma = \alpha + i\beta$, $\alpha, \beta \in \mathscr{R}$, then the complex number $\alpha - i\beta$ is called the conjugate, or complex conjugate of γ and is denoted by $\bar{\gamma}$. The following formulas are probably familiar:

(32.8) $$\overline{\gamma_1 + \gamma_2} = \overline{\gamma_1} + \overline{\gamma_2},$$

(32.9) $$\overline{\gamma_1 \gamma_2} = \overline{\gamma_1} \cdot \overline{\gamma_2}, \text{ and}$$

(32.10) $$\gamma\bar{\gamma} \geqslant 0.$$

Equation (32.10) must be taken with a small grain of salt. If $\gamma = \alpha + i\beta$, $\alpha, \beta \in \mathscr{R}$, then

$$\gamma\bar{\gamma} = (\alpha + i\beta)(\alpha - i\beta) = (\alpha^2 + \beta^2) + i \cdot 0.$$

This is a complex number whose imaginary part happens to be zero.

From a rigorously logical point of view such a complex number is not quite the same thing as its real part, $\alpha^2 + \beta^2$. Nevertheless, distinguishing between a complex number such as $\alpha + i \cdot 0$ and its real part α calls for inconvenient circumlocutions, while confusing them leads to no practical difficulties. Henceforth we will confuse them.

If $\gamma \in \mathscr{C}$ then, since $\gamma\bar{\gamma}$ is a non-negative real number, $\gamma\bar{\gamma}$ has a non-negative square root. We call this real number, $\sqrt{\gamma\bar{\gamma}}$, the absolute value of the complex number γ and denote it by $|\gamma|$. We need to know little about $|\gamma|$ except its definition and the fact that $|\alpha + \beta| \leqslant |\alpha| + |\beta|$ for all $\alpha, \beta \in \mathscr{C}$.

Using this bar notation for complex conjugate, we can now define a complex inner product space.

DEFINITION 32.2. A *complex inner product space* is a complex vector space $\mathscr{V}$ together with a function $\langle\ ,\ \rangle$, called the *inner product*, which satisfies the conditions: For all $x, y, z \in \mathscr{V}$ and all $\alpha, \beta \in \mathscr{C}$,

(32.11) $$\langle x, y \rangle \in \mathscr{C},$$

(32.12) $$\langle \alpha x + \beta y, z \rangle = \alpha \langle x, z \rangle + \beta \langle y, z \rangle,$$

(32.13) $$\langle x, y \rangle = \overline{\langle y, x \rangle},$$

(32.14) $$\langle x, x \rangle \geqslant 0, \quad \text{and}$$

(32.15) $$\langle x, x \rangle = 0 \quad \text{if and only if } x = 0.$$

Aside from the so called Hermitian* symmetry condition,

$$\langle x, y \rangle = \overline{\langle y, x \rangle},$$

we have simply replaced $\mathscr{R}$ by $\mathscr{C}$ throughout Definition 32.1, but equation (32.13) has one sad consequence. In a complex inner-product space, the inner product is no longer quite linear. We still have

(32.16) $$\langle x, y + z \rangle = \langle x, y \rangle + \langle x, z \rangle,$$

but instead of $\langle x, \alpha y \rangle = \alpha \langle x, y \rangle$ we have

(32.17) $$\langle x, \alpha y \rangle = \bar{\alpha} \langle x, y \rangle.$$

* Charles Hermite (French, 1822–1901) introduced this type of symmetry in a paper published in 1854. The forms used by Hermite were certain quadratic functions rather than bilinear functions, and the work was more concerned with number theory than with pure algebra.

The proof of (32.17) is trivial. If x and y belong to a complex inner product space and $\alpha \in \mathscr{C}$ then

$$\langle x, \alpha y \rangle = \overline{\langle \alpha y, x \rangle} \qquad \text{[by (32.13)]}$$

$$= \overline{\alpha \langle y, x \rangle} \qquad \text{[by (32.12)]}$$

$$= \overline{\alpha} \cdot \overline{\langle y, x \rangle} \qquad \text{[by (32.9)]}$$

$$= \bar{\alpha} \cdot \langle x, y \rangle. \qquad \text{[by (32.13)]}$$

If α is a purely real number, then $\alpha = \bar{\alpha}$; so (32.17) yields $\langle x, \alpha y \rangle = \alpha \langle x, y \rangle$ for $\alpha \in \mathscr{R}$.

Although the phrase "complex inner-product space" is more descriptive, we will usually use the briefer synonym "unitary space."

In spite of the difference between the real number symmetry of equation (32.3) and the Hermitian symmetry of (32.13), we can do much of our work in a way that handles both cases at once. If we agree that the conjugate of a real number is the number itself then (32.13) can be used instead of (32.3), in the real case as well as in the complex case. Differences will appear later.

Section 33. Norms and Orthogonality

In this section we can treat real and complex inner-product spaces together. Remember that if $\alpha \in \mathscr{R}$ then $\bar{\alpha} = \alpha$, and (32.8), (32.9), and (32.10) are valid in either $\mathscr{R}$ or $\mathscr{C}$.

Our introduction to inner products, in Section 6, was based on the concepts of distance and perpendicularity and on the Pythagorean theorem. These concepts continue to play a dominant role in the abstract theory.

To save repeating such phrases as "if $\mathscr{V}$ is an inner-product space whose inner product is denoted by $\langle \ , \ \rangle$" we shall assume that we are provided, once and for all, with a finite-dimensional inner-product space $\mathscr{V}$ with inner product $\langle \ , \ \rangle$. The letter N will, as previously, stand for dim $\mathscr{V}$.

DEFINITION 33.1. If $x \in \mathscr{V}$, then the real number $\sqrt{\langle x, x \rangle}$ is called the *norm* of x and is denoted by $\|x\|$.

Note that even if x belongs to a unitary space, $\|x\|$ is real.

THEOREM 33.2. *If $\mathscr{V}$ is an inner product space and $x \in \mathscr{V}$ then*

(33.1) $x \neq 0 \quad implies \quad \|x\| > 0 \ and \ conversely.$

Also, for all $\alpha \in \mathscr{F}$,

(33.2) $$\|\alpha x\| = |\alpha| \cdot \|x\|.$$

PROOF. The first assertion simply rephrases (32.14) and (32.15). To prove the second we simply observe

$$\|\alpha x\| = \sqrt{\langle \alpha x, \alpha x \rangle} = \sqrt{\alpha \bar{\alpha} \langle x, x \rangle}$$
$$= \sqrt{\alpha \bar{\alpha}} \sqrt{\langle x, x \rangle} = |\alpha| \cdot \|x\|.$$

Q.E.D.

Remembering the situation in $\mathscr{R}^2$, you will recall that if x and y are two sides of a triangle then the third side is $x - y$. If x is to behave like a distance we expect to find $\|x - y\| \leqslant \|x\| + \|y\|$ or, replacing y by $-y$ and using (33.2), $\|x + y\| \leqslant \|x\| + \|y\|$. We will soon prove this, but the essential step in the proof is more important than the final result and we state it as a theorem in its own right.

THEOREM 33.3 (SCHWARZ'S INEQUALITY*). *If* $x, y \in \mathscr{V}$, *then*

(33.3) $$|\langle x, y \rangle| \leqslant \|x\| \cdot \|y\|.$$

PROOF. The proof in Section 6 is valid if $\mathscr{V}$ is a real inner-product space, but needs modification in the complex case.

If $y = 0$, then both sides of (33.3) are zero and no more need be said.

If $y \neq 0$, let $z = y/\|y\|$ and $\alpha = \langle x, z \rangle$. (Your hackles should rise when you see $y/\|y\|$ because this symbol has not had a formal definition. We omit the formalities since it seems reasonably clear that $y/\|y\|$ should mean $(1/\|y\|) \cdot y$. Whenever we can save writing by expressing a product of a scalar and a vector as a fraction with a vector numerator and a scalar denominator, we will do so. The meaning is always quite obvious and the algebraic manipulations are often simplified by this notation.) Now let β be the real number $1/\|y\|$; so $z = \beta y$ and

$$\langle z, z \rangle = \langle \beta y, \beta y \rangle = \beta \beta \langle y, y \rangle = \beta^2 \|y\|^2 = 1.$$

---

* The name "Schwarz's inequality" is deeply entrenched in the literature, but is misleading historically. In the space of continuous functions on the interval $[\alpha, \beta]$ an inner product can be defined by the formula

$$\langle x, y \rangle = \int_\alpha^\beta x(\tau) \overline{y(\tau)} \, d\tau.$$

For this inner product Schwarz's inequality asserts

$$\left| \int_\alpha^\beta x(\tau) \overline{y(\tau)} \, d\tau \right| \leqslant \left\{ \int_\alpha^\beta |x(\tau)|^2 \, d\tau \right\}^{1/2} \cdot \left\{ \int_\alpha^\beta |y(\tau)|^2 \, d\tau \right\}^{1/2}.$$

The double integral version of this formula was proved by H. R. Schwarz in 1885. However, the corresponding formula for sums had been given by Cauchy in 1821 and the simple integral form appeared in work by V. Bunyakovsky in 1859.

Using the fact that $\langle z, x \rangle = \overline{\langle x, z \rangle} = \bar{\alpha}$, we have

$$
\begin{aligned}
0 \leqslant \|x - \alpha z\|^2 &= \langle x - \alpha z, x - \alpha z \rangle \\
&= \langle x, x \rangle - \langle \alpha z, x \rangle - \langle x, \alpha z \rangle + \langle \alpha z, \alpha z \rangle \\
&= \langle x, x \rangle - \alpha \langle z, x \rangle - \bar{\alpha} \langle x, z \rangle + \alpha \bar{\alpha} \langle z, z \rangle \\
&= \|x\|^2 - \alpha \bar{\alpha} - \bar{\alpha} \alpha + \alpha \bar{\alpha} = \|x\|^2 - |\alpha|^2.
\end{aligned}
$$

Since $\|x\|$ and $|\alpha|$ are both non-negative, we may infer

$$
\|x\| \geqslant |\alpha| = |\langle x, z \rangle| = |\langle x, \beta y \rangle| = |\beta \langle x, y \rangle| = \frac{1}{\|y\|} |\langle x, y \rangle|,
$$

and $\|x\| \cdot \|y\| \geqslant |\langle x, y \rangle|.$

Q.E.D.

THEOREM 33.4.   *If* $x, y \in \mathscr{V}$, *then*

(33.4) $\|x + y\| \leqslant \|x\| + \|y\|.$

PROOF.   If α and β are known to be non-negative real numbers, then $\alpha^2 \leqslant \beta^2$ implies $\alpha \leqslant \beta$. Since both sides of (33.4) are non-negative, that inequality will follow if we can prove $\|x + y\|^2 \leqslant (\|x\| + \|y\|)^2$. Using Schwarz's inequality we find

$$
\begin{aligned}
\|x + y\|^2 &= |\langle x + y, x + y \rangle| = |\langle x, x \rangle + \langle x, y \rangle + \langle y, x \rangle + \langle y, y \rangle| \\
&\leqslant |\langle x, x \rangle| + |\langle x, y \rangle| + |\langle y, x \rangle| + |\langle y, y \rangle| \\
&\leqslant \|x\|^2 + \|x\| \cdot \|y\| + \|y\| \cdot \|x\| + \|y\|^2 \\
&= (\|x\| + \|y\|)^2.
\end{aligned}
$$

Q.E.D.

Let us turn to perpendicularity. Our definition is suggested by the situation in $\mathscr{R}^2$. There the vectors x and y are perpendicular if and only if the Pythagorean relation

$$
\|x\|^2 + \|y\|^2 = \|x - y\|^2
$$

holds. In a real inner-product space this Pythagorean relation is equivalent to the simpler condition $\langle x, y \rangle = 0$. (See Problem 38.5.)

DEFINITION 33.5.   We say that two vectors x and y in $\mathscr{V}$ are *orthogonal* if $\langle x, y \rangle = 0$.

In this context the synonyms "orthogonal" and "perpendicular" are about equally common, but there are a few phrases in which it is customary to use one and not the other.

In Euclidean solid geometry one also defines the notion of perpendicularity between a plane and a line. In N dimensions we obviously need a more general concept. We ask three questions. When is a vector x orthogonal to a subspace? When are two subspaces perpendicular? What is the analogue of the line through a given point and perpendicular to a given plane? The first definitions come straight out of Euclid (Book XI, Definitions 3 and 4).

DEFINITION 33.6. A vector x is *perpendicular* to a subspace $\mathscr{X}$ if, for all $y \in \mathscr{X}$,

$$\langle x, y \rangle = 0.$$

DEFINITION 33.7. We say that the subspaces $\mathscr{X}$ and $\mathscr{Y}$ are *orthogonal* and write $\mathscr{X} \perp \mathscr{Y}$ if, for all $x \in \mathscr{X}$, $y \in \mathscr{Y}$,

$$\langle x, y \rangle = 0.$$

We need these definitions only for subspaces, but they make perfectly good sense if $\mathscr{X}$ and $\mathscr{Y}$ are arbitrary subsets of $\mathscr{V}$.

In three-dimensional Euclidean space a plane passing through the origin is a certain subspace; let us call it $\mathscr{X}$. The line through the origin and perpendicular to $\mathscr{X}$ consists of all vectors x which are perpendicular to $\mathscr{X}$. This example suggests that if we have any subspace $\mathscr{X}$ of $\mathscr{V}$, we may be interested in the set of all vectors which are perpendicular to $\mathscr{X}$.

DEFINITION 33.8. The *orthogonal complement* of a subspace $\mathscr{X}$ of $\mathscr{V}$ is the set

(33.5) $\mathscr{X}^{\perp} = \{x \mid x \text{ is perpendicular to } \mathscr{X}\}.$

Using Definition 33.6, we can rewrite (33.7) as

$$\mathscr{X}^{\perp} = \{x \mid \text{for all } y \in \mathscr{X}, \langle x, y \rangle = 0\}.$$

The name "orthogonal complement" is intended to suggest that $\mathscr{X}^{\perp}$ is a subspace complementary to $\mathscr{X}$. To show that $\mathscr{X}^{\perp}$ is a subspace is a routine exercise (see below), but our proof that $\mathscr{X}$ and $\mathscr{X}^{\perp}$ are complementary requires a special kind of basis. The symbol "$\mathscr{X}^{\perp}$" is usually read "$\mathscr{X}$ perpendicular."

THEOREM 33.9. *If $\mathscr{X}$ is a subspace of $\mathscr{V}$, so is $\mathscr{X}^{\perp}$.*

PROOF. Problem 38.9.

THEOREM 33.10. *If $x]_1^n$ is a basis for a subspace $\mathscr{X}$ of $\mathscr{V}$, then $y \in \mathscr{X}^{\perp}$ if and only if*

(33.6) $\langle y, x_i \rangle = 0 \quad \text{for } i = {}'1, 2, \ldots, n.$

PROOF. We must show that if (33.6) holds and $z \in \mathscr{X}$, then $\langle y, z \rangle = 0$. But if $z \in \mathscr{X}$, then z has coordinates, say $\zeta^1, \zeta^2, \ldots, \zeta^n$, relative to $x]_1^n$,

$$z = \sum_{i=1}^{n} \zeta^i x_i,$$

and $$\langle y, z \rangle = \langle y, \sum_{i=1}^{n} \zeta^i x_i \rangle = \sum_{i=1}^{n} \overline{\zeta^i} \langle y, x_i \rangle = 0.$$

The converse is so trivial that we do not even include it among the problems.

Q.E.D.

Section 34.   Orthonormal Bases

In Section 21 we found dual bases most convenient. With inner-product spaces we can do even better and obtain bases which are essentially their own duals. Then we asked that

$$\tilde{x}^i(x_j) = \delta_j^i;$$

now we ask that

(34.1) $$\langle x_i, x_j \rangle = \delta_{ij} = \begin{cases} 1 & \text{if } i = j, \\ 0 & \text{if } i \neq j. \end{cases}$$

This is the first formula which suggests that, in inner-product spaces, the superscript-subscript conventions of preceding sections cease to be of much use. In a sense, a real inner-product space is its own dual and a complex inner-product space is almost its own dual, so the location of the indices is no longer a help. Because exponents will be needed, it is better to use subscripts only. Henceforth, indices, whether on elements of $\mathscr{V}$ or on coordinates, will usually be written as subscripts.

Our real aim is to find bases satisfying (34.1), but the easiest route to the bases is to consider arbitrary sets which satisfy the equation.

DEFINITION 34.1.   A finite set of vectors $x_1, x_2, \ldots, x_n$ is called an *orthonormal set* if

$$\langle x_i, x_j \rangle = \delta_{ij}.$$

An orthonormal set which is also a basis is called an *orthonormal basis*.

THEOREM 34.2.   *If $x]_1^N$ is an orthonormal basis for $\mathscr{V}$ and y is any vector in $\mathscr{V}$, then the coordinates of y, relative to $x]$, are $\langle y, x_i \rangle$.   Thus*

$$y = \sum_{i=1}^{N} \langle y, x_i \rangle x_i.$$

Moreover

$$\| y \|^2 = \sum_{i=1}^{N} |\langle y, x_i \rangle|^2.$$

PROOF. Consider an orthonormal basis $x]$ and an arbitrary $y \in \mathscr{V}$. Let $\eta_1, \eta_2, \ldots, \eta_N$ be the coordinates of y. Then $y = \sum_j \eta_j x_j$ and

$$\langle y, x_i \rangle = \langle \sum_j \eta_j x_j, x_i \rangle = \sum_j \eta_j \langle x_j, x_i \rangle$$

$$= \sum_j \eta_j \delta_{ji} = \eta_i, \quad \text{for } i = 1, 2, \ldots, N.$$

Also

$$\| y \|^2 = \langle y, y \rangle = \langle \sum_j \eta_j x_j, \sum_k \eta_k x_k \rangle$$

$$= \sum_j \sum_k \eta_j \bar{\eta}_k \langle x_j, x_k \rangle = \sum_j \sum_k \eta_j \bar{\eta}_k \delta_{jk}$$

$$= \sum_j \eta_j \bar{\eta}_j = \sum_j |\eta_j|^2 = \sum_j |\langle y, x_j \rangle|^2.$$

$$\text{Q.E.D.}$$

THEOREM 34.3. *An orthonormal set of vectors is linearly independent.*

PROOF. Let $x_1, x_2, \ldots, x_n$ be any orthonormal set. If

$$\sum_i \alpha_i x_i = 0,$$

then for $j = 1, 2, \ldots, n$,

$$0 = \langle \sum_{i=1}^{n} \alpha_i x_i, x_j \rangle = \sum_{i=1}^{n} \alpha_i \langle x_i, x_j \rangle = \sum_{i=1}^{n} \alpha_i \delta_{ij} = \alpha_j.$$

$$\text{Q.E.D.}$$

COROLLARY 34.4. *An orthonormal set of vectors in $\mathscr{V}$ is a basis for $\mathscr{V}$ if and only if it spans $\mathscr{V}$.*

COROLLARY 34.5. *A set of n orthonormal vectors in $\mathscr{V}$ is a basis for $\mathscr{V}$ if and only if $n = \dim \mathscr{V}$.*

Our object is to prove that every finite-dimensional inner-product space has an orthonormal basis. In fact we do a bit more. We show that starting from any orthonormal set, we can enlarge the set until we obtain a basis. The first step is to show how to add one more vector to the set in such a way that the enlarged set also is orthonormal.

THEOREM 34.6. *If $x_1, x_2, \ldots, x_n$ is an orthonormal set in $\mathscr{V}$ and y is an element of $\mathscr{V}$, then*

$$z = y - \sum_{i=1}^{n} \langle y, x_i \rangle x_i$$

is orthogonal to each x_j. Moreover, if $y \notin \mathrm{Sp}[x_1, x_2, \ldots, x_n]$, then $\|z\| \neq 0$, and if we let $x_{n+1} = z/\|z\|$, the set $x_1, \ldots, x_n, x_{n+1}$ is ortho-normal.

PROOF. The theorem makes three assertions, each of which is easily established.

For $j = 1, 2, \ldots, n$ we have

$$(34.2) \qquad \langle z, x_j \rangle = \left\langle y - \sum_{i=1}^{n} \langle y, x_i \rangle x_i, x_j \right\rangle$$

$$= \langle y, x_j \rangle - \sum_{i=1}^{n} \langle y, x_i \rangle \langle x_i, x_j \rangle$$

$$= \langle y, x_j \rangle - \sum_{i=1}^{n} \langle y, x_i \rangle \delta_{ij}$$

$$= \langle y, x_j \rangle - \langle y, x_j \rangle = 0.$$

Now assume $y \notin \mathrm{Sp}[x_1, x_2, \ldots, x_n]$. Were $\|z\| = 0$, we would have $z = 0$ and $y = \sum_{i=1}^{n} \langle y, x_j \rangle x_i$. This last equation is impossible because it asserts that y is a linear combination of the x's, i.e., an element of $\mathrm{Sp}[x_1, x_2, \ldots, x_n]$.

The hypothesis of the theorem is that $\langle x_i, x_j \rangle = \delta_{ij}$ for $i, j = 1, 2, \ldots, n$; so all we need to show is that

$$\langle x_{n+1}, x_i \rangle = 0 \quad \text{for } i = 1, 2, \ldots, n;$$

$$\langle x_i, x_{n+1} \rangle = 0 \quad \text{for } i = 1, 2, \ldots, n; \quad \text{and}$$

$$\langle x_{n+1}, x_{n+1} \rangle = 1.$$

The first two follow immediately from (34.2) and the third is so easy that you should certainly be able to make the computation mentally.

Q.E.D.

THEOREM 34.7. *Every finite-dimensional inner-product space has an orthonormal basis.*

PROOF. Choose any non-zero vector y_1 and "normalize" it, i.e., let $x_1 = y_1/\|y_1\|$. Then the set consisting of x_1 alone is an orthonormal set. If $N = \dim \mathscr{V} > 1$, then x_1 alone cannot span $\mathscr{V}$ and we can choose $y_2 \notin \mathrm{Sp}[x_1]$. By Theorem 34.6 we can find x_2; so x_1, x_2 is an ortho-normal set. Repeating this process we can enlarge our orthonormal set, one vector at a time, until we have a set with exactly N vectors in it. By Corollary 34.5 this set is a basis.

Q.E.D.

At the n-th step of this enlarging process we must choose a $y_n \notin$ Sp$[x_1, x_2, \ldots, x_{n-1}]$. If we are given a basis $z_1, z_2, \ldots, z_n$ to start with, we can choose $y_n = z_n$. The stepwise orthonormalization of a given basis in this manner is called the Gram-Schmidt orthogonalization process.

Our first application of orthonormal bases is to prove that an orthogonal complement really is a complement.

THEOREM 34.8. *If* $x]_1^m$ *is an orthonormal basis for* $\mathscr{X}$ *and* $y]_1^n$ *is an orthonormal basis for* $\mathscr{X}^\perp$, *then* $x_1, \ldots, x_m, y_1, \ldots, y_n$ *is an orthonormal basis for* $\mathscr{V}$.

PROOF. To say that $x_1, \ldots, x_m, y_1, \ldots, y_n$ is an orthonormal set is to say that

(34.3) $\langle x_i, x_j \rangle = \delta_{ij}$ for $i, j = 1, 2, \ldots, m$;

(34.4) $\langle y_i, y_j \rangle = \delta_{ij}$ for $i, j = 1, 2, \ldots, n$; and

(34.5) $\langle x_i, y_j \rangle = 0$ for $i = 1, 2, \ldots, m; j = 1, 2, \ldots, n$.

Equations (34.3) and (34.4) are among the hypotheses of the theorem. To say that $y_j \in \mathscr{X}^\perp$ is to say that, for all $x \in \mathscr{X}^\perp$, $\langle x, y_j \rangle = 0$. In particular $\langle x_i, y_j \rangle = 0$.

We now know that $x_1, \ldots, x_m, y_1, \ldots, y_n$ are linearly independent; so the theorem will be proved as soon as we know that they span $\mathscr{V}$. If they did not, we could choose $y \notin$ Sp$[x_1, \ldots, x_m, y_1, \ldots, y_n]$ and apply Theorem 34.6 to choose a vector y_{n+1} so that $x_1, \ldots, x_m, y_1, \ldots, y_n, y_{n+1}$ would be an orthonormal set. Thus y_{m+1} would be orthogonal to $x_1, x_2, \ldots, x_m$ and hence (by Theorem 33.10) $y_{n+1} \in \mathscr{X}^\perp$. Thus the n-dimensional space $\mathscr{X}^\perp$ would contain $n+1$ linearly independent vectors $y_1, y_2, \ldots, y_{n+1}$, which is impossible.

Q.E.D.

COROLLARY 34.9. *If* $\mathscr{X}$ *is a subspace of* $\mathscr{V}$, *then* $\mathscr{X}$ *and* $\mathscr{X}^\perp$ *are complementary subspaces.*

COROLLARY 34.10. *If* $\mathscr{X}$ *is a subspace of* $\mathscr{V}$, *then*

$$\dim \mathscr{X}^\perp = N - \dim \mathscr{X}.$$

COROLLARY 34.11. *If* $\mathscr{X}$ *is a subspace of* $\mathscr{V}$, *then* $\mathscr{X}^{\perp\perp} = \mathscr{X}$.

PROOF. Problem 38.13.

Section 35.   Eigenvalues

In a variety of physical problems, interest centers around a given linear transformation A and those scalars λ and vectors x which satisfy the equation

$$(35.1) \qquad\qquad Ax = \lambda x.$$

We cannot go into the physics here; we will simply mention two applications.   In the theory of vibrations one is interested in the frequencies with which a given system can oscillate.   For many important systems these can be determined by finding those $\lambda < 0$ such that (35.1) has a non-zero solution, x.   Each such λ corresponds to a possible oscillation of frequency $\sqrt{-\lambda}/2\pi$ and the corresponding x's serve to describe the way the system can oscillate.

In parts of quantum theory each physical system determines an infinite-dimensional complex inner-product space.   Each linear transformation of a certain type corresponds to some physical quantity, like the energy or momentum, of the system.   In such an infinite-dimensional space, equation (35.1), alone, is not adequate; one needs to seek some more general condition.   Nevertheless, each value of λ such that (35.1) has a non-zero solution x is a possible value of the physical quantity corresponding to the transformation A.   For example, the wave lengths of the bright lines in the spectrum of an element are easily computed as soon as one has found the non-trivial solutions of a certain equation in the form (35.1).

DEFINITION 35.1.   If A is a linear transformation on $\mathscr{V}$, we say that a scalar λ is an *eigenvalue* of A if, for some vector $x \neq 0$,

$$Ax = \lambda x.$$

Such a vector x is called an *eigenvector* of A corresponding to the eigenvalue λ.

There is a host of synonyms for "eigenvalue" and "eigenvector." Purists who like to speak only one language at a time, may use "proper value" and "proper vector" or "Eigenwert" and "Eigenvektor."   The adjective "characteristic" often replaces "proper," and various other synonyms are to be found in the literature.

In Definition 35.1 there is no mention of inner products, and eigenvalues and eigenvectors are useful in arbitrary vector spaces as well as in inner-product spaces.

In this and the two following sections we give one answer to a fundamental question: Can we reconstruct the transformation A from a knowledge of its eigenvalues and eigenvectors? In general the answer is no. In fact a very simple example (Problem 38.17) shows that some transformations have no eigenvalues at all. In this section we shall show that every transformation on a complex vector space does have at least one eigenvalue. In the next section we introduce a special class of transformations which are particularly important for applications. Even in the real case, transformations in this class always have eigenvalues. Finally we show that all such transformations can be described completely in terms of their eigenvalues and eigenvectors.

THEOREM 35.2. *The eigenvalues of a linear transformation A are the scalars λ which satisfy the equation*

$$(35.2) \qquad \det(\lambda I - A) = 0,$$

where I is the identity transformation on $\mathscr{V}$.

PROOF. This is just Corollary 23.13 or Theorem 30.3 applied to the transformation $\lambda I - A$. To say that λ is an eigenvalue is to say that there is an $x \neq 0$ such that $Ax = \lambda x$ or, equivalently, $(\lambda I - A)x = 0$. Both Corollary 23.13 and Theorem 30.3 say that the latter condition is equivalent to (35.2).

Q.E.D.

THEOREM 35.3. *If A is a linear transformation on $\mathscr{V}$, then the function p which assigns to each scalar λ the value*

$$p(\lambda) = \det(\lambda I - A)$$

is a polynomial* of degree dim $\mathscr{V}$.

We give two proofs. The first is very easy for those who can visualize the behavior of linear forms. It may be quite transparent after you have done Problem 38.18.

FIRST PROOF. Let $x]_1^n$ be a basis for $\mathscr{V}$ and let φ be the alternating N-form such that $\varphi(x_1, x_2, \ldots, x_N) = 1$. Then

$$(35.3) \qquad p(\lambda) = \det(\lambda I - A)$$
$$= \varphi(\lambda x_1 - A x_1, \lambda x_2 - A x_2, \ldots, \lambda x_N - A x_N).$$

Use the linearity of φ to expand the right-hand side of (35.3). There are 2^N terms in the expansion. Each is of the form $(-1)^{N-k} \lambda^k \varphi(y_1, y_2, \ldots, y_N)$ where, for some k different values of the index i, $y_i = x_i$; while for the remaining $N-k$ values, $y_i = A x_i$. There is only one term of the highest possible degree in λ and it is $\lambda^N \varphi(x_1, x_2, \ldots, x_N) = \lambda^N$.

Q.E.D.

---

* One word of warning: at places in advanced mathematics the approach to polynomials undergoes a subtle change. In this text polynomials are always the old familiar polynomial functions.

SECOND PROOF.   Let $x]$ be a basis for $\mathscr{V}$ and let $[\alpha]=[A\,;x],x]]$.   If just one basis is used, the matrix of the identity transformation is the identity matrix so $[I\,;x],x]]=[\delta]$ where δ is the Kronecker δ.   According to Definition 27.1,

$$\det[\lambda I-A\,;x],x]]$$

$$= \sum_{f\in S_N} \operatorname{sgn} f\cdot(\lambda\delta^1_{f(1)}-\alpha^1_{f(1)})(\lambda\delta^2_{f(2)}-\alpha^2_{f(2)})\cdots(\lambda\delta^N_{f(N)}-\alpha^N_{f(N)}).$$

Consider the term corresponding to a particular f.   Apart from the sign, it is a product of N factors, the i-th one being

$$\lambda\delta^i_{f(i)}-\alpha^i_{f(i)} = \begin{cases} \alpha^i_{f(i)} & \text{if}\quad f(i)\ne i, \\ \lambda-\alpha^i_{f(i)} & \text{if}\quad f(i)=i. \end{cases}$$

Clearly this term is a polynomial whose degree is not greater than N. Furthermore, the polynomial contains λ to the N-th power if and only if every factor is of the form $\lambda-\alpha^i_{f(i)}$, i.e., if $f(i)=i$ for $i=1,2,\ldots,N$. In this case f is the special permutation e (see Definition 26.1) and the term is

$$\operatorname{sgn} e\cdot(\lambda-\alpha^1_1)(\lambda-\alpha^2_2)\cdots(\lambda-\alpha^N_N)$$

$$= \lambda^N-\left(\sum_{i=1}^N \alpha^i_i\right)\lambda^{N-1}+\cdots+(-1)^N\alpha^1_1\alpha^2_2\cdots\alpha^N_N.$$

What we have just said amounts to this: (i) $\det[\lambda I-A\,;x],x]]$ is a sum of polynomials in λ, (ii) exactly one of these polynomials is of degree N and in it the coefficient of λ^N is 1, and (iii) all the other polynomials are of lower degree.   When we add such polynomials the result is obviously a polynomial whose leading term is λ^N.

Q.E.D.

DEFINITION 35.4.   The polynomial $\det(\lambda I-A)$ is called the *characteristic polynomial** of A and the equation $\det(\lambda I-A)=0$ is called the characteristic equation of A.

Now, for the first time, we need to appeal to a theorem wholly outside our present subject—the so called *Fundamental Theorem of Algebra*.†

---

* Some authors define the characteristic polynomial as $\det(A-\lambda I)$, but $\det(A-\lambda I)=(-1)^N\det(\lambda I-A)$.   For neatness' sake, we prefer that the coefficient of λ^N be 1 rather than $(-1)^N$.

† In spite of its name, the theorem really belongs to analysis rather than to algebra. The great Carl Friedrich Gauss (1777–1855) gave the first adequate proof of it in his doctoral dissertation : "Demonstratio nova theorematis omnem functionem algebraicam rationalem integram unius variabilis in factores reales primi vel secundi gradus resolvi posse," Helmstedt : 1799.

Gauss himself published four proofs of the theorem and many more have appeared since.   Several of them can be found in the *American Mathematical Monthly*.   Gauss' third proof remains one of the easiest and clearest.

FUNDAMENTAL THEOREM OF ALGEBRA.   *If $p(\lambda)$ is a polynomial (with real or complex coefficients) of degree $N \geqslant 1$, then there is at least one complex number λ_0 such that $p(\lambda_0) = 0$.*

In other words every polynomial equation has at least one complex root.

THEOREM 35.5.   *Every linear transformation on a finite-dimensional $(N \geqslant 1)$ complex vector space has at least one eigenvalue.*

PROOF.   By Theorem 35.2 the eigenvalues are the roots of the characteristic equation, by Theorem 35.3 this is a polynomial equation, and by the fundamental theorem of algebra it has at least one root.

Q.E.D.

Section 36.   Symmetric Transformations

In Section 35 we mentioned the fact that some transformations have no eigenvalues whatever.   Even in complex spaces, where every transformation has at least one eigenvalue, a transformation may not possess an adequate set of eigenvectors.   So far we have made no connection between inner products and eigenvectors, but in the majority of cases where eigenvalues are important, a special type of transformation is involved.

DEFINITION 36.1.   A linear transformation A on an inner-product space $\mathscr{V}$ is called *symmetric* if

$$\langle Ax, y \rangle = \langle x, Ay \rangle$$

for all $x, y \in \mathscr{V}$.

For reasons which we do not explore here, symmetric transformations are often called self-adjoint, or sometimes, in the unitary case only, Hermitian.

THEOREM 36.2.   *The eigenvalues of a symmetric transformation are real.*

PROOF.   For real spaces the theorem is nothing but an obvious tautology.

Assume that λ is an eigenvalue of a symmetric transformation A. That is to say, there is an $x \neq 0$ such that $Ax = \lambda x$.   We want to show that if $\lambda = \mu + i\nu$, $\mu, \nu \in \mathscr{R}$, then $\nu = 0$.   Saying that $\nu = 0$ is the same thing as saying that

$$\bar{\lambda} = \mu - i\nu = \mu + i\nu = \lambda.$$

However,

$$\lambda \langle x, x \rangle = \langle \lambda x, x \rangle = \langle Ax, x \rangle = \langle x, Ax \rangle = \langle x, \lambda x \rangle = \bar{\lambda} \langle x, x \rangle.$$

Since $\langle x, x \rangle \neq 0$, we may divide by it to get $\lambda = \bar{\lambda}$.

Q.E.D.

One useful connection between symmetric transformations and orthogonality is given by the following easy theorem.

THEOREM 36.3. *If A is a symmetric transformation and x and y are eigenvectors of A corresponding to different eigenvalues, then $\langle x, y \rangle = 0$.*

PROOF. Assume that x corresponds to the eigenvalue λ and y to the eigenvalue $\mu \neq \lambda$. Then, since A is symmetric,

(36.1) $$\langle Ax, y \rangle = \langle \lambda x, y \rangle = \lambda \langle x, y \rangle \quad \text{and}$$

(36.2) $$\langle Ax, y \rangle = \langle x, Ay \rangle = \langle x, \mu y \rangle = \bar{\mu} \langle x, y \rangle.$$

But Theorem 36.2 tells us that μ is real, so $\mu = \bar{\mu}$; and subtracting (36.2) from (36.1) yields

$$(\lambda - \mu)\langle x, y \rangle = 0.$$

If we divide by the non-zero number $\lambda - \mu$, we get

$$\langle x, y \rangle = 0$$

Q.E.D.

To prove that every transformation on a complex vector space has an eigenvalue we needed one hard theorem from analysis—the fundamental theorem of algebra. The fact that the eigenvalues of symmetric transformations are real suggests that, for such transformations, we might be able to transfer the complex theorem to the real case. This can be done by means of a slightly artificial construction, but we prefer to get the real result by a purely real variable method. The advantage of this method is that it exhibits an important minimal property of the eigenvectors. Here, too, we need one hard theorem, which we borrow (without proof) from analysis. We state only the special case which we need.

WEIERSTRASS MINIMUM PRINCIPLE* (SPECIAL CASE). *If f is a*

---

* In the second half of the nineteenth century Weierstrass (1815–1897) was the leader in the movement to put the calculus on a sounder logical foundation—to prove basic results previously taken for granted. I have not been able to trace the history of this particular theorem beyond references to his lectures in the 1860's. (See, for example, the footnote on page 14 of W. F. Osgood's *Lehrbuch der Funktionentheorie*, 2nd ed., Leipzig and Berlin, 1912.) In 1870 Weierstrass published a famous example showing that the corresponding conclusion in infinite-dimensional spaces may be false.

For a proof of the theorem, consult any up-to-date book on advanced calculus.

Weierstrass is also responsible for a proof (in 1858) of a version of the spectral theorem.

continuous function of N real variables, defined and continuous on the unit sphere,

$$\{(\xi_1, \xi_2, \ldots, \xi_N) \mid \sum_{i=1}^{N} \xi_i^2 = 1\},$$

then f has a minimum value, i.e., there is a point $(\xi_1, \xi_2, \ldots, \xi_N)$ on the sphere such that, for all $(\eta_1, \eta_2, \ldots, \eta_N)$ on the sphere,

$$f(\xi_1, \xi_2, \ldots, \xi_N) \leqslant f(\eta_1, \eta_2, \ldots, \eta_N).$$

We need only an even more specialized version of this principle, but we want it in vector form.

MINIMUM PRINCIPLE (VERY SPECIAL CASE). *If A is a linear transformation on an N-dimensional real* inner-product space $\mathscr{V}$, then there is an $x \in \mathscr{V}$ such that*

$$\|x\| = 1$$

and, for all $y \in \mathscr{V}$,

(36.3) $\langle Ax, x\rangle \|y\|^2 \leqslant \langle Ay, y\rangle.$

Let $x]_1^N$ be an orthonormal basis for $\mathscr{V}$, and consider the function f defined by

$$f(\eta_1, \eta_2, \ldots, \eta_N) = \langle A \sum_i \eta_i x_i, \sum_j \eta_j x_j\rangle$$

$$= \sum_i \sum_j \eta_i \eta_j (Ax_i, x_j).$$

Since f is a quadratic function, it is continuous.   Let $(\xi_1, \xi_2, \ldots, \xi_N)$ be a point where f assumes its minimum on the unit sphere.   (There may be more than one such point.   In fact, the special form of f guarantees that there are either exactly two or infinitely many, but we simply choose a particular one.)   Let x be the fixed vector

$$x = \sum_{i=1}^{N} \xi_i x_i.$$

Since $(\xi_1, \xi_2, \ldots, \xi_N)$ is on the sphere, $\sum_i \xi_i^2 = 1$, and hence

$$\|x\|^2 = \langle x, x\rangle = \langle \sum_i \xi_i x_i, \sum_j \xi_j x_j\rangle$$

$$= \sum_i \sum_j \xi_i \xi_j \langle x_i, x_j\rangle = \sum_i \sum_j \xi_i \xi_j \delta_{ij}$$

$$= \sum_i \xi_i \xi_i = 1.$$

---

* The conclusion is valid also for symmetric transformations on a complex space. The proof of this assertion is very like the one given.

When $y = 0$, the equation (36.3) reduces to $0 \leqslant 0$. Thus all we have to do is to establish the equation (36.3) under the assumption $y \neq 0$. Actually we establish the equivalent relation $\langle Ax, x \rangle \leqslant \| y \|^{-2} \langle Ay, y \rangle$.

Consider the arbitrary vector $y \neq 0$, and let $\eta_i = \langle y, x_i \rangle / \| y \|$. Since $\langle y, x \rangle$ is real, $\langle y, x \rangle^2 = |\langle y, x \rangle|^2$, and Theorem 34.2 gives

$$\sum_i \eta_i^2 = \sum_i [\langle y, x_i \rangle / \| y \|]^2 = \sum_i \langle y, x_i \rangle^2 / \| y \|^2$$

$$= \| y \|^2 / \| y \|^2 = 1.$$

Thus $(\eta_1, \eta_2, \ldots, \eta_N)$ is on the unit sphere, and hence

$$f(\xi_1, \xi_2, \ldots, \xi_N) \leqslant f(\eta_1, \eta_2, \ldots, \eta_N).$$

Since the $\langle y, x_i \rangle$'s are the coordinates of y we also have

$$\sum_i \eta_i x_i = \sum_i [\langle y, x_i \rangle / \| y \|] x_i = \| y \|^{-1} \sum_i \langle y, x_i \rangle x_i = \| y \|^{-1} y.$$

Hence

$$\langle Ax, x \rangle = \langle A \sum_i \xi_i x_i, \sum_j \xi_j x_j \rangle = f(\xi_1, \xi_2, \ldots, \xi_N) \leqslant f(\eta_1, \eta_2, \ldots, \eta_N)$$

$$= \langle A \sum_i \eta_i x_i, \sum_j \eta_j x_j \rangle = \langle A \| y \|^{-1} y, \| y \|^{-1} y \rangle = \| y \|^{-2} \langle Ay, y \rangle.$$

$$\text{Q.E.D.}$$

As we will soon show, if A is symmetric then every x which satisfies (36.3) is an eigenvector of A. This fact is important for infinite-dimensional spaces and for complex spaces. Our proof covers these cases even though we will use the theorem only for the finite-dimensional, real case.

THEOREM 36.4. *Assume that A is a symmetric linear transformation on an inner-product space $\mathscr{V}$. If x is a vector such that for all $y \in \mathscr{V}$*

(36.4) $$0 \leqslant \langle Ay, y \rangle \langle x, x \rangle - \langle Ax, x \rangle \langle y, y \rangle,$$

then

(36.5) $$\langle x, x \rangle Ax = \langle Ax, x \rangle x.$$

PROOF. Let $z = Ax$ and apply (36.4) to $y = z + \tau x$ where τ is an arbitrary *real* number. To save writing let

$$\alpha = \langle x, x \rangle,$$

$$\beta = \langle x, z \rangle = \langle x, Ax \rangle = \langle Ax, x \rangle = \langle z, x \rangle,$$

$$\gamma = \langle z, z \rangle = \langle Ax, z \rangle = \langle z, Ax \rangle = \langle Az, x \rangle, \quad \text{and}$$

$$\delta = \langle Az, z \rangle.$$

Then

$$\langle Ay, y \rangle = \langle Az + \tau Ax, z + \tau x \rangle$$
$$= \langle Az, z \rangle + \tau \langle Ax, z \rangle + \tau \langle Az, x \rangle + \tau^2 \langle Ax, x \rangle$$
$$= \delta + 2\gamma\tau + \beta\tau^2,$$

and, similarly,

$$\langle y, y \rangle = \langle z + \tau x, z + \tau x \rangle = \gamma + 2\beta\tau + \alpha\tau^2.$$

Substituting into (36.4) we see that, for all τ,

(36.6) $$0 \leqslant (\delta + 2\gamma\tau + \beta\tau^2)\alpha - \beta(\gamma + 2\beta\tau + \alpha\tau^2)$$
$$= (\alpha\delta - \beta\gamma) + 2(\gamma\alpha - \beta^2)\tau.$$

Remember that (36.6) is valid for *all* τ. This can occur only if $\alpha\delta - \beta\gamma \geqslant 0$ and $\gamma\alpha - \beta^2 = 0$. The former is of no interest to us, but the latter is just what we need.

Our object is to show that $0 = \langle x, x \rangle Ax - \langle Ax, x \rangle x = \alpha z - \beta x$ or, equivalently—see Definition 32.2—that $\langle \alpha z - \beta x, \alpha z - \beta x \rangle = 0$. We find

$$\langle \alpha z - \beta x, \alpha z - \beta x \rangle = \alpha^2 \langle z, z \rangle - \beta\alpha \langle x, z \rangle - \alpha\beta \langle z, x \rangle + \beta^2 \langle x, x \rangle$$
$$= \alpha^2 \gamma - \beta\alpha\beta - \alpha\beta^2 + \beta^2\alpha$$
$$= \alpha(\alpha\gamma - \beta^2) = 0.$$

$$\text{Q.E.D.}$$

COROLLARY 36.5. *If A is a symmetric transformation on an inner-product space $\mathscr{V}$, $\|x\| = 1$, and $\langle Ax, x \rangle \| y \|^2 \leqslant \langle Ay, y \rangle$ for all $y \in \mathscr{V}$, then x is an eigenvector of A corresponding to the eigenvalue $\langle Ax, x \rangle$.*

PROOF. Problem 38.26.

COROLLARY 36.6. *Every symmetric linear transformation on a finite-dimensional real inner-product space has an eigenvalue.*

For any transformation A, Theorem 17.4 in Chapter IV gave the relation between the dimensions of its null space $\mathscr{N}(A)$ and its range rng A. For symmetric operators, there is a far stronger result connecting the null space and the range.

THEOREM 36.7. *If A is a symmetric linear transformation on the finite-dimensional space $\mathscr{V}$, then rng $A = \mathscr{N}(A)^{\perp}$.*

PROOF. Theorem 13.5 asserts: If a subspace has the same dimension as the whole space, then it is equal to the whole space. Theorem 17.4 and Corollary 34.10 say that rng A and $\mathscr{N}(A)^{\perp}$ have the same dimension, namely $N - \dim \mathscr{N}(A)$. Thus all we need to do is to show either rng A is a subspace of $\mathscr{N}(A)^{\perp}$ or $\mathscr{N}(A)^{\perp}$ is a subspace of rng A. The former is easy.

Assume $x \in \operatorname{rng} A$. Then, for some $z \in \mathscr{V}$, $x = Az$. Hence, for all $y \in \mathscr{N}(A)$,

$$\langle x, y \rangle = \langle Az, y \rangle = \langle z, Ay \rangle = \langle z, 0 \rangle = 0; \quad \text{so } x \in \mathscr{N}(A)^{\perp}.$$
$$\text{Q.E.D.}$$

Section 37. The Spectral Theorem

Consider a symmetric transformation, A. We wish to solve two problems: (i) describe A in terms of its eigenvalues and eigenvectors, and (ii) find an orthonormal basis, $x]$, so that the matrix $[A; x], x]]$ is particularly simple. Once we have solved the former, the latter proves to be an easy corollary.

In attacking (i) it is convenient, not to look at the individual eigenvectors, but to collect together all the eigenvectors corresponding to a given eigenvalue. Let us denote the eigenvalues of A by $\lambda_1, \lambda_2, \ldots, \lambda_n$, and let us write A_i for $A - \lambda_i I$.   (In listing the eigenvalues we count each distinct value only once, even though some may be multiple roots of the characteristic equation.)

A vector x is an eigenvector corresponding to λ_i if and only if $x \neq 0$ and $Ax = \lambda_i x$. The latter is equivalent to

$$0 = Ax - \lambda_i x = Ax - \lambda_i Ix = (A - \lambda_i I)x = A_i x.$$

Thus a non-zero vector is an eigenvector corresponding to λ_i if and only if it is in the null space of A_i. The restriction to non-zero vectors is essential in speaking of eigenvectors, but at this stage it begins to get in the way. Let us look, then, at the whole null space $\mathscr{N}(A_i)$ and let us abbreviate this to $\mathscr{N}_i$.

The crucial fact is that these null spaces, or eigenspaces, span the whole of $\mathscr{V}$.

THEOREM 37.1 (SPECTRAL THEOREM, 1ST VERSION). *If A is a symmetric linear transformation on a finite-dimensional inner-product space $\mathscr{V}$, if $\lambda_1, \lambda_2, \ldots, \lambda_n$ are the eigenvalues of A, and if $\mathscr{N}_i$ is the null space of $A - \lambda_i I$, then for each x in $\mathscr{V}$ there is one and only one set of vectors $x_1, x_2, \ldots, x_n$ such that*

$$x_i \in \mathscr{N}_i \quad \text{for } i = 1, 2, \ldots, n$$

and $$x = \sum_{i=1}^{n} x_i.$$

PROOF. Look at the set of all vectors y which can be written as a sum of n vectors, one from each $\mathscr{N}_i$. As in Section 13, we denote this set by $\sum_{i=1}^{n} \mathscr{N}_i$, and we now set $\mathscr{N} = \sum_{i=1}^{n} \mathscr{N}_i$. The existence part of the theorem simply asserts that $\mathcal{N} = \mathcal{V}$. To prove this we proceed by contradiction.

Were $\mathcal{N} \neq \mathcal{V}$, then its orthogonal complement $\mathcal{N}^{\perp}$ would be some honest vector space and not just the zero vector. Let us see how A behaves on $\mathcal{N}$ and on $\mathcal{N}^{\perp}$.

If y is any element of $\mathcal{N}$, then $y = y_1 + y_2 + \cdots + y_n$ for some choice of $y_i \in \mathcal{N}_i$. Since $y_i \in \mathcal{N}_i$, $Ay_i = \lambda_i y_i \in \mathcal{N}_i$. Thus

$$Ay = Ay_1 + Ay_2 + \cdots + Ay_n = \lambda_1 y_1 + \lambda_2 y_2 + \cdots + \lambda_n y_n$$

is also a sum of vectors chosen from the $\mathcal{N}_i$ and hence $Ay \in \mathcal{N}$.

Now consider any $z \in \mathcal{N}^{\perp}$. We want to show that $Az \in \mathcal{N}^{\perp}$, i.e., for all $y \in \mathcal{N}$, $(Az, y) = 0$. The symmetry assumption is now essential. We have, for $y \in \mathcal{N}$, $Ay \in \mathcal{N}$; and since z is assumed to be perpendicular to anything in $\mathcal{N}$, it follows that $(Az, y) = (z, Ay) = 0$. This fact— that $z \in \mathcal{N}^{\perp}$ implies $Az \in \mathcal{N}^{\perp}$—may be described by saying that A maps $\mathcal{N}^{\perp}$ into $\mathcal{N}^{\perp}$. In the standard technical phrase: $\mathcal{N}^{\perp}$ is an *invariant* subspace of A.

It is now quite easy to see that $\mathcal{N}^{\perp}$ cannot contain anything except the zero vector. We have a symmetric transformation on $\mathcal{N}^{\perp}$ to $\mathcal{N}^{\perp}$. If you want, you may think of this as A itself or you may be more precise and define the restriction of A to $\mathcal{N}^{\perp}$ by letting

$$Bz = Az \quad \text{for } z \in \mathcal{N}^{\perp}.$$

From the point of view of $\mathcal{N}^{\perp}$ alone, $\langle\ ,\ \rangle$ is still a perfectly good inner product and B is obviously symmetric. If $\mathcal{N}^{\perp}$ were not the trivial space $\{0\}$, B would have an eigenvector and this would also be an eigenvector of A. Since each eigenvector of A lies in some $\mathcal{N}_i$ and hence in $\mathcal{N}$, none of the eigenvectors can possibly lie in $\mathcal{N}^{\perp}$. This completes the first part of the theorem.

It remains to show that any given vector x has only one representation as a sum of vectors chosen from the $\mathcal{N}_i$. We assume

$$x = \sum_{i=1}^{n} x_i = \sum_{i=1}^{n} y_i$$

and $\qquad x_i, y_i \in \mathcal{N}_i \quad \text{for } i = 1, 2, \ldots, n.$

Our object is to show that $x_i = y_i$ for $i = 1, 2, \ldots, n$. Let $z_i = x_i - y_i$. Then $z_i \in \mathcal{N}_i$ and $\sum_{i=1}^{n} z_i = 0$. For $i \neq j$, z_i and z_j are either zero vectors or eigenvectors corresponding to different eigenvalues. Hence $\langle z_j, z_j \rangle = 0$ and, for $i = 1, 2, \ldots, n$,

$$0 = \left\langle \sum_{i=1}^{n} z_i, z_j \right\rangle = \sum_{i=1}^{n} \langle z_i, z_j \rangle = \langle z_j, z_j \rangle.$$

Thus $z_j = 0$.

$$\text{Q.E.D.}$$

The most interesting interpretation of this theorem is geometrical. For $x \in \mathcal{N}_i$, $Ax = \lambda_i x$; so all vectors in $\mathcal{N}_i$ are stretched in the same proportion. The whole of $\mathcal{N}_i$ is simply stretched (or compressed) without any rotation or distortion. The theorem says that the whole of $\mathcal{V}$ is spanned by a set of mutually perpendicular subspaces each of which undergoes a simple expansion or contraction when acted upon by A.

THEOREM 37.2 (SPECTRAL THEOREM, 2ND VERSION). *If A is a symmetric transformation on a finite-dimensional inner-product space $\mathcal{V}$, then $\mathcal{V}$ has an orthonormal basis $x]_1^N$ such that each x_i is an eigenvector.*

PROOF. Using the notation of the previous theorem, we can choose an orthonormal basis for each subspace $\mathcal{N}_i$. Put all the vectors so chosen into a single set and call them $x_1, x_2, \ldots, x_M$. At this point we have no guarantee that $M = N$.

We chose the x's so that each is normalized, $\|x_i\| = 1$. If we look at x_i and x_j, $i \neq j$, then either x_i and x_j belong to the same $\mathcal{N}_k$, in which case we chose them to be orthogonal, or x_i and x_j are eigenvectors for different eigenvalues, in which case they are orthogonal by Theorem 36.3. Thus the x's form an orthonormal set.

If y is any vector in $\mathcal{V}$, then y is a sum of vectors, $y_1, y_2, \ldots, y_n$, with $y_i \in \mathcal{N}_i$. Each y_i is a linear combination of certain x's and it follows that y itself is a linear combination of the x's. Thus the x's span $\mathcal{V}$ and, since they are orthonormal, form a basis.

Q.E.D.

COROLLARY 37.3 (SPECTRAL THEOREM, 3RD VERSION). *If A is a symmetric transformation on a finite-dimensional inner-product space $\mathcal{V}$, then $\mathcal{V}$ has an orthonormal basis $x]$ such that*

$$(37.1) \qquad [A\,; x],\, x]] = \begin{bmatrix} \lambda_1 & 0 & 0 & \ldots & 0 \\ 0 & \lambda_2 & 0 & \ldots & 0 \\ 0 & 0 & \lambda_3 & \ldots & 0 \\ \vdots & \vdots & \vdots & & \vdots \\ 0 & 0 & 0 & \ldots & \lambda_N \end{bmatrix}$$

where $\lambda_1, \lambda_2, \ldots, \lambda_N$ are the eigenvalues of A.

In this corollary some of the λ's may be equal. As a matter of fact, if you think how the matrix describes the transformation, you should see that if a particular eigenvalue λ appears exactly m times, then $\dim \mathcal{N}(A - \lambda I) = m$ and that λ is an m-fold root of the characteristic equation.

None of these three versions of the spectral theorem is suitable for generalization to infinite-dimensional inner-product spaces. A different version, which can be generalized, is suggested in Problems 38.27 through 38.31.

Section 38. Problems

1. In each part, (a) to (k), we name a vector space and give a formula defining $\langle \ , \ \rangle$. For each part, (i) state whether the given formula defines an inner product on the given space, (ii) if $\langle \ , \ \rangle$ is an inner product, prove those formulas among (32.1), (32.2), (32.3), and (32.7) which are not obvious, and (iii) if $\langle \ , \ \rangle$ is not an inner product, give an explicit example showing that $\langle \ , \ \rangle$ does not satisfy some one of (32.1), (32.2), (32.3), and (32.7).

(a) $\mathscr{P}$; $\langle x, y \rangle = \displaystyle\int_{-1}^{+1} x(\tau)y(\tau)\, d\tau.$

(b) $\mathscr{C}(-\infty, +\infty)$; $\langle x, y \rangle = \displaystyle\int_{-1}^{+1} x(\tau)y(\tau)\, d\tau.$

(c) $\mathscr{P}$; $\langle x, y \rangle = \displaystyle\int_{-1}^{+1} \tau x(\tau)y(\tau)\, d\tau.$

(d) $\mathscr{P}$; $\langle x, y \rangle = \displaystyle\int_{-\infty}^{+\infty} e^{-\tau^2} x(\tau)y(\tau)\, d\tau.$

(e) $\mathscr{C}(-\infty, +\infty)$; $\langle x, y \rangle = \displaystyle\int_{-\infty}^{+\infty} e^{-\tau^2} x(\tau)y(\tau)\, d\tau.$

(f) $\mathscr{P}$; $\langle x, y \rangle = \displaystyle\int_{-1}^{+1} [x(\tau)+y(\tau)]\, d\tau.$

(g) $\mathscr{P}$; $\langle x, y \rangle = \displaystyle\int_{0}^{+1} x(\tau)y(\tau^2)\, d\tau.$

(h) $\mathscr{P}$; $\langle x, y \rangle = \displaystyle\int_{0}^{1} x(\tau)y(1-\tau)\, d\tau.$

(In the rest of this problem and throughout this chapter indices are usually written as subscripts. Superscripts are exponents.)

(i) $\mathscr{R}^2$; $\left\langle \begin{bmatrix} \xi_1 \\ \xi_2 \end{bmatrix}, \begin{bmatrix} \eta_1 \\ \eta_2 \end{bmatrix} \right\rangle = \xi_1\eta_1 + 2\xi_2\eta_2.$

(j) $\mathscr{R}^2$; $\left\langle \begin{bmatrix} \xi_1 \\ \xi_2 \end{bmatrix}, \begin{bmatrix} \eta_1 \\ \eta_2 \end{bmatrix} \right\rangle = \xi_1\eta_1 - \xi_2\eta_2.$

(k) $\mathscr{R}^2$; $\left\langle \begin{bmatrix} \xi_1 \\ \xi_2 \end{bmatrix}, \begin{bmatrix} \eta_1 \\ \eta_2 \end{bmatrix} \right\rangle = \xi_1^2 + \eta_2^2.$

2. Prove that if $x]_1^N$ is any basis for vector space $\mathscr{V}$ and if we define a function $\langle \ , \ \rangle$ by the formula

$$(38.1) \qquad\qquad\qquad \langle x, y \rangle = \sum_{i=1}^{N} \xi_i \bar{\eta}_i$$

where the ξ's and η's are the coordinates of x and y relative to $x]$, then $\mathscr{V}$ becomes an inner product space with $\langle \ , \ \rangle$ as inner product.

NOTE: It is common practice to speak of $\mathscr{R}^N$ and $\mathscr{C}^N$ as inner product spaces without specifying the inner product. It is taken for granted that the inner product is defined by (38.1) where $x]_1^N$ is the natural basis. With this basis the coordinates are simply the entries in the columns so

$$\left\langle \begin{bmatrix} \xi_1 \\ \xi_2 \\ \vdots \\ \xi_N \end{bmatrix}, \begin{bmatrix} \eta_1 \\ \eta_2 \\ \vdots \\ \eta_N \end{bmatrix} \right\rangle = \xi_1\bar{\eta}_1 + \xi_2\bar{\eta}_2 + \cdots + \xi_N\bar{\eta}_N.$$

3. Let $\mathscr{V}$ consist of all continuous complex-valued functions on the interval $\{\tau \mid \alpha \leqslant \tau \leqslant \beta\}$, with the operations defined by (2.12) and (2.13). For $x, y \in \mathscr{V}$ let

$$\langle x, y \rangle = \int_{\alpha}^{\beta} x(\tau)\overline{y(\tau)} \, d\tau.$$

Show that $\langle \ , \ \rangle$ is an inner product for $\mathscr{V}$.

4. Prove (32.16) from (32.12) and (32.13). More generally, show that for all $x, y, u, v \in \mathscr{V}$ and all $\alpha, \beta, \gamma, \delta \in \mathscr{F}$.

$$\langle \alpha x + \beta y, \gamma u + \delta v \rangle = \alpha\bar{\gamma}\langle x, u \rangle + \beta\bar{\gamma}\langle y, u \rangle + \alpha\bar{\delta}\langle x, v \rangle + \beta\bar{\delta}\langle y, v \rangle.$$

5. Show that:

(a) In any inner-product space, $\langle x, y \rangle = 0$ implies

$$\|x\|^2 + \|y\|^2 = \|x+y\|^2.$$

(b) In a real inner-product space, $\|x\|^2 + \|y\|^2 = \|x+y\|^2$ implies $\langle x, y \rangle = 0$.

(c) In a unitary space, if $y = ix \neq 0$, then

$$\|x\|^2 + \|y\|^2 = \|x+y\|^2 \quad \text{but} \quad \langle x, y \rangle \neq 0.$$

(d) In a unitary space, if both

$$\|x\|^2 + \|y\|^2 = \|x+y\|^2 \quad \text{and} \quad \|x\|^2 + \|iy\|^2 = \|x+iy\|^2,$$

then $\langle x, y \rangle = 0$.

6. Let $\mathscr{V}$ be a *complex* vector space and let φ be a bilinear form on $\mathscr{V}$. Show that φ cannot satisfy the condition: For all $x \in \mathscr{V}$, if $x \neq 0$ then $\varphi(x, x) > 0$.

NOTE: This shows that the "positive definiteness" conditions, (32.14) and (32.15), are incompatible with genuine bilinearity.

7. Consider the space $\mathscr{P}_3$ with the inner product $\langle \ , \ \rangle$ defined by

$$\langle x, y \rangle = \int_0^1 x(\tau)y(\tau)\,d\tau,$$

and treat $\mathscr{P}_1$ as a subspace of $\mathscr{P}_3$.

(a) What is the orthogonal complement of $\mathscr{P}_1$?

(b) Find a basis for $\mathscr{P}_1^\perp$.

8. Let

$$\left\langle \begin{bmatrix} \xi_1 \\ \xi_2 \end{bmatrix}, \begin{bmatrix} \eta_1 \\ \eta_2 \end{bmatrix} \right\rangle = \xi_1\eta_1 + \xi_1\eta_2 + \xi_2\eta_1 + 5\xi_2\eta_2.$$

(a) Show that $\langle \ , \ \rangle$ is an inner product for $\mathscr{R}^2$.

(b) With respect to this inner product find the orthogonal complement of

$$\mathscr{X} = \{ \begin{bmatrix} \xi_1 \\ \xi_2 \end{bmatrix} \mid \xi_1 = \xi_2 \}.$$

(c) Graph $\mathscr{X}$ and $\mathscr{X}^\perp$.

(d) Graph also the orthogonal complement of $\mathscr{X}$ with respect to the usual inner product for $\mathscr{R}^2$.

9. Without referring to the results in Section 34, prove: If $\mathscr{X}$ is a subspace of $\mathscr{V}$, then so is $\mathscr{X}^\perp$ and $\mathscr{X} \cap \mathscr{X}^\perp = 0$.

10. Prove:

Theorem 38.1. *If $x]_1^N$ is an orthonormal basis for an inner-product space $\mathscr{V}$, then for all $y, z \in \mathscr{V}$,*

$$\langle y, z \rangle = \sum_{i=1}^N \langle y, x_i \rangle \langle x_i, z \rangle.$$

11. Using the usual inner product for $\mathscr{R}^3$ (see Problem 2) apply the Gram-Schmidt process to obtain orthonormal bases starting from the bases:

(a) $$\begin{bmatrix} -1 \\ 1 \\ 1 \end{bmatrix}, \begin{bmatrix} 1 \\ -1 \\ 1 \end{bmatrix}, \begin{bmatrix} 1 \\ 1 \\ -1 \end{bmatrix};$$

(b) $$\begin{bmatrix} 1 \\ 2 \\ 2 \end{bmatrix}, \begin{bmatrix} 0 \\ 0 \\ 1 \end{bmatrix}, \begin{bmatrix} 0 \\ 1 \\ 0 \end{bmatrix}.$$

(c) Apply the Gram-Schmidt process to the natural basis for $\mathscr{R}^3$ in order to get a basis orthonormal with respect to the inner product defined by

$$\left\langle \begin{bmatrix} \xi_1 \\ \xi_2 \\ \xi_3 \end{bmatrix}, \begin{bmatrix} \eta_1 \\ \eta_2 \\ \eta_3 \end{bmatrix} \right\rangle = \xi_1\eta_1 + \xi_1\eta_2 + \xi_1\eta_3 + \xi_2\eta_1 + 2\xi_2\eta_2 + \xi_2\eta_3$$
$$+ \xi_3\eta_1 + \xi_3\eta_2 + 5\xi_3\eta_3.$$

12. In Problem 11 the use of the Gram-Schmidt process is completely artificial and rather trivial, but the process does have non-trivial applications.

Several different inner products for the space $\mathscr{P}$ have important applications. For example, let

$$\langle x, y \rangle = \int_{-1}^{+1} x(\tau)y(\tau)\,d\tau,$$

$$(x, y) = \int_{0}^{\infty} e^{-\tau}x(\tau)y(\tau)\,d\tau,$$

$$[x, y] = \int_{-\infty}^{+\infty} e^{-\tau^2/2}x(\tau)y(\tau)\,d\tau.$$

You may take for granted the obvious fact that $\langle \ , \ \rangle, (\ , \ )$, and $[\ , \ ]$ are inner products for $\mathscr{P}$.

Let $y_n(\tau) = \tau^n$, for $n = 0, 1, 2, \ldots$. If you apply the Gram-Schmidt process to the sequence $y_0, y_1, y_2, \ldots$, you will obtain a sequence $x_0, x_1, x_2, \ldots$ of polynomials, orthonormal with respect to the given inner product, and such that x_n is of the n-th degree. It is customary to use, not the x's so obtained, but certain multiples of them.

(a) Calculate $\langle y_i, y_j \rangle$, (y_i, y_j), and $[y_i, y_j]$.   HINT:

$$\int_{-\infty}^{+\infty} e^{-\tau^2/2}\tau^n\,d\tau = \begin{cases} \sqrt{2\pi} & \text{if } n = 0, \\ 1.3 \cdot \ \cdots \ \cdot (n-1) \cdot \sqrt{2\pi} & \text{if } n = 2, 4, \ldots, \\ 0 & \text{if } n = 1, 3, \ldots, \end{cases}$$

(b) Find x_0, x_1, x_2, x_3, and x_4, using the inner product $\langle \ , \ \rangle$.

(c) Find x_0, x_1, x_2, and x_3, using the inner product $(\ , \ )$.

(d) Find x_0, x_1, x_2, x_3, and x_4, using the inner product $[\ , \ ]$.

13. Prove Corollary 34.11.

14. For any subspaces $\mathscr{X}$ and $\mathscr{Y}$ of $\mathscr{V}$, show that

$$(\mathscr{X} + \mathscr{Y})^{\perp} = \mathscr{X}^{\perp} \cap \mathscr{Y}^{\perp} \quad \text{and}$$

$$(\mathscr{X} \cap \mathscr{Y})^{\perp} = \mathscr{X}^{\perp} + \mathscr{Y}^{\perp}.$$

Interpret these results geometrically for the special cases where $\mathscr{X}$ and $\mathscr{Y}$ are lines in three-space and for the case where they are planes in three-space.

15. Suppose

$$[A; x], x]] = \begin{bmatrix} 2 & -2 & -1 \\ -1 & 3 & 1 \\ 2 & -4 & -1 \end{bmatrix},$$

where $x]$ is the natural basis for $\mathscr{R}^3$.

(a) What are the eigenvalues of A?

(b) Find three linearly independent eigenvectors of A.

16. Let $\mathscr{V}$ be an N-dimensional vector space, not necessarily an inner-product space. Assume that A is a linear transformation on $\mathscr{V}$ to $\mathscr{V}$ and that $x_1, x_2, \ldots, x_N$ are linearly independent eigenvectors of A. Let λ_i be the eigenvalue associated with x_i. What is $[A; x], x]]$?

17. Show that the transformation on $\mathscr{R}^2$ whose matrix (relative to the natural basis) is

$$\begin{bmatrix} 0 & 1 \\ -1 & 0 \end{bmatrix}$$

has no eigenvalues.

18. Let φ be a 2-form on a vector space $\mathscr{V}$, and assume $x_1, x_2, y_1, y_2 \in \mathscr{V}$. Show that

$$\varphi(\lambda x_1 + y_1, \lambda x_2 + y_2) = \alpha \lambda^2 + \beta \lambda + \gamma,$$

where

$$\alpha = \varphi(x_1, x_2),$$

$$\beta = \varphi(x_1, y_2) + \varphi(x_2, y_1), \quad \text{and}$$

$$\gamma = \varphi(y_1, y_2).$$

Find similar expressions for α, β, γ, and δ, if φ is a 3-form on $\mathscr{V}$ and

$$\alpha \lambda^3 + \beta \lambda^2 + \gamma \lambda + \delta = \varphi(\lambda x_1 + y_1, \lambda x_2 + y_2, \lambda x_3 + y_3).$$

19. Prove:

THEOREM 38.2. *If A is a linear transformation on a finite-dimensional inner-product space $\mathscr{V}$, then there is one and only one transformation A^* such that*

$$\langle A^* x, y \rangle = \langle x, Ay \rangle$$

for all $x, y \in \mathscr{V}$.   HINT: Use Theorem 34.2 to derive a formula for A^*.

DEFINITION 38.3.   If A is a linear transformation on an inner-product space $\mathscr{V}$, then its *adjoint* is the transformation A^* such that

$$\langle A^* x, y \rangle = \langle x, Ay \rangle$$

for all $x, y \in \mathscr{V}$.

---

20. Let A be a linear transformation on an inner-product space $\mathscr{V}$. Show that:

(a) $(A^*)^* = A$.

(b) For all $x, y \in \mathscr{V}$

$$\langle Ax, y \rangle = \langle x, A^* y \rangle.$$

(c) $A^* A$ is symmetric.

21. Let A be a linear transformation on a unitary space $\mathscr{V}$. Show that:

(a) $(A + A^*)/2$ is symmetric.

(b) $(A - A^*)/2i$ is symmetric.

(c) If $A^* A = A A^*$ and x is an eigenvector of A corresponding to the eigenvalue λ, then x is an eigenvector of A^* corresponding to the eigenvalue $\bar{\lambda}$.

(d) If $[\alpha] = [A; x], x]$ and $[\beta] = [A^*; x], x]$, then $\alpha_j^i = \bar{\beta}_i^j$. (Here the superscripts are indices, not exponents.)

DEFINITION 38.4.   A linear transformation A on a unitary space is called a *unitary transformation* if

$$A^* = A^{-1}.$$

Summary

In a real vector space an inner product is a bilinear form which is symmetric, i.e., $\langle x, y \rangle = \langle y, x \rangle$, and "positive definite", i.e., $\langle x, x \rangle > 0$ if $x \neq 0$. In a complex space the symmetry is Hermitian symmetry, $\langle x, y \rangle = \overline{\langle y, x \rangle}$, and linearity in the second argument is replaced by

$$(x, \alpha y + \beta z) = \bar{\alpha}(x, y) + \bar{\beta}(x, z).$$

Schwarz's inequality, $|(x, y)|^2 \leqslant (x, x)(y, y)$, is useful in countless different contexts, and so is its corollary: $\|x + y\| \leqslant \|x\| + \|y\|$.

You must be thoroughly familiar with perpendicularity of two vectors, of a vector and a subspace, and of two subspaces. Orthogonal complements are equally important. A vector is perpendicular to subspace if it is perpendicular to each element of a basis for the subspace.

Orthonormal bases are convenient and can be obtained by the Gram-Schmidt process. If $x]_1^N$ is an orthonormal basis, the coordinates of y are $\langle y, x_i \rangle$, $i = 1, 2, \ldots, N$.

Eigenvalues and eigenvectors are tremendously important. Eigenvalues can be found by solving the characteristic equation. For a symmetric transformation, the eigenvalues are real and eigenvectors corresponding to different eigenvalues are orthogonal.

All three forms of the spectral theorem are needed. Learn them.

APPENDICES

Appendix A. Equations and Identities

1. When you enter a new realm of mathematics it takes constant care to be sure that you work within the framework appropriate to the new area. With experience this care becomes more automatic and less conscious, but even the best mathematicians are liable to errors. Adequate caution is impossible without a thorough understanding of the nature and use of equations and identities.

You must understand both the basic principles involved and the means of communication employed. About the principles there is wide agreement, but in the matter of style you will find enormous variation from writer to writer. If you have a command of the English language, an instinct to anticipate the reader's difficulties, and good taste in the arrangement of formulas, you may safely neglect everything we say about purely stylistic questions. In any case, you should not accept it uncritically. If you wish to depart from our suggestions, do so whenever you believe that the departure makes for greater clarity or elegance.

2. We will use the term "equation" in the broadest possible sense, meaning thereby any formula containing the sign "$=$". Typical equations contain letters which may be playing either of two roles. They may be standing for specific objects or for arbitrary objects to be chosen at will from some particular class of objects. Both uses are familiar in elementary algebra. If you see the equation

$$2x+3 \;=\; 7,$$

experience has taught you that x is standing for a particular object, and you see at a glance that if the equation is valid, then x is standing for the number 2. On the other hand, if you meet the equation

$$x+y \;=\; y+x,$$

you will not attempt to solve for x because you know that this equation is valid for all possible choices of x and y.

This double role played by our symbols is discussed more fully in Appendix B, "Variables and Unknowns." Here we need only remark that one must know whether an equation is universally true for all reasonable values of the

233

variables appearing in it or whether it is true only for certain particular values. The usual agreement is:

> *If there is no preceding statement telling what the letters stand for, the reader is to assume that the equation is universally valid.*

Of course, the universality is subject to limitations. If you take "$x+y=y+x$" and replace the "x" and "y" by the names of numbers, you always get a true statement. If you replace the "x" by "3" and the "y" by "George Washington", you get only nonsense. The task of deciding what sort of object may replace the variables in a universal equation is often left to the reader.

In Section 1, equations (1.1)–(1.6) are universally valid, provided the x, y, and z stand for "arrows" and the α and β for numbers. When we turn to (1.8) and (1.9), we find equations which are clearly not true for all possible arrows $x, z, y, w_0, x_0,$ and z_0. This is quite proper because each of these symbols has been assigned a definite meaning.

3. Careful logicians may vary in their interpretation of the meaning of mathematical reasoning, but when a mathematician sets out to show that a certain equation is true, the symbols he uses stand each for a particular object. In establishing general propositions this object may be any object chosen from a whole class of objects, but throughout a given argument the letter is to stand for just one particular thing. Universally valid equations play a part in the argument, but usually in the background.

Look at equation (1.11), for example. The aim here is to get a simple formula expressing w in terms of the two arrows, x and z. All the letters are standing for particular arrows obtained from a single triangle ABC. The fact that the reasoning applies to any triangle whatsoever is important—it means that our conclusion is true quite generally—but in the argument, we are talking about just one triangle.

What you find in (1.11) is a display which can be represented schematically as

$$\cdots = \text{- - -}$$
$$= /\,/\,/$$
$$= :\,:\,:$$
$$\text{etc.}$$

Such a scheme asserts that

$$\cdots = \text{- - -},$$
and
$$\text{- - -} = /\,/\,/,$$
and
$$/\,/\,/ = :\,:\,:, \text{ etc.}$$

You are invited to check each of these separate assertions and to recognize that from them it follows that $\cdots$, - - -, $/\,/\,/$, and $:\,:\,:$, are all just different names for the same quantity (in this case, w).   Usually we are interested only in the fact that the first and the last are equal.

How do you check the individual assertions?   Compare the expressions to the right of the "$=$" on the first two lines of (1.11).   Examining their form you see that they differ in that the second line has

$$\left\{\left(\frac{1}{\|x\|}*x\right)\oplus\left(\frac{1}{\|z\|}*z\right)\right\}$$

where the first line has w_0.   You are supposed to remember that

$$\left\{\left(\frac{1}{\|x\|}*x\right)\oplus\left(\frac{1}{\|z\|}*z\right)\right\}$$

and w_0 are really one and the same thing, but in case you have forgotten, there is a parenthetical reference to (1.10) where their identity was established.

In going from the second to the third line we use a universally valid equation, namely (1.5):

$$\alpha*(x\oplus y) = (\alpha*x)\oplus(\alpha*y).$$

To say that (1.5) is universally valid is to say that we obtain a true statement whenever we replace its variables "α", "x", and "y", by the names of objects from the appropriate *universe of discourse*.   In this case we may replace "α" by the name of a number and "x" and "y" by the names of arrows, being sure to replace every occurrence of "α" by the name of the same number, every occurrence of "x" by the name of the same arrow, and every occurrence of "y" by the name of the same arrow (which may or may not be different from that used in replacing "x").   Note that the "x" in (1.5) and the "x" in (1.11) are quite unrelated.   The former is simply a dummy awaiting replacement; the latter is the name of a specific arrow—that from B to C.   Similarly the "α" in (1.5) is a dummy; that in (1.11) is a particular number.

The reasoning you are supposed to go through runs roughly as follows: We need to know that

$$\alpha*\left\{\left(\frac{1}{\|x\|}*x\right)\oplus\left(\frac{1}{\|z\|}*z\right)\right\}\quad\text{and}$$

$$\left\{\alpha*\left(\frac{1}{\|x\|}*x\right)\right\}\oplus\left\{\alpha*\left(\frac{1}{\|z\|}*z\right)\right\}$$

are the same thing.   The hint suggests we look at (1.5).   Can we make a substitution in (1.5) to get the desired equality:

$$\alpha*\left\{\left(\frac{1}{\|x\|}*x\right)\oplus\left(\frac{1}{\|z\|}*z\right)\right\} = \left\{\alpha*\left(\frac{1}{\|x\|}*x\right)\right\}\oplus\left\{\alpha*\left(\frac{1}{\|z\|}*z\right)\right\}?$$

Of course ! Replace the dummy "α" of (1.5) by the real number "α", replace the "x" by "$\left(\dfrac{1}{\|x\|}*x\right)$" and replace "$y$" by "$\left(\dfrac{1}{\|z\|}*z\right)$". (We have made one other change for aesthetic reasons. We have used braces, { }, where (1.5) has ordinary parentheses.)

In the next step (1.3) must be used twice. Replacing "α" by "α", "β" by "$1/\|x\|$" and "x" by "x" shows us that the "$\{(\alpha \cdot 1/\|x\|) *x\}$" which starts the fourth line is just another name for the $\left\{\alpha*\left(\dfrac{1}{\|x\|}*x\right)\right\}$ which appears immediately above it. A slightly different application of (1.3) tells us that the remaining terms are equal.

No hint is given for the next equality. You note what has changed: $(\alpha \cdot 1/\|x\|)$ has become $\alpha/\|x\|$ and $(\alpha \cdot 1/\|z\|)$ has become $\alpha/\|z\|$. You are expected to recognize that $\alpha \cdot 1/\|x\|$ and $\alpha/\|x\|$ are equal without any special knowledge. Since α and $\|x\|$ are numbers, this is the most elementary of elementary algebra.

Naturally, it is not intended that you go into one bit more of this reasoning than is necessary to carry conviction. One great object of mathematical notation is to make such steps as quick and automatic as possible.

4. Of all methods for establishing the equality of two expressions, the serial equality like $\cdots = \cdots = /// = ::: $, etc., is the easiest to write and to explain. In general, what is helpful to you in keeping track of your reasoning will be a help to your reader and, vice versa, what will help your reader will help you to work with assurance and accuracy. As always, neatness is essential to accuracy. Never crowd your work; paper is cheap compared with time. In going to a new line, never break a formula in the middle of a natural unit. The most natural place for a break is at an "$=$" and the universal custom is to put the "$=$" at the beginning of a new line, never at the end of the old one. At the beginning of a new line it catches the eye and tells the reader what to look for. In simple formulas of this kind it is quite proper to have several "$=$"'s on a single line, but it is usually easiest to read a long series of equalities when each line has only the one "$=$" at the beginning. If a formula is so complicated that it must be broken somewhere else, try to pick the major dividing point. This will come at a symbol for an operation, e.g., "$+$" or "$\div$"; put this symbol at the start of the new line and indent further than you indent at an "$=$".

There are many special notations involving one type of bracket—( ), [ ], { }, or $\langle$ $\rangle$—where no other will do; but for general purposes these are completely interchangeable. In complicated formulas you will find that a shrewd choice of which type to use where can be a great help in focusing attention on the crucial points. In general, try to use the same type for comparable parts of the formula.

The hints are optional. It is always a ticklish question to decide how much explanatory matter to include in a mathematical argument. Too little leaves the reader at a loss to follow your reasoning; too much distracts him from the true issues and, what is worse, bores him. This book is largely concerned with questions of reasoning and the explanations tend towards excessive length. You should practice greater brevity.

Examination papers present an exception. Within the limited time available you should ordinarily make your explanations as complete as possible. In grading, mathematicians are usually loath to penalize verbosity, but often object to obscurity.

5. In establishing an equation, the serial equality method is ideally simple to write and to explain, but often other methods of argument are more natural and hence clearer.

One method is to start from a known equation, such as (1.15), and from it to infer various consequences. The types of substitution employed are identical with those we have just been considering.

For example, to obtain (1.16) from (1.15) we first apply (1.2) to get

$$(1*z \oplus \beta*y) \oplus \frac{-\alpha}{\|x\|}*y = 1*z \oplus \left(\beta*y \oplus \frac{-\alpha}{\|x\|}*y\right)$$

and

$$(A.1) \quad \left(\left[\alpha\frac{\|x\|+\|z\|}{\|x\|\cdot\|z\|}\right]*z \oplus \frac{\alpha}{\|x\|}*y\right) \oplus \frac{-\alpha}{\|x\|}*y$$
$$= \left[\alpha\frac{\|x\|+\|z\|}{\|x\|\cdot\|z\|}\right]*z \oplus \left(\frac{\alpha}{\|x\|}*y \oplus \frac{-\alpha}{\|x\|}*y\right).$$

On the left-hand side of (1.15) we replace

$$\text{``}(1*z \oplus \beta*y) \oplus \frac{-\alpha}{\|x\|}*y\text{''} \quad \text{by} \quad \text{``}1*z \oplus \left(\beta*y \oplus \frac{-\alpha}{\|x\|}*y\right)\text{''}$$

which we now know to be another name for the same arrow. Similarly the right-hand side of (1.16) is obtained from that of (1.15) by making the substitution authorized by equation (A.1).

The step from (1.14) to (1.15) is of quite a different nature. Equation (1.15) is of the form

$$\cdots \oplus \{(- - -) \oplus ///\} = \cdots \oplus \{(:::) \oplus ///\}.$$

Here $\cdots$ stands for $(-1)*z$ and $///$ for $(-\alpha/\|x\|)*y$. Moreover equation (1.14) assures us that the - - -, namely, $1*z \oplus \beta*y$, and the :::, namely,

$$\left[\alpha\frac{\|x\|+\|z\|}{\|x\|\cdot\|z\|}\right]*z \oplus \frac{\alpha}{\|x\|}*y,$$

are synonymous. In a sense (1.15) is a triviality.

Trivial though it be, this step raises an important point. Equation (1.16) is simply a revised version of its predecessor. So is (1.17). But (1.15) is not a revised version of (1.14); it is an essentially new equation whose validity follows from that of (1.14).

We must make a careful distinction between a pair of equivalent equations and a pair one of which implies the other.

The type of reasoning that leads from (1.14) to (1.15) is not always reversible. Confusion arises only because there are so many, many special circumstances in which one can turn such an argument backwards. For instance, in elementary algebra one constantly meets equations of the form

$$(\cdots)+[\text{-}\text{-}\text{-}] = (\cdots)+\{///\}$$

and, without conscious thought, infers that

$$[\text{-}\text{-}\text{-}] = \{///\}.$$

Of course, this is absolutely right, but the analogous inference from

$$(\cdots)\cdot[\text{-}\text{-}\text{-}] = (\cdots)\cdot\{///\}$$

to $$[\text{-}\text{-}\text{-}] = \{///\}$$

is permissible only if one has prior assurance that $(\cdots)$ is not zero. Failure to remember this point is a frequent source of error.

6. In mathematics we usually start from the known and proceed to the unknown. The common connective phrases: "hence", "thus", "we conclude that", etc., etc., all assert that what comes next is true because it follows from what went before. Occasionally it is convenient to reverse this order—to start with the thing we wish to prove and to show that it is equivalent to something else, known to be true. In writing such a reverse argument you must make crystal clear what is going on. If what you write, taken literally, says only that from the abstruse identity you seek to prove follows some triviality like $0=0$, you are simply inviting sarcasm from your reader.

7. In no argument, direct or reverse, are the equations alone sufficient. The reader cannot be expected to know what the equation is all about unless you tell him. The relation $=$ is a verb and the expressions on the two sides of it are nouns; but a sentence made up of a formula alone seems incomplete. Often the explanation can be very brief; a single word like "hence" may be sufficient. Some mathematicians insist that every sentence must begin with an English word, but there are rare occasions when this becomes awkward.

Proper punctuation also helps. In a formula there can be no punctuation but that provided by the symbols themselves—the most important being parentheses—but between formulas some separation is essential. Several equations may be collected in a single sentence. The context determines whether they are separate assertions, each following from what has gone before, or whether each is to be inferred from its immediate predecessor.

8. In summary we offer the following bits of advice.

(1) Be sure you understand the dual role played by letters in formulas. In universally valid formulas they are dummies awaiting replacement; in most mathematical arguments they are names of definite objects.

(2) Remember the two types of substitution: (i) replacement of one name by another name for the same thing and (ii) substitution of specific names for the variables in universally valid formulas.

(3) Complicated serial equalities should be arranged with care. (Our only specific advice is: When possible, start each new line with "$=$".)

(4) With each equation, put enough plain English to tell the reader the status of the equation.

Appendix B.   Variables and Quantifiers, Unknowns

1. The general propositions of mathematics—the axioms and theorems— typically make assertions about all objects of a given type.   For example:

All equilateral triangles are equiangular;

or

For all real numbers x and y, $x+y-y+x$.

When we use such a proposition, however, we do not care about its generality. We care only about its applicability to the particular case at hand.   The universal proposition is interesting just because it says something about each and every particular instance.

Such universal statements can be made using only the English language, but this is often clumsy.   Try, for instance, rephrasing our second example without the use of the letters "x" and "y" or the symbols "$+$" and "$=$".

On the other hand, the bare expression

$$x+y = y+x$$

standing alone is utterly meaningless.   The symbol "$+$" has a meaning; so does "$=$"; but "x" and "y" are simply letters and acquire meaning only when they are strung together to form words or are put to some other well-defined use.   When you saw

$$x+y = y+x$$

in an algebra book, you supplied the meaning.   In elementary school you had learned that "$3+2$" and "$2+3$" were both names of the number 5. Hence $3+2=2+3$.   You also knew that $1+2=2+1$, $2+2=2+2$, and many more such special results.   You realized that

$$x+y = y+x$$

in some way summarized all of these and infinitely many more special formulas involving numbers. To put it precisely:

> If, in the formula "$x+y=y+x$", each occurrence of the symbol "x" is replaced by the name of some number (the same number at each occurrence of "x"), and if each occurrence of "y" is similarly replaced by the name of some number, then the result will be a true statement.

Fortunately, there is no need to use such long, pedantic, sentences. There are several brief phrases in standard use to convey the same idea. Among commonest are "for all numbers x and y," "for every pair of numbers x and y," "for each pair of numbers x and y," and "for any numbers x and y." Unfortunately, the last often leads to misunderstanding and it is to be hoped that this use of the word "any" will drop out of the mathematical vocabulary. The symbols "(x,y)" and "$\underset{x,y}{\forall}$" are also used, particularly in work on symbolic logic.

2. When used in this way, the letters "x", "y", etc., are called variables. They may be regarded as marking blank spaces in a form to be filled out. Repeated use of the same letter indicates that certain blanks are to be filled in the same way. Some recent algebra books go so far as to use squares, circles, etc., to stress the blank space idea, writing

$$\Box \; + \; \bigcirc \; = \; \bigcirc \; + \; \Box$$

and inviting the student to turn this into

$$\boxed{3} \; + \; \textcircled{2} \; = \; \textcircled{2} \; + \; \boxed{3}$$

3. The phrase "for all numbers x and y" spells out which substitutions are allowed in "$x+y=y+x$." When this is clear from the context there is no harm in writing just "for all x and y." Going further, the whole phrase is often omitted. When a formula contains variables, the phrase "for all - - -" is to be understood unless it is quite clear from the context that it is inappropriate.

In Chapter I you will find both forms. In (2.1)–(2.9) the "for all" appears explicitly. In (3.1)–(3.9) it is to be understood. Since we are dealing with two distinct types of object, vectors and numbers, we have to be specific as to which may be substituted where.

4. A new use for variables appears in (2.4) and (3.4). Let us look at an analogous statement in the familiar context of elementary algebra:

For all numbers x and y there is a number z such that $x+z=y$.

The variables "x" and "y" are playing a now familiar role. This proposition is a summary of an infinite number of special cases, each obtained by a suitable substitution. One such substitution gives:

There is a number z such that $2+z=5$;

another:

There is a number z such that $3+z=7$.

The original statement asserts that these and all other similar statements are true. When we assert:

There is a z such that $2+z=5$,

we are still talking about possible substitutions for the variable z. We are saying that there is at least one substitution for the variable, "z", in "$2+z=5$" which yields a true statement. In this particular case there is only one such replacement—we must substitute a name of the number 3—but the phrase "for some z" carries no implication of uniqueness.

Alternatives to "for some z..." are "there is a z...", "there exists a z...". The corresponding symbol used in symbolic logic is "$\underset{z}{\exists}$".

5. The phrases "for all..." and "for some..." are often called the *universal quantifier* and the *existential quantifier*.

The order of the quantifiers is crucial. The statement

for each x there is a y such that $x+y=0$

is true. It asserts that each number has a negative. Reversing the quantifiers yields

there is a y such that for all x, $x+y=0$,

i.e., there is a number which is simultaneously the negative of all other numbers—an obvious falsehood.

On the other hand, "for all x and for all y" and "for all y and for all x" say the same thing and are usually replaced by "for all x and y." Similarly "there are x and y..." usually replaces "there is an x and there is a y...."

6. Which letters we use in statements with quantifiers is completely immaterial.

For each x there is a y such that $x+y=0$

and

For each t there is a z such that $t+z=0$

are really the same statement. The only thing you must guard against is using a single letter for two incompatible tasks.

7. The denial of a universal statement is an existential statement and vice versa. To say

> For all x . . .

is to say that every reasonable substitution for x in . . . yields a true statement. Hence to deny

> For all x . . .

is to assert that there is at least one such substitution which yields a false statement. In other words, the denial of

> For all x . . . ,

is

> For some x it is not the case that . . . .

Similarly the denial of

> For some x . . . ,

is

> For every x, . . . is false.

Definition 10.1 provides a good example. In each specific application of the definition the letters $x_1, x_2, \ldots, x_n$ will stand for particular vectors. The quantifiers will go with the α's. We consider two conditions which the α's may or may not satisfy. One condition is

$$\sum_{i=1}^{N} \alpha_i x_i = 0;$$

the other is

$$\alpha_1 = \alpha_2 = \cdots = \alpha_n = 0.$$

Let us call these conditions P and Q. The first part of the definition says

> The x's are linearly independent if (and only if) P implies Q.

Since P and Q both contain the variables $\alpha_1, \alpha_2, \ldots, \alpha_n$, a universal quantifier must be understood. The phrase "P imples Q" means: if P is true then so is Q. In full, then, the first part of the definition is:

> The x's are linearly independent if and only if, for all α_1, α_2, $\ldots, \alpha_n$, if P is true then Q is true also.

We want to say that linear dependence is the denial of linear independence: i.e.,

> The x's are linearly dependent if and only if it is not the case that for all $\alpha_1, \alpha_2, \ldots, \alpha_n$, if P is true then Q is true also.

Using the principle that the denial of a universal statement is an existential statement, we see that this may be rephrased:

> The x's are linearly dependent if and only if, for some α_1, α_2, ..., α_n, it is not the case that if P is true then Q is true also.

Finally, the phrase "if P then Q" is false only when P happens to be true but Q is not. (This is discussed at length in Appendix C.9.) We may replace "it is not the case that if P is true then Q is true also" by the simpler "P is true and Q is false." In this way we obtain:

> The x's are linearly dependent if and only if, for some α_1, α_2, ..., α_n, $\sum_{i=1}^{N} \alpha_i x_i = 0$ and not $\alpha_1 = \alpha_2 = \cdots = \alpha_n = 0$.

8. Variables and quantifiers are sufficient for stating all our general propositions—our theorems—but when we start proving the theorems, we run into difficulty. It is easy enough to state something about all numbers, but it is difficult to reason about all numbers simultaneously. The typical procedure in a proof is to introduce a letter not as a variable, but as the name of one particular number. We then reason about that number and draw some conclusion concerning it. If we are careful that our reasoning applies, no matter which number the letter stands for, we may infer that the final conclusion is true of all numbers. Roughly speaking, we prove a universal statement by proving it for any old number.

Of course, these remarks are not limited to statements about numbers.

In elementary algebra the term "unknown" is used for a letter which stands for a particular, but not explicitly known, number. We will use the same word in a slightly more general sense. An unknown stands for a particular object, but that object is either an unspecified object of a certain sort or one imperfectly known.

You should not pay too much attention to the distinction between variables and unknowns. Once you realize that letters lead such a double life, you will automatically assign them to their proper role. Do not think about the distinction unless you find a proof really obscure. Then it may help to write down exactly what each unknown stands for. The few letters unaccounted for must be variables. If no quantifier appears with a variable, you know that the universal quantifier is implicit.

The symbols sometimes shift, without warning, from one role to the other. Some examples are discussed in Appendix D.1. It may be useful exercise in logic to see which part each letter plays at each occurrence, but attention to this detail is liable to distract you from the mathematics.

The use of unknowns raises some philosophical problems, but presents no practical difficulties. The interested reader will find an illuminating discussion in Chapter VI of J. B. Rosser's *Logic for Mathematicians*, McGraw-Hill, New York, 1953.

9. The most important rule in mathematical writing is the most obvious. Each symbol and expression should have a definite meaning. Never introduce a symbol without telling the reader what it stands for. Always check a compound expression to see that it is meaningful.

Usually some symbols appear in the statement of a theorem. The theorem itself introduces the symbols—which may change from variables to unknowns, either with or without warning. All other symbols must be accompanied by enough explanation to tell the reader exactly what they signify. Often "let $\cdots$ be a - - -" is enough. Other common phrases are "consider a $\cdots$ such that - - -"; "choose a $\cdots$"; "$\cdots$ tells us that there is a - - - such that $///$"; etc.

After you have introduced the individual symbols you may combine them to form compound expressions. Some compounds are names, some are statements, some are mere gibberish.

There are conventions—axioms and definitions—whereby author and reader agree that certain combinations of symbols shall be the names of certain objects. For instance, axiom (3.1) says that if the blanks $\cdots$ and - - - in

$$(\cdots + \text{- - -})$$

are filled with the names of vectors, the result is the name of a vector. Theorem 3.4 asserts that there is exactly one vector with a certain property; Definition 3.5 says that henceforth a certain compound symbol will be a name for that particular vector. Many possible compounds remain forever undefined.

Assume, for example, that the symbols "x" and "y" have been properly introduced and are names of certain elements in a vector space. Consider the three expressions

$$\text{(i)} \ \ x + (2 \cdot y), \qquad \text{(ii)} \ \ x + 2y, \quad \text{and} \quad \text{(iii)} \ \ (x + 2) \cdot y.$$

Axiom (3.5) guarantees that $(2 \cdot y)$ is a vector. Hence axiom (3.1) assures us that (i) is a name of a vector. On the other hand (ii) is not a name in good standing until there is an agreed convention saying that it is to denote the same vector as (i). Finally, (iii) is nothing but a collection of marks. It has no more meaning than a bunch of hen tracks in the dust. There is no reason why we should not attach a meaning to an expression of the form "$\cdots + \text{- - -}$" when the first blank is filled with the name of a vector and the second with the name of a number, but we have not found it convenient to do so.

10. Some expressions are gibberish because they contain collections of symbols which should be names but are not. Others are nonsense because they apply inappropriate predicates to perfectly good subjects.

The statement

John Kennedy was elected president in 1960

is a true assertion.   The sentence

Richard Nixon was elected president in 1960

happens to be false, but it is not ridiculous.   Contrast these with the collection of words:

17 was elected president in 1960.

Possibly this is a sentence, but if so, you need no knowledge of political history to realize that it is false.   It is worse than false; it is silly.

Students frequently write mathematical sentences just as nonsensical as "17 was elected president in 1960".   Sometimes the unfamiliar symbols trap them into thinking that nonsense is sense.   More often they simply fail to think.   Until you become thoroughly familiar with the language of a new part of mathematics, you should pause often to scrutinize your statements.   Check each predicate and be sure that it makes sense to attach it to its subject.   If so, the sentence may still be false.   If not, the sentence is certainly false if, indeed, it has any meaning at all.

The principal mathematical verbs in this book are

APP.
c.2 &
c.7
SETS

$$=, \quad \in, \quad \text{and} \quad \subseteq.$$

A sentence of the form

$$\cdots = \text{---}$$

asserts that "$\cdots$" and "---" are names of the same object.*   If the objects named are not even of the same kind, the error is flagrant.   Occasionally students fill one blank with something that is not even a name.   Note that "$=$" and "is" are not truly synonymous.   For example,

The sky is blue

and

17 is a number

are true.   On the other hand

The sky$=$blue

is certainly not grammatical, while

$17=a$ number

is a most awkward construction, of doubtful correctness.

In a sentence of the form

APP.
c.2
SETS

$$\cdots \in \text{---},$$

the left-hand blank, $\cdots$, must be filled with the name of a suitable object

---

* Some authors use "$=$" in a more general sense.

The right-hand blank, - - -, must be occupied by the name of a set. In the case of

$$\cdots \subseteq \text{---},$$

both blanks call for names of sets.

Appendix C.   Sets

1. The idea of a set or collection of objects is completely natural and intuitive.   There is an enormous variety of words in everyday use for sets in general or sets of a particular kind.   Several—"set", "collection", "group", "class", "flock", "herd", etc.—are common; and for special purposes there are such esoteric terms as "a pride of lions", "a pod of whales", or "an exaltation of larks".   In mathematics, the word "set"* is the standard term.   Other words are occasionally used informally or are reserved for special purposes.

For centuries mathematicians have operated with sets in a natural and obvious way, but within the last hundred years it has become clear that a few notational devices can simplify and clarify work with sets.   These notations are an essential part of a mathematical education, but it is easy to make too much of them.   The uninitiated have gotten the impression that sets are something new, and that their elementary properties are somehow deep and subtle.   Nothing could be farther from the truth!   In this appendix we are simply formalizing ideas intuitively familiar to us since infancy.

2. The fundamental concepts are those of set, element, and belonging. We cannot define these in terms of more basic ideas because they are themselves absolutely basic.   All we can do is to say how the words will be used and to give examples showing that you are already familiar with the concepts.   If we have a set and an object or element, there are just two mutually exclusive possibilities—either the element belongs to the set or it does not. Consider the Brown Class of 1960.   This is a well-defined set whose elements are certain alumni of Brown University.   Any given person either belongs to this Class or he does not.   One more example should suffice.   Consider the disc consisting of all points (x,y) such that $x^2 + y^2 \leqslant 1$.   This is a set whose members or elements are points in the plane.   The point $(\frac{1}{2}, \frac{1}{3})$ lies in the disc; the point $(1,2)$ does not.

If $\mathscr{S}$ is a set and a is an object, we write $a \in \mathscr{S}$ to signify that a is an element of $\mathscr{S}$ and $a \notin \mathscr{S}$ to signify that a is not one of the elements of $\mathscr{S}$. Grammatically "$\in$" is a verb and "$a \in \mathscr{S}$" is a declarative sentence asserting

* Some logicians distinguish two types of collection, the more general being called classes.

that a belongs to the set $\mathscr{S}$.   One may read "$a \in \mathscr{S}$" as "a belongs to $\mathscr{S}$", "a is an element of $\mathscr{S}$", "a is a member of $\mathscr{S}$", "a is in $\mathscr{S}$", etc.   Frequently we want to use the predicate "$\in \mathscr{S}$" as an adjectival clause modifying the noun "a".   Thus "choose an $a \in \mathscr{S}$, then ..." may be read "choose an a which lies in $\mathscr{S}$, then ..." or, briefly, "choose an a in $\mathscr{S}$, then ...".

3. Any old collection of elements is a set, but the sets we really care about consist of elements sharing some common property.   A moment ago we introduced the unit disc.   It consisted of those points (x, y) which fulfilled the condition $x^2 + y^2 \leqslant 1$.   It is a great convenience to have a brief notation for the set consisting of all those objects which satisfy a particular condition. We will use

$$\{x \mid \cdots\}$$

to denote the set of those x such that $\cdots$.*   Thus $\{x \mid x^2 < 1\}$ is the set of numbers whose squares are less than 1, i.e., the set of numbers between -1 and $+1$.   Similarly $\{(x, y) \mid \cdots\}$ is the set of all pairs which satisfy the condition $\cdots$.   For instance, the unit disc is $\{(x, y) \mid x^2 + y^2 \leqslant 1\}$.

In the expression "$\{(x, y) \mid x^2 + y^2 \leqslant 1\}$" the "$x$" and "$y$" are variables, dummies awaiting replacement.   To check whether $(\frac{1}{2}, \frac{1}{3})$ belongs to the unit disc we see whether it satisfies the defining condition.   We ask: what happens when we replace the "x" and "y" in "$x^2 + y^2 \leqslant 1$" by "$\frac{1}{2}$" and "$\frac{1}{3}$" respectively?   We get

$$(\tfrac{1}{2})^2 + (\tfrac{1}{3})^2 \leqslant 1$$

or
$$\tfrac{13}{36} \leqslant 1$$

—a true statement.   Thus $(\frac{1}{2}, \frac{1}{3})$ does satisfy the condition and $(\frac{1}{2}, \frac{1}{3}) \in \{(x, y) \mid x^2 + y^2 \leqslant 1\}$.   In fact,

$$(\tfrac{1}{2}, \tfrac{1}{3}) \in \{(x, y) \mid x^2 + y^2 \leqslant 1\}$$

is just an elaborate way of saying

$$(\tfrac{1}{2})^2 + (\tfrac{1}{3})^2 \leqslant 1.$$

Since the letters in "$\{(x, y) \mid \cdots\}$" are dummies, we can change them at will, so long as the change does not conflict with some other use of a letter. The set $\{(x, y) \mid x = y^2\}$ is identical with $\{(s, t) \mid s = t^2\}$ and with

$$\{(y, x) \mid y = x^2\}.$$

In analytic geometry it is customary to reserve "x" for the first coordinate and "y" for the second, so the use of $\{(y, x) \mid y = x^2\}$ is unwise; but it is not incorrect.

In the expression "$\{(x, y) \mid \cdots\}$" it is not essential that the "x" and "y"

---

* Bertrand Russell was the first to point out that the naive assumption that every meaningful condition determines a set leads to logical difficulties.   A lucid and amusing discussion of the problem appears in W. V. Quine's article "Paradox," *Scientific American*, Vol. 206, No. 4 (April 1962), pp. 84–96.

appear explicitly in the "$\cdots$". The set $\{(x, y) \mid x = 1\}$ is a vertical straight line one unit to the right of the vertical axis. It is not the same as $\{x \mid x = 1\}$, which is a set with just one element—the number 1.

4. For sets with only a finite number of elements another notation is convenient. To name the set we simply write down a list of its members and enclose the list in braces. For instance, $\{1,3\}$ is the set with just two members 1 and 3. It is identical with $\{3,1\}$ and with $\{x \mid x^2 - 4x + 3 = 0\}$, since these sets have precisely the same members as $\{1,3\}$. If convenient, the list may contain duplications, either intentionally or inadvertently. Thus $\{1,1,2,1,2,3\}$ is the set whose members appear in the list. It is just the same as $\{1,2,3\}$.

5. If $\mathscr{A}$ and $\mathscr{B}$ are two sets, we can determine certain other sets related to this pair. Consider a mundane example. Let $\mathscr{A}$ be the set of all families which include a teen-age driver and let $\mathscr{B}$ be the set of all families which include someone who has been convicted of a traffic violation. In setting its rates an insurance company may wish to set a high premium for any family which contains either a teen-ager or a traffic violator.

The company has an IBM card for each family. They run the cards through a sorter, pulling out all which indicate that some member of the family has a traffic conviction. They put these cards aside and run the remainder through the sorter again, to get all those marked for a teen-age driver. They put this new pile on top of the one for traffic offenders and list all the names in the combined pile. This is a list of a certain set of families—those which the actuaries worry about. This set is called the union of $\mathscr{A}$ and $\mathscr{B}$. Some of the members belong to $\mathscr{A}$ only, some to $\mathscr{B}$ only, and some both to $\mathscr{A}$ and to $\mathscr{B}$.

The insurance company will be particularly concerned about families which have both a teen-ager and a traffic violator—the set of families which belong both to $\mathscr{A}$ and to $\mathscr{B}$. This set is called the intersection of $\mathscr{A}$ and $\mathscr{B}$.

Another set of interest consists of families with a teen-age driver but no traffic offences on record—the families which belong to set $\mathscr{A}$, but not to $\mathscr{B}$. It is known as the relative complement of $\mathscr{B}$ with respect to $\mathscr{A}$.

The notations for the union and intersection of two sets are completely standard, while that for a relative complement is widespread, but not universal. In formal terms:

If $\mathscr{A}$ and $\mathscr{B}$ are sets then

(i) the union of $\mathscr{A}$ and $\mathscr{B}$ is the set
$$\mathscr{A} \cup \mathscr{B} = \{x \mid x \in \mathscr{A} \quad \text{or} \quad x \in \mathscr{B}\};$$

(ii) the intersection of $\mathscr{A}$ and $\mathscr{B}$ is the set
$$\mathscr{A} \cap \mathscr{B} = \{x \mid x \in \mathscr{B} \quad \text{and} \quad x \in \mathscr{B}\}; \quad \text{and}$$

(iii) the relative complement of $\mathscr{B}$ with respect to $\mathscr{A}$ (or the difference of $\mathscr{A}$ and $\mathscr{B}$) is the set

$$\mathscr{A} - \mathscr{B} = \{x \mid x \in \mathscr{A} \quad \text{and} \quad x \notin \mathscr{B}\}.$$

In (i) the word "or" is being used in the inclusive sense meaning "either ... or ... or both," a usage universal in mathematics. The use of "and" in the definition: $\mathscr{A} \cap \mathscr{B} = \{x \mid x \in \mathscr{A} \text{ and } x \in \mathscr{B}\}$ confuses the unwary. They think that the "and" somehow puts the sets together to get a big set. In fact it puts the conditions together to give a restrictive condition and hence a small set.

6. The symbols "$\cup$", "$\cap$", and "$-$", denote operations on sets, rules for combining two sets to get new sets. It is quite possible to study the algebra of these operations and to prove such theorems as:

For all sets $\mathscr{A}$, $\mathscr{B}$, and $\mathscr{C}$, $\mathscr{A} \cap (\mathscr{B} \cup \mathscr{C}) = (\mathscr{A} \cap \mathscr{B}) \cup (\mathscr{A} \cap \mathscr{C})$.

This algebra of sets is called Boolean algebra in honor of the English mathematician George Boole (1815–1864), who first recognized its import-ance and formalized it in his epoch-making book on logic, *An Investigation of the Laws of Thought*, 1854 (reprinted by Dover, New York, 1951).

We do not need to study Boolean algebra in detail, but we do need to extend the notions of union and intersection. These extensions are given formally the body of the text (see Definition 13.3) and require little com-ment. The set $\bigcup_{i=1}^{N} \mathscr{A}_i$ consists of those elements which belong to at least one of the sets $\mathscr{A}_1, \mathscr{A}_2, \ldots, \mathscr{A}_n$; while the set $\bigcap_{i=1}^{N} \mathscr{A}_i$ consists of those elements which belong to each and every one of $\mathscr{A}_1, \mathscr{A}_2, \ldots, \mathscr{A}_n$.

7. In addition to the operations on sets, we need to study one relation which may hold between two sets. If $\mathscr{A}$ and $\mathscr{B}$ are two sets, it may happen that every element which belongs to $\mathscr{A}$ necessarily also belongs to $\mathscr{B}$. If this is the case, we say, naturally enough, that $\mathscr{A}$ is contained in $\mathscr{B}$ or that $\mathscr{A}$ is a *subset* of $\mathscr{B}$ and write $\mathscr{A} \subseteq \mathscr{B}$. For instance, if $\mathscr{A}$ is the set of all United States senators, and $\mathscr{B}$ is the set of American citizens over thirty years of age, Article I, Section 3, Paragraph 3, of the Constitution of the United States, guarantees that $\mathscr{A} \subseteq \mathscr{B}$. When we say that $\mathscr{A}$ is contained in $\mathscr{B}$, we do not insist that $\mathscr{A}$ and $\mathscr{B}$ be different. If we wish to say that $\mathscr{A}$ is contained in $\mathscr{B}$ but not equal to it, we may say that $\mathscr{A}$ is *properly contained* in $\mathscr{B}$ or that $\mathscr{A}$ is a *proper subset* of $\mathscr{B}$ and write $\mathscr{A} \subset \mathscr{B}$.

Unfortunately the notation is not standard. It is more usual to find "$\subset$" used for "is contained in" than for "is properly contained in."

We need only two obvious facts about the relation $\subseteq$. If $\mathscr{A} \subseteq \mathscr{B}$ and $\mathscr{B} \subseteq \mathscr{C}$, then every element of $\mathscr{A}$ belongs to $\mathscr{B}$ and hence to $\mathscr{C}$. Thus:

If $\mathscr{A} \subseteq \mathscr{B}$ and $\mathscr{B} \subseteq \mathscr{C}$, then $\mathscr{A} \subseteq \mathscr{C}$.

If $\mathscr{A} \subseteq \mathscr{B}$ and $\mathscr{B} \subseteq \mathscr{A}$, then the two sets have exactly the same members. In other words:

If $\mathscr{A} \subseteq \mathscr{B}$ and $\mathscr{B} \subseteq \mathscr{A}$, then $\mathscr{A} = \mathscr{B}$.

The latter fact is in constant use to prove that two sets are equal. Such a proof runs roughly as follows. Consider any $x \in \mathscr{A}$. Then ..., etc., etc. Hence $x \in \mathscr{B}$. Now consider any $x \in \mathscr{B}$. Then ..., etc., etc. Hence $x \in \mathscr{A}$. Q.E.D.

Note that the x in the first half is not the same as that in the second half. Sometimes it is convenient to use a new unknown, sometimes not; but if you use the same letter in both halves, you must be careful not to confuse the two parts.

The proof of Theorem 7.3 provides a typical example. We are interested in two sets,

$$\{x \mid \text{for some } \tau, x = \tau b + (1 - \tau)a\}$$

and the straight line through a and b. Let us call them $\mathscr{A}$ and $\mathscr{B}$. We look at an arbitrary point x of the former and show that it belongs to the latter. This shows that every element of $\mathscr{A}$ is also in $\mathscr{B}$ or, in symbols, $\mathscr{A} \subseteq \mathscr{B}$. Note that the "$x$" in

"$\{x \mid \text{for some } \tau, x = \tau b + (1 - \tau)a\}$"

is a variable, a dummy, while the other "x" in the argument is the name of a particular, but unspecified, point of this set.

Similarly, in the second half of the proof we do not spell out the fact that we are proving $\mathscr{B} \subseteq \mathscr{A}$. Here "$x$" is a new unknown, the name of an unspecified element of $\mathscr{B}$.

The conclusion does not say explicitly that $x \in \mathscr{A}$. It is assumed that the reader has enough sense to recognize the conclusion as the statement that x satisfies the condition defining $\mathscr{A}$. Note that the existence of a τ with the desired property is proved by giving a formula, β/α, for such a τ.

8. There is one very important set of a peculiar nature. What is $\{1,3\} \cap \{2,4,6\}$? Obviously, there are no elements which belong both to $\{1,3\}$ and to $\{2,4,6\}$, so we are on the horns of a dilemma. Either we must admit the existence of a strange "empty" set which has no elements or we must declare the expression $\{1,3\} \cap \{2,4,6\}$ to be meaningless. There is no doubt which is the better choice. To reject the empty set leads to countless different kinds of inconvenience, while its admission causes no real difficulty. Accordingly, we admit the empty set as a set in good standing. Other names for the empty set are "the void set", "the vacuous set", and "the null set".

9. The only trouble with the empty set is that arguments involving it call for excessive literal-mindedness. In particular, one must pay attention to the exact significance of statements in the form

If $\cdots$ then - - -.

In everyday life one seldom uses "if $\cdots$ then - - -" unless there is doubt about the "$\cdots$," but our understandings about variables and quantifiers require that "if $\cdots$ then - - -" be meaningful whenever the "$\cdots$" and "- - -" are simple verifiable statements. It is customary to call "$\cdots$" the hypothesis and "- - -" the conclusion of the implication "if $\cdots$ then - - -".

APP. B.1 & B.4 VAR.

For instance, in number theory the word "divides" means "divides evenly" and the theorem

> *If a number divides one factor of a product then it divides the product*

is familiar from elementary arithmetic. Written with variables and quantifiers this theorem is

> *For all a, b, c, if a divides b then a divides bc.*

This is a universal proposition and every reasonable substitution for the variables will yield a true statement. Making such substitutions, we find that the following three statements must all be true:

If 2 divides 6 then 2 divides 6×5;

if 2 divides 3 then 2 divides 3×5;

and

if 2 divides 3 then 2 divides 3×6.

Thinking of these as examples of the general form "if $\cdots$ then - - -", we see that the latter is true in the three cases:

(i) $\cdots$ and - - - are both true,

(ii) $\cdots$ and - - - are both false, and

(iii) $\cdots$ is false and - - - is true.

If you were to examine a large number of mathematical examples, you would discover that this one is typical. An implication is true if and only if it is not the case that its hypothesis is true and its conclusion is false. Examples from outside mathematics are less clear-cut, but show that this precise, mathematical use of "if $\cdots$ then - - -" is very close to its use in standard English.

10. We are now prepared to give one example of an argument involving the empty set. Our object is to show that the empty set does not provide an exception to the general statement of Theorem 10.2.

First observe that the empty set, Λ, is a subset of every set. To say $\Lambda \subseteq \mathscr{A}$ is to say:

For all x if $x \in \Lambda$ then $x \in \mathscr{A}$.

Consider any particular object x and look at the implication:

If $x \in \Lambda$ then $x \in \mathscr{A}$.

No matter what x may be, the hypothesis, $x \in \Lambda$, is false, since Λ has no members. Accordingly, we must have either the case (ii) or case (iii) described above, and in both these cases the implication is true.

Since the empty set Λ is a subset of every set, Theorem 10.2 asserts that Λ is linearly independent. We wish to verify that this is, indeed, correct. Unfortunately, the natural, conventional form of the definition of linear independence is ill-adapted to dealing with the empty set. Definition 10.1 hides three difficulties which are important only in this special case.

The first is the relationship between the α's and the x's. What we need is an α for each x. An appropriate notation is that of functions. Remembering that the universal quantifier, "$\alpha_1, \alpha_2, \ldots, \alpha_n$", was understood in Definition 10.1, we can rephrase the start of the definition as:

A set $\mathscr{A}$ of vectors is said to be linearly independent if for each function α which assigns a scalar $\alpha(x)$ to each $x \in \mathscr{A}$, etc.

In these terms we need a new notation for the sum. In Appendix E.10 we mention that one good notation is $\sum_{x \in \mathscr{A}} \alpha(x) \cdot x$. This brings up the second difficulty: What is the sum of no vectors? A natural solution is to say that the sum of no vectors is the zero vector, and we adopt this convention.

The final difficulty rests in the phrase "$\alpha_i = 0$ for $i = 1, 2, \ldots, n$". In our functional notation for the α's this would be "$\alpha(x) = 0$ for $x \in \mathscr{A}$", or more precisely, "for all x if $x \in \mathscr{A}$, $\alpha(x) = 0$". With these changes Definition 10.1 becomes:

A set, $\mathscr{A}$, of vectors is said to be linearly independent if, for all functions α, the condition

$$\sum_{x \in \mathscr{A}} \alpha(x) \cdot x = 0,$$

implies the conclusion: for all x, if $x \in \mathscr{A}$ then $\alpha(x) = 0$.

It is now easy to see that the empty set Λ is linearly independent. When we replace $\mathscr{A}$ by Λ, the conclusion:

For all x, if $x \in \Lambda$ then $\alpha(x) = 0$,

is true, because in the "if $\cdots$ then $---$" the "$\cdots$" is always false.

As we saw earlier, to say that one condition implies another is to say that it is never the case that the latter is false and the former true. In our particular instance the condition

$$\sum_{x \in \mathscr{A}} \alpha(x) \cdot x = 0$$

implies the conclusion:

For all x, if $x \in \Lambda$ then $\alpha(x) = 0$,

because the latter is always true.

Appendix D.   Proofs

1. The simplest type of theorem is one which looks something like:

For all $\cdots x$ if $---$ then $///$,

where $---$ and $///$ are statements involving the variable x.* A straight- forward proof starts by turning x from a variable into an unknown with some such phrase as "let x be a $\cdots$ such that $---$". This does more than change the role of "x". It tells the reader that the particular object x satisfies the condition $---$. Hereafter $---$, the hypothesis of the theorem, is to be used as a known fact. There follow a series of inferences from things already known, including $---$, and the last of the inferences is $///$, the conclusion of the theorem.

APP.
B.8
VAR.

Section 1 contains a complicated example of such a proof. The theorem is phrased in English without the use of quantifiers, but it might be put:

For all points A, B, and C, if ABC is a triangle with two of its angle bisectors equal, then ABC is isosceles.

To be sure, the hypothesis that the bisectors are equal is introduced into the proof late rather than early.

The step of turning the variables into unknowns and assuming that they fulfill the hypotheses of the theorem is so standard that it is often taken for granted. Look at Theorem 10.4. Neglect the roles of y and the α's. In the theorem the x's appear without explanation so the quantifier: "for all vectors $x_1, x_2, \ldots, x_n$" is understood. Immediately after we next meet the x's, comes the phrase "since the x's are linearly independent," etc. Here we are talking about the x's as definite objects and the reader must make the transition for himself, preferably without conscious thought.

For further examples compare Theorems 10.2, 10.8, 10.12, 11.3, and 11.4. Each of these is a universal statement and each refers to an arbitrary set of n vectors. In the statements of 10.4, 10.8, 10.12, and 11.3, the vectors are represented by the variables $x_1, x_2, \ldots, x_n$ and the universal quantifier

---

* Strictly speaking, they cannot really be statements because they contain the variable "x", indicating a blank to be filled in. They look like statements and become statements as soon as "x" is replaced by a suitable name.

"for all $x_1, x_2, \ldots, x_n$," is understood.   In the proof of Theorem 10.12 there is a sentence pointing out that, in the proof, the x's stand for particular (but still arbitrary) vectors.   In the proofs of Theorems 10.8 and 11.3, the reader must realize for himself that the symbols have changed meaning in this way.   Theorems 10.2 and 11.4 are written differently.   Because they do not appear in the statements of the theorems, the x's must be politely introduced when they make their first appearance.   The x's play precisely the same role in these proofs as in the others.

2. After you have introduced your symbols, you must decide what to do with them.   A typical theorem asserts that some object or objects have a certain property.   Reexamine the theorem and see what it says *in terms of the symbols you are using*.   It often helps to write this out explicitly— to set up a signpost showing the route to be followed.

Look again at the proof of Theorem 10.2.   The second sentence of the second paragraph simply translates the conclusion of the theorem into a statement about the $x_1, x_2, \ldots, x_m$.   The second sentence in the proof of Theorem 10.4 is another such guidepost.

Sometimes such route signs belong at the beginning of a proof.   Sometimes you need to pause in the middle to clarify your present position and to plot your future course.   Theorem 21.2 is strewn with such reappraisals and guiding hands—some very explicit, some partly hidden.

Whenever you are in doubt how to start a proof, try writing out such a restatement of your aim.   You will be surprised how often it will help.

3. Theorems containing existential quantifiers usually involve universal quantifiers as well, and the reader must take care to keep the order straight.

> *The simplest way to prove that something exists is to hold it up for all the world to see.   To show that it has certain desired properties use methods similar to those used in proving universal statements.*

Theorem 3.2 is a good example.   This asserts:

There is an o such that - - -.

To find such an o we need some previous known fact.   As this is our first theorem, the only known facts are the axioms (3.1)–(3.9) and the only ones of these which tell us that something exists are (3.1), (3.4), and (3.5).   Axiom (3.4) tells us that a certain vector z exists, provided we have two others, x and y, to start with.   We choose an arbitrary vector v and let it serve for both x and y.   Now v is a particular vector chosen once and for all.   Remembering that "for all x and y" is understood before (3.4), we know that replacing these variables by the name of a definite vector yields a true statement.   In this way we get:

For some z, $v + z = v$.

At this point it would be standard practice to assume that from now on "z" is no longer a variable, but the name of one particular vector and that for this vector $v+z=v$. To emphasize the change from variable to unknown we use a new letter "o". Since o has been exhibited it is known to exist; it remains to show that it has the required property. What we must show is:

For all vectors x, $x+o=x$.

The first line of the second paragraph says that x is now to be a particular vector, an arbitrary vector in $\mathscr{V}$, but just that one, throughout the proof. An auxiliary vector w is needed, but after its introduction everything proceeds smoothly to the conclusion $x+o=x$.

Far less detail is given in the second half of the proof. By this time the reader is supposed to be able to supply most of the reasons for himself.

4. Both Theorems 3.2 and 3.4 are double-barreled. The first half says that there is something with a certain property, the second that there is no more than one object with this property. In technical terms the first halves are existence theorems, the second halves, uniqueness theorems.

The existence part of Theorem 3.4 is trivial—simply quoting axiom (3.4). The uniqueness part is straightforward but illuminating. We know that there is one object with a certain property, in this case z. The simple-minded way to prove uniqueness is to assume that some other object, z', has the given property and then to prove that z' and z are really one and the same. This is precisely what we do here.

5. Theorems 3.6–3.9 all illustrate one way of using uniqueness theorems. The second part of Theorem 3.2 tells us that, for each y, the only way of filling the blank in

$$y + \cdots = y$$

so as to get a true statement is to put in some name of the vector 0. In Theorem 3.6 we take this universal statement and replace the variable y by the unknown x. Equation (3.13) establishes

APP. B.8 VAR.

$$x + 0 \cdot x = x;$$

i.e., filling the blank space with $0 \cdot x$ yields a true statement. Hence $0 \cdot x$ must be another name for 0.

6. It is impossible to summarize all the different forms which proofs can take, but it may be helpful to describe a few of them.

The proof of Theorem 10.8 contains three parts, each a proof by contradiction. In each part we want to show that $\mathscr{A}$ has a certain property. To do so we assume that $\mathscr{A}$ does not have the property. We then show that from this assumption and certain known facts we could infer an obviously false proposition. Except for this one assumption, everything we use is known to be correct—an axiom, a definition, a previous theorem, or one of the hypotheses of the present theorem. The only place where falsity could have crept in is through the assumption. Since falsity did, indeed, creep in, the assumption must be to blame. But if the assumption—that $\mathscr{A}$ lacks the property—is untenable, then $\mathscr{A}$ must have the property.*

7. Straightforward proofs by induction are discussed in the body of the text (see Theorem 10.12), but part (iii) of the proof of Theorem 10.8 contains a hidden induction. We could avoid a proof by contradiction and prove directly that $x_1 \in \mathrm{Sp}\mathscr{A}$ and that if $x_1, x_2, \ldots, x_i \in \mathrm{Sp}\mathscr{A}$ for $i = 1, 2, \ldots, n$, then $x_{n+1} \in \mathrm{Sp}\mathscr{A}$. Instead we use the fact that if there were any i such that $x_i \notin \mathrm{Sp}\mathscr{A}$ then there would be a least such integer i. The principle used— that every non-empty set of positive integers has a least element—is part of a more general proposition, the so-called well ordering principle. Any proof by well ordering can be converted to one by induction and vice versa.

8. For some obscure reason, proofs involving linear dependence and independence cause an unreasonable amount of trouble for many students. The essential thing to keep in mind is that mathematics is a most literal-minded subject. The straightforward way to show that a set of vectors $x_1, x_2, \ldots, x_n$ is linearly independent is to follow the definition verbatim. One must prove:

For each set of scalars $\alpha_1, \alpha_2, \ldots, \alpha_n$, if $\sum_{i=1}^{N} \alpha_i x_i = 0$ then

$$\alpha_1 = \alpha_2 = \cdots = \alpha_n = 0.$$

Accordingly, one assumes that $\alpha_1, \alpha_2, \ldots, \alpha_n$ are scalars and that $\sum_{i=1}^{n} \alpha_i x_i = 0$. There follows some argument involving what is known about the x's and terminating in the conclusion $\alpha_1 = \alpha_2 = \cdots = \alpha_n = 0$.

To prove that $x_1, x_2, \ldots, x_n$ are linearly dependent one exhibits a particular set of scalars $\alpha_1, \alpha_2, \ldots, \alpha_n$, gives evidence that at least one of the α's is not zero, and finally establishes that $\sum_{i=1}^{n} \alpha_i x_i = 0$.

9. Theorem 11.4 takes the form:

if $\cdots$, then the conditions $---$ and $///$ are equivalent,

where "$\cdots$" is "$x_1, x_2, \ldots, x_n$ is a set of n linearly independent vectors in the finite-dimensional space $\mathscr{V}$," "$---$" is "$x_1, x_2, \ldots, x_n$ is a maximal linearly independent set," and "$///$" is "$n = \dim \mathscr{V}$." Throughout the proof we assume $\cdots$ and use it wherever we wish. The first paragraph points out that $n \leqslant \dim \mathscr{V}$ irrespective of the truth or falsity of $---$ and

---

* During the twentieth century a small but very able group of mathematicians have come to doubt the validity of such reasoning. A relatively non-technical exposition of their views will be found in the book, *Intuitionism: An Introduction*, by A. Heyting (North-Holland Publishing Company, Amsterdam, 1956).

///. The second points out that /// implies - - - (always under the assumption · · ·).

The final paragraph does not, however, show that - - - implies ///. Instead it shows that - - - implies $n \geqslant \dim \mathscr{V}$. This is enough because the two statements $n \leqslant \dim \mathscr{V}$ and $n \geqslant \dim \mathscr{V}$ together say just $n = \dim \mathscr{V}$, i.e., ///.

10. Problem 4.10(b) involves a simple logical question that troubles many students. Schematically, the assertion to be proved takes the form:

(A) If · · ·, then either - - - or ///.

One easy proof consists in showing:

(B) If · · · and not - - -, then ///.

The schemes (A) and (B) are simply different ways of saying exactly the same thing !

If this is not obvious to you, think about (B). Assume you know · · · to be true. What can you infer from (B)? You will see that it tells you that /// must be true whenever - - - fails to be true. That is to say: at least one of the two, /// or - - -, must be true. This is precisely what (A) says also. If · · · happens to be false then no inferences can be drawn either from (A) or from (B).

11. Before writing out a proof you must decide how much intelligence to expect of your reader. Different proofs in the text contain very different amounts of detail, so you will become accustomed to such variations in mathematical style.

The proof of Theorem 10.2, for example, contains a great deal that is unnecessary to the proof proper. The first sentence is important, but seems so obvious that it might well be left to the reader. Alternatively, it and the next sentence might be combined, using a customary phrase, to yield:

> Without loss of generality, assume $x_1, x_2, \ldots, x_n$ linearly independent and $m \leqslant n$.

The second sentence of the second paragraph really lies quite outside the proof. As explained in D.2, it is simply a road sign pointing the proper direction. As you gain mathematical maturity, such signposts are less needed. You get in the habit of analyzing the theorem before you start on the proof. You think to yourself, "Just what conclusion do we want here?" If the proof promises to be complicated and the author does not provide such clues, it may help to jot them down for yourself. Examine the conclusion and see exactly what it says in terms of the unknowns being used in the proof.

The end of the proof of Theorem 10.2 can also be greatly abbreviated. It might go:

Since $x_1, x_2, \ldots, x_n$ are linearly independent, all the α's are zero.   Q.E.D.

Here the reader is expected to know exactly what linear dependence means, but if he is uncertain, still he should have no difficulty.   He knows enough to go back to the definition.   The last sentence is there only because the proof is being given in great detail.   Some readers will regard its inclusion as an insult to their intelligence.

Theorem 13.4 is an example of a proof written without such a guiding hand.   You are expected to see, automatically, just what is demanded, namely, that $x, y \in \bigcap_i \mathscr{X}_i$ implies $x + y \in \bigcap_i \mathscr{X}_i$, etc.   Notice that the genuinely important fact that a subset is a subspace if it satisfies (3.1) and (3.5) is regarded as so obvious that it has not even been honored with the title of theorem.

Appendix E.   Indices and Summation

1. Most of our arguments involve an arbitrary number of vectors.   To have enough symbols to work with we add various distinguishing marks to the letters, e.g., x', $\tilde{x}$, $\bar{x}$, x_1, and so forth.   In some contexts the original letter and its variant both appear and are intimately related.   Thus in Chapter V the dual of any operator A is denoted by $\tilde{A}$.   In such cases the device of differencing is simply another way of writing functions and is discussed in Appendix F.   More often the original symbol and its varied forms are related only in that they are doing more or less similar jobs.

The most useful distinguishing marks are numerical subscripts and superscripts.   Here, also, the concept of function is involved, but for elementary work this aspect of the notation is not helpful.   We will mention it again only briefly in the next appendix.

To talk about an arbitrary number of vectors we often let n stand for the number of vectors in the set and denote the individuals by $x_1, x_2, \ldots, x_n$. There is no reason why n might not be 1, 2, or 3.   The ever-present three dots suggest, but do not guarantee, that something is missing in the list. If we knew that n was 2, we would write just "x_1, x_2," not "$x_1, x_2, \ldots, x_2$," but there is nothing positively wrong with the latter nor with the even more ridiculous "$x_1, x_2, \ldots, x_1$" instead of "x_1".

Of course there is no special virtue in using the letter n for the number of elements.   It is a help to use a letter which has come to suggest an integer— the commonest are i, j, k, l, m, n, M, N, and ν—but there is no necessity for doing so.   Sometimes the indices do not start with 1.   It may be convenient to number the elements, $x_0, x_1, \ldots, x_n$ or $y_{m+1}, y_{m+2}, \ldots, y_{m+n}$ or $y_{m+1}, y_{m+2}, \ldots, y_n$.   In the last, of course, $n > m$.

2. The power to talk about arbitrary numbers of objects is only one of the benefits conferred by the subscript notation. If we wish to talk about the sum of $x_1, x_2, \ldots, x_n$ we may use $x_1 + x_2 + \cdots + x_n$ or the condensed notation $\sum_{i=1}^{n} x_i$. Every mathematician must be able to manipulate with the summation sign "$\sum$" easily and correctly and must know *exactly* what it signifies.

The sign "$\sum_{i=1}^{n}$" has one feature in common with the quantifiers. It turns the i into a dummy, but a dummy quite different from those in quantified statements. Roughly speaking the "$\sum_{i=1}^{n}$" says:

> Take the expression to which the summation sign applies. Write it down n different times, the first time replacing every occurrence of i by 1, the second time replacing i by 2, and so on until, in the n-th repetition, you replace it by n. Finally, add all the terms you have written.

For example, in the proof of Theorem 10.8 we find

$$\sum_{i=i}^{k-1} (-\alpha_{j_i}/\alpha_{j_k})x_{j_i}.$$

To be painfully explicit, we write the expression to which the summation applies, replacing the dummy variable by blanks, getting

$$(-\alpha_{j_-}/\alpha_{j_k})/x_{j_-}.$$

Next we rewrite it, filling the blanks with integers, beginning with 1 and ending with $k-1$. Then we add to get

$$[(-\alpha_{j_1}/\alpha_{j_k})x_{j_1}] + [(\alpha_{j_2}/\alpha_{j_k})x_{j_2}] + \cdots + [(-\alpha_{j_{k-1}}/\alpha_{j_k})x_{j_{k-1}}].$$

Note that, except for the dummy variable of summation, all symbols remain the same from term to term.

In parts of mathematics (there are no examples in this book) one encounters a sum where the index of summation does not appear in the terms to be summed. The same prescription applies, but now there is no place to substitute different values for the dummy variable, so all the terms you write down are identical. For instance, to evaluate $\sum_{i=1}^{n} 1$ you put down n 1's and add them. Thus $\sum_{i=1}^{n} 1 = n$.

The sign "$\sum_{i=1}^{n}$" is commonly read "the sum as i ranges from 1 to n" or "sigma as i runs from 1 to n."

Like most of our symbols, $\sum$ must do more than one job. The $\sum$ in Definition 13.3 is *defined* there. It is not quite the same as the $\sum$ we have been discussing.

Often the limits of summation, the 1 and the n in $\sum_{i=1}^{n}$, are quite clear from the context. If they play no essential role in the computation, they may be omitted. Strictly speaking, however, the expression $\sum_{i} \alpha_i x_i$ is incomplete and incorrect. It may be used only when there can be no reasonable doubt what the complete expression would be. Then it may be a small help because the reader cannot be distracted by unimportant limits of summation. By the same token, one may sometimes omit even the indication of the variable of summation, writing, for example, just $\sum \alpha_i x_i$ instead of the correct $\sum_{i=1}^{n} \alpha_i x_i$.

3. Generalizations of the associative law, $(x+y)+z=x+(y+z)$; the commutative law, $x+y=y+x$; and the distributive law, $x(y+z)=xy+xz$: are needed to manipulate sums.

For example, in the proof of Theorem 10.2 we have the sum $\sum_{i=1}^{n} \alpha_i x_i$. Written out this is

$$\alpha_1 x_1 + \alpha_2 x_2 + \cdots + \alpha_n x_n.$$

We want to look at two parts of this sum, the part consisting of the first m terms and that consisting of the remaining terms. Accordingly, we rewrite the sum, making the middle terms explicit. In this form the sum is

$$\alpha_1 x_1 + \cdots + \alpha_m x_m + \alpha_{m+1} x_{m+1} + \cdots + \alpha_n x_n,$$

or, to suggest the next step,

$$(\alpha_1 x_1 + \cdots + \alpha_m x_m) + (\alpha_{m+1} x_{m+1} + \cdots + \alpha_n x_n).$$

Finally, reverting to the sigma notation, this becomes

$$\sum_{i=1}^{m} \alpha_i x_i + \sum_{i=m+1}^{n} \alpha_i x_i.$$

4. Use of the commutative law entails simultaneous application of the associative law. To use them separately involves a prohibitively long, explicit calculation. Together they tell us that the terms in a finite sum can be rearranged and regrouped in any way we choose. The proof of this well-known fact is, however, a taxing exercise in mathematical induction. Even to state it precisely demands some ingenuity and the precise statement is not very illuminating.

Equation (10.1) in the proof of Theorem 10.4 provides an example. Written without the summation sign, the expression after the second "$=$" is

$$\alpha_1' x_1 + \alpha_2' x_2 + \cdots + \alpha_n' x_n$$
$$- (\alpha_1 x_1 + \alpha_2 x_2 + \cdots + \alpha_n x_n).$$

Taking account of the minus sign and grouping together the terms which appear above and below one another, this is

$$(\alpha_1' x_1 - \alpha_1 x_1) + (\alpha_2' x_2 - \alpha_2 x_2) + \cdots + (\alpha_n' x_n - \alpha_n x_n).$$

On applying axiom (3.9) it becomes

$$(\alpha_1' - \alpha_1) x_1 + (\alpha_2' - \alpha_2) x_2 + \cdots + (\alpha_n' - \alpha_n) x_n$$

or, in the sigma notation, $\sum_i (\alpha_i' - \alpha_i) x_i$.

In practice you should read such equations rather quickly, simply checking that every term on each side of the equation is accounted for on the other side.   This soon becomes a matter of habit.

5. Applications of the distributive law consist of taking out a common factor.   If there is a factor which remains unchanged from term to term, it may be removed from them and be written as a factor multiplying the whole sum.

Thus in the proof of Theorem 10.12 the second step in equation (10.4) is

$$\sum_i \alpha_k^i x_i - (\alpha_k^n/\alpha_j^n) \sum_i \alpha_j^i x_i = \sum_i (\alpha_k^i - \alpha_k^n \alpha_j/\alpha_j^n) x_i.$$

This includes applications of the associative and commutative laws as well as the distributive law.   If we put in the details, the equation becomes

$$\sum_i \alpha_k^i x_i - (\alpha_k^n/\alpha_j^n) \sum_i \alpha_j^i x_i = \sum_i \alpha_k^i x_i - \sum_i (\alpha_k^n/\alpha_j^n)\alpha_j^i x_i$$

$$= \sum_i [\alpha_k^i x_i - (\alpha_k^n/\alpha_j^n)\alpha_j^i x_i]$$

$$= \sum_i [\alpha_k^i - \alpha_k^n \alpha_j^i/\alpha_j^n] x_i.$$

Here the first step uses the generalized distributive law, the second the associative and commutative laws, and the last the ungeneralized distributive law—our axiom (3.9).

Equation (15.5) provides typical examples of the application of the commutative, associative, and distributive laws.   Written out, the expression on the second line is

(E.1)
$$(\alpha\alpha_1^j\xi^1 + \beta\alpha_1^j\eta^1)$$
$$+ (\alpha\alpha_2^j\xi^2 + \beta\alpha_2^j\eta^2)$$
$$+ \cdots$$
$$+ (\alpha\alpha_N^j\xi^N + \beta\alpha_N^j\eta^N).$$

To get the third line of (15.5) we apply the commutative law and the associative law.   We collect together all the terms in the first column of (E.1).   To this sum we add the sum of the terms in the second column. This gives the expression on the third line of (15.5) which is, written out,

(E.2)
$$\alpha\alpha_1^j\xi^1 + \alpha\alpha_2^j\xi^2 + \cdots + \alpha\alpha_N^j\xi^N$$
$$+ \beta\alpha_1^j\eta^1 + \beta\alpha_2^j\eta^2 + \cdots + \beta\alpha_N^j\eta^N.$$

To go from this to the fourth line of (15.5), take out common factors, i.e. α from the first line of (E.2) and β from the second.   This yields

$$\alpha(\alpha_1^j\xi^1 + \alpha_2^j\xi^2 + \cdots + \alpha_N^j\xi^N)$$
$$+ \beta(\alpha_1^j\eta^1 + \alpha_2^j\eta^2 + \cdots + \alpha_N^j\eta^N),$$

which is just another way of writing the fourth line of (15.5).

6. The proof of Theorem 10.12 includes also an extension of the notation for sums. In equation (10.5) we have a sum of n terms, but the indices do not run from 1 to n. To preserve the connection between the indices on the z's and those on the y's the former had to be named $z_0, \ldots, z_{j-1}, z_{j+1}, \ldots, z_n$. There is no z_j! We could write (10.5) in the form

$$\sum_{k=0}^{j-1} \beta_k z_k + \sum_{k=j+1}^{n} \beta_k z_k,$$

but the expression

$$\sum_{k=0, k \neq j}^{n} \beta_k z_k$$

is shorter and emphasizes the essential fact—that there is no term with the subscripts j. This is brought out even more clearly if we assume the reader knows that the sum must be over indices from 0 to n and use the incomplete form

$$\sum_{k \neq j} \beta_k z_k.$$

It is worth noting how the missing index reappears in equation (10.6). Applying the distributive, commutative, and associative laws, we find that there is a term involving y_j, but with a complicated coefficient, $\sum_{k \neq j} (-\beta_k \alpha_k^n / \alpha_j^n)$, quite unlike the simple β's that go with the other y's. To make everything neat again, we introduce the abbreviation $\gamma_j = \sum_{k \neq j} (\beta_k \alpha_k^n / \alpha_j^n)$, but before we can use the sigma notation we must have a γ for each of the other y's. Accordingly, we let γ_k be the coefficient of y_k, namely β_k if $k \neq j$.

The same missing index notation is used in equation (10.4) where our object is to separate out the n-th term for special consideration. Here, however, the missing term is the last in the sum and we could equally well have written the third line as

$$= \sum_{i=0}^{n-1} (\alpha_k^i - \alpha_k^n \alpha_j^i / \alpha_j^k) x_i + (\alpha_k^n - \alpha_k^n \alpha_j^n / \alpha_j^n) x_n.$$

7. Often, a single index is not enough. Thus in the proof of Theorem 10.7 we have several x's, $x_1, x_2, \ldots, x_m$, and each of them is a sum of certain y's. We need to show that each y is associated with a certain x. To exhibit the connection we put a superscript on the y matching the subscript on the x. However, there are many y's associated with x_i and we cannot call them all y^i, so we distinguish between them by giving them different subscripts. Since the number of y's associated with x_i may change as i changes, we must use a symbol which indicates this possibility—we use n_i for the number of y's going with x_i.

There is no special virtue in the use of superscripts as opposed to subscripts. We could have called the y's attached to x_i, $y_i^1, y_i^2, \ldots, y_i^{n_i}$, instead of $y_1^i, y_2^i, \ldots, y_{n_i}^i$. We could equally well have used double subscripts and called them $y_{i,1}, y_{i,2}, \ldots, y_{i,n_i}$. In Chapters IV and V a systematic use of subscripts and superscripts is a helpful mnemonic, but elsewhere we put the indices up or down as the spirit moves us. Of course, in subjects where exponents are common it is wise to avoid superscripts entirely, because they may be confused with exponents.

8. In Chapter III double sums occur, but in a rather trivial way. Not until Section 19 do we have to apply the associative and commutative laws to double sums. In Equation (19.3) we find

$$\sum_{i=1}^{M} \left(\sum_{j=1}^{N} \xi^i \alpha_i^j y_j \right) = \sum_{j=1}^{N} \left(\sum_{i=1}^{M} \xi^i \alpha_i^j y_j \right).$$

Written without the sigmas, the left-hand side is

$$(\xi^1 \alpha_1^1 y_1 + \xi^1 \alpha_1^2 y_2 + \cdots + \xi^1 \alpha_1^N y_N)$$
$$+ (\xi^2 \alpha_2^1 y_1 + \xi^2 \alpha_2^2 y_2 + \cdots + \xi^2 \alpha_2^N y_N)$$
$$+ \cdots$$
$$+ (\xi^M \alpha_M^1 y_1 + \xi^M \alpha_M^2 y_2 + \cdots + \xi^M \alpha_M^N y_N).$$

If you think of adding together first all the terms in a single column and then adding these sums, you will see that this is the same as the double sum on the right-hand side.

The parentheses are wholly superfluous, but in expressions like $\sum_{i=1}^{m} \sum_{j=1}^{n_i} \alpha_i \beta_j^i y_j^i$ it is important to realize that the innermost sum must be performed first. The reason is that the $\sum_{i=1}^{m}$ turns the four "i's" in "$\sum_{j=1}^{n_i} \alpha_i \beta_j^i y_j^i$" into dummy indices, but if one tries to reverse the order and writes $\sum_{j=1}^{n_i} \sum_{i=1}^{m} \alpha_i \beta_j^i y_j^i$, there is nothing before the "i" in "$\sum_{j=i}^{n_i}$" to turn it into a dummy.

In equation (19.3) this difficulty does not arise, because the upper limit of summation in the inner sum does not vary. In this case the order of summation does not matter, and one often writes

$$`` \sum_{i=1, j=1}^{n, m} "\quad \text{instead of} \quad `` \sum_{i=1}^{n} \sum_{j=1}^{m} ".$$

9. The compound subscripts in the proof of Theorem 10.8 must not be confused with double subscripts. The object of the compound indices is to describe a subset. A small example may clarify the situation. Say we start with the set $\{x_1, x_2, x_3, x_4, x_5\}$ and want to consider the subset $\{x_1, x_3, x_4\}$. It is easy to write the sum of the elements of the subset. It is $x_1 + x_3 + x_4$, but this is simple only because the subset is given very explicitly. To use the sigma notation or to describe subsets in general the compound subscripts are most convenient. If we let $j_1 = 1$, $j_2 = 3$, and $j_3 = 4$, the subset is

$\{x_{j_1}, x_{j_2}, x_{j_3}\}$. The compounding has given us an index—the subscript to the subscript—which takes on successive integer values. Now the sigma notation is usable and we can express the sum of the elements in the subset as

$$\sum_{i=1}^{3} x_{j_i}.$$

10. We conclude this appendix with a brief description of an alternative to the compound subscripts.

Again we start with the set $\{x_1, x_2, x_3, x_4, x_5\}$ and look at $\{x_1, x_3, x_4\}$. The set of subscripts appearing here is the set of numbers $\{1,3,4\}$. Let $\mathscr{S} = \{1,2,3,4,5\}$ and $\mathscr{S}' = \{1,3,4\}$. Then

$$\{x_1, x_2, x_3, x_4, x_5\} = \{x \mid \text{for some } i \in \mathscr{S},\ x = x_i\}$$

and

$$\{x_1, x_3, x_4\} = \{x \mid \text{for some } i \in \mathscr{S}',\ x = x_i\}.$$

We can now define a new sigma notation:

$\sum_{i \in \mathscr{S}'} x_i$ is the sum of all terms obtained on replacing the "i" in "x_i" by the names of the elements in $\mathscr{S}'$.

Similarly, in Definition 26.3 the expression

$$\prod_{\{i,j\} \in P_N} \frac{f(j) - f(i)}{j - i}$$

stands for a product. For each element $\{i,j\}$ in the set P_N there is a corresponding factor in the product. For example, if $N = 4$ and f is the function corresponding to the list $(2,4,3,1)$ then $\{2,4\}$ is an element of P_4 and the corresponding factor is $[f(4) - f(2)]/[4 - 2] = [1 - 4]/2 = -3/2$.

Appendix F.   Functions

1. A function is a rule which assigns to each element of a certain set a uniquely determined corresponding object. For example, the sine function, as defined in elementary trigonometry, assigns to each angle, A, a corresponding number, $\sin A$; the square root function assigns to each positive number x the corresponding value $\sqrt{x}$. Elementary calculus is the study of functions which, like the square root function, assign numbers to numbers; but the calculus is not the only place where functions appear. They permeate every branch of mathematics. Often they occupy the center of the stage, and they are always present either openly or clandestinely.

Although studies in the foundations of mathematics require a more precise definition, the intuitive idea of a rule of assignment is the most natural approach to functions. What is important is an understanding of the notations and terminology.

2. Let f be a function. The standard notation for the object which f assigns to an element x is $f(x)$, read "f of x". Now $f(x)$ is not always meaningful. For example, if f is the square root function and we are confining our attention to real numbers, then $f(-4)$ is nonsense. A function f assigns correspondents only to the elements of a certain set and not to other objects. This set is called the domain of f and is often denoted by $\operatorname{dmn} f$. Thus $f(x)$ is meaningful if and only if $x \in \operatorname{dmn} f$.

The object, $f(x)$, which f assigns to x is called the value of f at x or the value assumed by f at x. The set of all values assumed by f is called the range of f and is commonly denoted by $\operatorname{rng} f$.

The formal definitions of the domain and range of f:

$$\operatorname{dmn} f = \{x \mid \text{for some } y, f(x) = y\}$$

and
$$\operatorname{rng} f = \{y \mid \text{for some } x, f(x) = y\},$$

appear similar, but the symmetry between domain and range is very limited. In particular, to each $x \in \operatorname{dmn} f$, f assigns exactly one corresponding value in $\operatorname{rng} f$, but it is quite possible that f assigns the same value, $y \in \operatorname{rng} f$, to several different elements of $\operatorname{dmn} f$. Thus if f is the square function, defined by

(F.1) $f(x) = x^2$ for all real numbers x,

$f(1)$ and $f(-1)$ are both 1.

In the older literature it was common to speak of multivalued functions—a multivalued function being a rule which assigned several values to elements in its domain. Such multivalued correspondences arise frequently, but the functional notation is not appropriate for them, and the term *multivalued function* is slowly being replaced by *multivalued relation*, or simply *relation*.

3. To describe a particular function it is necessary to tell both its domain and the value it assigns to each element of the domain. The same formula used with different domains gives different functions. Thus the square function defined by (F.1) is quite different from the function g defined by

$$g(x) = x^2 \quad \text{for } x \geqslant 0.$$

There is no reason why the rule must be given by a single formula. All that is needed is that it be unambiguous. Thus

$$f(x) = \begin{cases} x^2+1 & \text{for } x > 0 \\ 1-x & \text{for } x < 0 \end{cases}$$

defines f quite clearly. Since $0^2+1=1-0$ we could equally well write

$$f(x) = \begin{cases} x^2+1 & \text{for } x \geqslant 0 \\ 1-x & \text{for } x \leqslant 0 \end{cases}$$

without causing any confusion. However, the formula

$$g(x) = \begin{cases} 3+x & \text{for } x \geqslant 1 \\ 2+x^2 & \text{for } x \leqslant 1 \end{cases}$$

does not define a function because it gives the contradictory information $g(1)=4$ and $g(1)=3$.

> *To prove that two functions are equal you must show that they have the same domain and verify that for each x in that domain, $f(x)=g(x)$.*

4. Often the domain is clear from the context and its explicit description is omitted. If a function is described by a formula and no domain is specified, assume that the domain consists of those elements for which the formula is meaningful. For instance, the phrase:

$$\text{Let } f(x) = \sqrt{1-x^2},$$

means that f is a function whose domain is $\{x \mid -1 \leqslant x \leqslant +1\}$ and, for x in this domain, $f(x) = \sqrt{1-x^2}$.

5. It is important to realize that a function f and its value $f(x)$ at a particular point x are very different objects indeed. Nevertheless, mathematicians frequently blur the distinction in their writing. Often this is mere indifference—the careless phrase "let $f(x)$ be a function ..." could perfectly well be replaced by the correct "let f be a function ..."—but sometimes pedantic insistence on correctness would lead to completely unnecessary verbiage.

The easiest way to describe a function f is to give a formula for $f(x)$, but often this is impossible. Think about the problem of defining the square root function. Once, earlier, we introduced this function, calling it f and defining it by

$$f(x) = \sqrt{x} \quad \text{for } x \geqslant 0,$$

but this does nothing except replace one symbol, "$\sqrt{}$", by another, "$f(\ )$". How can we define f if we do not already know it? One way is to say:

> Let f be the function with domain $\{x \mid x \geqslant 0\}$ which satisfies the conditions (i) $f(x) \geqslant 0$ for $x \geqslant 0$, and (ii) $[f(x)]^2 = x$ for $x \geqslant 0$.

This definition is completely satisfactory as soon as one knows that there is exactly one function satisfying (i) and (ii).

This example also illustrates the fact that there are many symbols for functions besides the traditional letters f, g, φ, etc.; "$\sqrt{}$" is a name of a certain function. In the text we introduce the dual, $\mathscr{V}$, of any finite-dimensional vector space $\mathscr{V}$. Here we are using " ~ " as the name of a function whose domain consists of all finite-dimensional vector spaces. We also use " ~ " as a name of a function whose domain consists of certain linear transformations. Such variant notations for functions are customarily used when one is not particularly interested in the fact that a function is involved.

6. Earlier we stressed the point that a function may assign the same value to several different elements in its domain.

Of course, there are functions which always assign different values to different elements of their domains. Such a function is called univalent or one-to-one (often written 1-1). If f is a one-to-one function, then there is another function which undoes the work of f. The new function is usually denoted by f^{-1} and can be defined formally as follows.

DEFINITION: If f is a one-to-one function, the *inverse* of f is the function f^{-1} whose domain is the range of f and which satisfies

(F.2) $f^{-1}(f(x)) = x$ for $x \in \operatorname{dmn} f$.

Several easily proved facts about inverses deserve special mention.

If f is not one-to-one, then there is no function which satisfies (F.2). For if f is not one-to-one, then there is some value in $\operatorname{rng} f$ which f assigns to two different values in $\operatorname{dmn} f$. Say $y \in \operatorname{rng} f$, $x_1 \neq x_2$, and $f(x_1) = f(x_2) = y$. If we could find an f^{-1} then, using (F.2) twice, we would have

$$x_1 = f^{-1}(f(x_1)) = f^{-1}(y) = f^{-1}(f(x_2)) = x_2.$$

There is always at least one function g such that $\operatorname{dmn} g = \operatorname{rng} f$ and

(F.3) $f(g(y)) = y$ for $y \in \operatorname{rng} f$.

Moreover, f is one-to-one if and only if there is exactly one such function.

To see that there is such a g, note that to say

$$y \in \operatorname{rng} f = \{z \mid \text{for some } x, f(x) = z\}$$

is simply an elaborate way of saying:

For some x, $y = f(x)$.

For each $y \in \operatorname{rng} f$ choose one element x such that $y = f(x)$ and call it $g(y)$. This defines a function satisfying (F.3).

If f is not one-to-one, there will be at least one $y \in \operatorname{rng} f$ for which different choices of $g(y)$ are possible.

If f is one-to-one and g satisfies (F.3), then for all $y \in \operatorname{rng} f$, $g(y) \in \operatorname{dmn} f$ and, using (F.2) also,

$$g(y) = f^{-1}(f(g(y))) = f^{-1}(y).$$

Thus f^{-1} and g are identical.

7. A schematic figure is often a great help in thinking about functions. We picture $\operatorname{dmn} f$ and $\operatorname{rng} g$ (Fig. F.1) as if they were disjoint sets in the

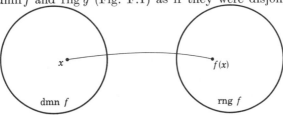

FIGURE F.1

plane and think of the rule as if it were a thread joining x and its corresponding value $f(x)$. Sometimes it is convenient to picture the range, and less often the domain, as lying in larger sets (Fig. F.2).

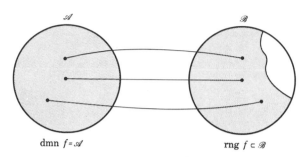

dmn $f = \mathcal{A}$ rng $f \subset \mathcal{B}$

FIGURE F.2

There is exactly one string starting at each point of dmn f, but if $f(x_1) = f(x_2) = y$, then the strings starting at x_1 and x_2 both lead to y. If f is one-to-one, each point of rng f has exactly one string running to it. In this case f^{-1} is pictured by the same strings used for f, but these are now to be thought of as running from points in the range to those in the domain (Fig. F.3).

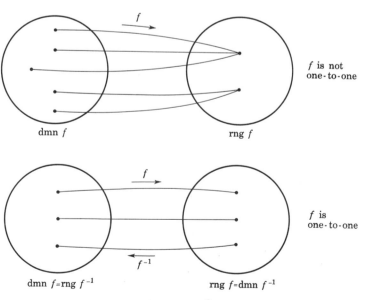

dmn f rng f f is not one-to-one

dmn f=rng f^{-1} rng f=dmn f^{-1} f is one-to-one

FIGURE F.3

8. Very commonly, it is necessary to superimpose one function on another. Consider two functions f and g and let h be a function such that

$$\text{dmn } h = \{x \mid x \in \text{dmn } g \text{ and } g(x) \in \text{dmn } f\}$$

and $$h(x) = f(g(x)).$$

There is no standard notation for this process of superimposing f on g to get h, but many authors write $h = f \circ g$.

9. Sequences are functions in disguise. When we write such a sequence as $x_1, x_2, \ldots, x_n$, we are describing a rule—the rule which assigns to each $i = 1, 2, \ldots, n$ the corresponding value x_i. Normally we write "$x_1, x_2, \ldots, x_n$" only when we want to neglect the function, but in Chapter VI the correspondence between functions and lists becomes all-important.

In Section 26 we consider a sequence, $k_1, k_2, \ldots, k_N$, whose entries are the integers $1, 2, \ldots, N$, arranged in some order. The corresponding function f assumes the value k_i at i. In other words, $f(i) = k_i$. Here the domain and range are finite sets and are most conveniently represented by sets of dots. To be specific let us illustrate (Fig. F.4) a case where $N = 6$.

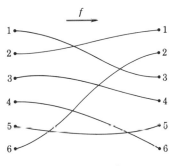

FIGURE F.4

There is no obvious, simple formula for the pictured function, f, but we can describe it completely by telling the values it assigns to each element of its domain:

$$f(1) = 3, \quad f(2) = 1, \quad f(3) = 4,$$
$$f(4) = 6, \quad f(5) = 5, \quad f(6) = 2.$$

In Fig. F.4 there are six "strings," one for each element in dmn f.

By a permutation of the integers 1, 2, 3, 4, 5, and 6, we mean a function whose domain and range both consist of the whole set $\{1,2,3,4,5,6\}$. If two strings led to the same point, there would not be enough to go round and the range could not be the *whole* of $\{1,2,3,4,5,6\}$. A permutation is a one-to-one function and hence has an inverse.

10. It is often convenient to use complicated names for certain functions. In the example $C(-\infty, +\infty)$ in Section 2, $x \oplus y$ is the name of a certain function; let us call it z. To specify z we give a formula for $z(\tau)$, namely,

$$z(\tau) = x(\tau) + y(\tau).$$

However, "$x \oplus y$" and "z" are names of the same object; so we may equally well write

$$(x \oplus y)(\tau) = x(\tau) + y(\tau).$$

The parentheses about "$x \oplus y$" are essential. The usual grouping conventions applied to

$$x \oplus y(\tau)$$

suggest to the eye that this expression should mean $x \oplus [y(\tau)]$, which is certainly not what we want.

11. As functional notations become more and more complicated, you
must be more and more careful that each compound expression designates precisely what you intend. Suppose f is a function; $f(\cdots)$ becomes meaningful only when the blank, $\cdots$, is filled by the name of some object in the domain of f. Furthermore, when the blank has been so filled, the result is a name for some element in rng f.

Look, for example, at equations (21.8) and (21.10). They *define* $\tilde{A}$. As explained in the text, $\tilde{A}$ is a function whose domain is $\tilde{\mathscr{W}}$ and whose range is in $\tilde{\mathscr{V}}$. Moreover, $\tilde{A}$ is a linear transformation; so we often write $\tilde{A}\tilde{y}$ instead of the more complete $\tilde{A}(\tilde{y})$. Assume $\tilde{y} \in \tilde{\mathscr{W}}$. Then $\tilde{A}\tilde{y}$ is the result of filling the blank in "$A(\cdots)$" with an element in the domain of $\tilde{A}$ Accordingly "$\tilde{A}\tilde{y}$" is the name of something in $\tilde{\mathscr{V}}$. Elements of $\tilde{\mathscr{V}}$ are themselves functions—functions on $\mathscr{V}$ to its scalar field $\mathscr{F}$; so when the blank in "$(\tilde{A}\tilde{y})(\cdots)$" is filled by the name of something in $\mathscr{V}$ the result is some scalar.

Unwary students trying to apply (21.10) sometimes write "$\tilde{A}(\tilde{y}(x))$". This can lead only to disaster. Observe that "$\tilde{y}(x)$", if it stands for anything at all, can only denote some scalar. We cannot conceivably have $\tilde{y}(x) \in$ dmn $\tilde{A}$.

INDEX OF SYMBOLS

$\oplus$ Addition of "arrows", 3
Addition in other systems, 12 ff.
Direct sum, 61

$\| \ \|$ Length of an "arrow", 2
Distance in the plane, 27
Norm of a vector, 206

$|\ \ |$ Absolute value, 4, 205

$*$ Multiplication of an "arrow" by a number, 4
Multiplication in other systems, 12 ff.

$\left.\begin{array}{l}\mathcal{R}^n \\ \mathcal{C}^n\end{array}\right\}$ Spaces of n-tuples, 14, 15

$\left.\begin{array}{l}C(-\infty, +\infty) \\ C[\alpha, \beta] \\ \mathcal{S}\end{array}\right\}$ Spaces of continuous functions, 15, 16

$\left.\begin{array}{l}\mathcal{P} \\ \mathcal{P}_n\end{array}\right\}$ Spaces of polynomials, 16, 17

$\in$ Is an element of, 17, 246
$\notin$ Is not an element of, 17, 246

$\mathcal{V}, \mathcal{W}, \mathcal{U}$ Vector spaces, 13, 18
$\mathcal{F}$ Scalar field, 18, 38

x, y, z, etc.   Vectors
α, β, γ, etc.   Scalars

$+$ Addition of numbers
Addition of vectors, 17, 18
Addition of subspaces, 55
Addition of transformations, 72
Addition of matrices, 103
Addition of n-forms, 128

271

THE GREEK ALPHABET

A	α	*Alpha*	H	η	*Eta*	N	ν	*Nu*	T	τ	*Tau*
B	β	*Beta*	Θ	θ	*Theta*	Ξ	ξ	*Xi*	Υ	υ	*Upsilon*
Γ	γ	*Gamma*	I	ι	*Iota*	O	o	*Omicron*	Φ	φ	*Phi*
Δ	δ	*Delta*	K	κ	*Kappa*	Π	π	*Pi*	X	χ	*Chi*
E	ϵ	*Epsilon*	Λ	λ	*Lambda*	P	ρ	*Rho*	Ψ	ψ	*Psi*
Z	ζ	*Zeta*	M	μ	*Mu*	Σ	σ	*Sigma*	Ω	ω	*Omega*

INDEX

LIST OF NUMBERED DEFINITIONS, THEOREMS, COROLLARIES, AND LEMMAS